" Banker by day, stripper by night. Twer Marino invites you to be a voyeur on a year exuberance and mistakes, loves and loves lost. Enjoy through the late eighties from Philadelphia to New York. You will cry, laugh and grow angry along with Tom as the man he loves takes advantage of him. But anyone who has been in love will understand why it happened. Tom holds nothing back nor does he blame anyone but himself for his errors in judgment. Despite his setbacks, he ends in a good place having learned many lessons as a result of his experiences. His honesty makes this a compelling read and perhaps you will avoid his mistakes, or if you don't, perhaps you will have as much fun making those mistakes as he did. **THE REAL LESSON** IS THAT WHAT WE THINK ARE MISTAKES AT THE TIME CAN BE STEPPING STONES TO A BETTER LIFE.
RICH MERRITT, author of SECRETS OF A GAY MARINE PORN STAR and CODE OF CONDUCT

" TOMORROW MAY BE TOO LATE IS A STORY ALL GAY MEN CAN RELATE TO. To the ones who have been around it will bring back memories. To twenty-something readers it will seem contemporary. Tom's honesty in laying bare his past adventures is a cautionary tale about growing up. As I read, I found myself reassessing past actions and emotions, along with wiping away a tear or two. It's a wonderful take on the pitfalls and glorious passions flooding through us as we come to terms with our own sexuality.
TERRY OLDES, author of DANCING WITH TINA

" TOMORROW MAY BE TOO LATE satisfies in all the wonderful ways sneaking a read of someone's diary would— voyeuristic, and honest in the extreme. Marino allows the reader to see his twentysomething self without any of the soft-focus editing of memory that can occur in memoir writing: here is a young gay man's journey to discovery.
J. WARREN, author of STEALING GANYMEDE

" Marino's book certainly touches and reminds us all of the tender time in our youth of coming out to ourselves.
MARK SEGAL, publisher of PHILADELPHIA GAY NEWS

TOMORROW
MAY BE
TOO LATE

THOMAS MARINO

Published in the United States of America

Printed in the United States of America

Edited by:
Floyd Largent/StormWriter Writing & Editing Services

Cover, Layout & Website Design:
Cecilia Sorochin/SoroDesign

The author gratefully acknowledges the following publishers for permission to reprint the following lyrics:

Permission to reprint Hallmark Card, written by the talented Terry Matz, was granted by Hallmark Incorporated.

IF YOU DON'T KNOW ME BY NOW
Words and Music by KENNETH GAMBLE and LEON HUFF
© 1973 (Renewed) WARNER-TAMERLANE PUBLISHING CORP. and MIJAC MUSIC
All Rights Administered by WARNER-TAMERLANE PUBLISHING CORP.
All Rights Reserved Used by permission from ALFRED PUBLISHING CO., INC.

TAKE ME TO YOUR HEART
© 1988 Mike Stock Publishing Ltd., Sony/ATV Music Publishing UK Ltd., Publisher(s) Unknown. All rights on behalf of Mike Stock Publishing Ltd. and Sony/ATV Music Publishing UK Ltd. administered by Sony/ATV Music Publishing LLC,
8 Music Square West, Nashville, TN 37203. All rights reserved. Used by permission.

"Take Me To Your Heart" by Matt Aitken, Peter Waterman, and Mike Stock
©1988 Universal Songs of PolyGram Int., Inc., Universal Music - Careers, Sids Songs Ltd., All Boys Music Ltd., and *[Michael Stock publishing designee]*
All Rights for Sids Songs Ltd., Administered in the U.S. and Canada by Songs Of PolyGram Int., Inc. (BMI)
All Rights for All Boys Music Ltd., Administered in the U.S. and Canada by Universal Music - Careers (BMI)
Used By Permission. All Rights Reserved.

●

ACKNOWLEDGEMENTS

I am extremely grateful to the Heavenly Father. You have given me many gifts, one of the greatest being homosexuality. Thank you for lighting the way and keeping me safe. Holy Mother Mary, thank you for holding me in your arms.

To my husband Noe Sepulveda, thank you for a love that finally nourished me. Thanks for believing in me when I needed it and patience when I lacked it. You have been a constant source of inspiration and motivation. I love you.

•

Bringing this book in for a landing could not have been possible without the dedicated efforts of a diverse team of talented friends who have served as writing coaches; helped design and shape the final product you hold in your hands, and made me feel confident in the process of creation. You've all got hearts that give and give.

Floyd Largent, many thanks for assisting me with the editing process, welcoming the project and helping me do what I thought I couldn't do.

Ceci Sorochin, sincere appreciation for the care you took to masterfully create a design concept for the book. Thank you for providing guidance, materials and support that went beyond what anyone could ask for.

Terry Oldes, words can't express my gratefulness for your willingness to guide and teach me how to be a better writer. Thank you for being there to step in and provide gallant influence and direction always well balanced and blended with warm words of encouragement.

TABLE OF

9
CHECK-IN

13
1·BOARDING

50
2·TAKE OFF

171
5·AUTOPILOT

214
6·TURBULENCE

367
9·SEARCH & RESCUE

379
THE AUTHOR

CONTENTS

99
3·ASCENDING

141
4·CRUISING

255
7·CRASHING

311
8·CASUALTIES

380
THE MUSIC

382
EPILOGUE

CHECK-IN

Feeling his big strong arms wrapped around me as we lay in bed kissing only solidifies the love I feel for him. This moment is everything I've dreamed of.

He rolls me over on my back and grasps my hands interlocking his fingers in mine. As he stares down, we lock eyes and communicate an unspoken shared joy. I feel higher and happier than I've ever felt. Woven deep into the fabric of my being, somehow I have connected to what I've been yearning for my entire life – right here in this bed with him.

He lowers his head and his lips touch mine. It's in this precious moment of bliss that I realize this is where I belong.

The story you're about to read is true.

Memories of this love have sustained and consumed me for years and I can now say I have my answers.

DO NOT WORRY ABOUT TOMORROW;
TOMORROW WILL TAKE CARE OF ITSELF
Matthew, 6:34

BOARDING

Monday, August 22, 1988: 11:45 a.m.
Mount Holly, New Jersey

T here's a large window behind my desk that I'm staring out of, gazing across the street at nothing in particular. "There's a call for you on 2202," Janet interjects.

I sit up, turn around to face front, and blink both eyes toward Janet, offering her an acknowledging smile as I answer the phone. "First Commercial Bank, Tom Marino speaking."

It's Mitch.

I spin my chair back around to the window and lean back, twirling one of my business cards in one hand. The title on the card reads Personal Banker — which is a catch-all job in retail banking, covering all aspects of customer service from concierge to underwriting loans.

"Hey, Tommy, I got some more jobs for you this weekend."

"Cool, Mitch," I smile. "Where are they?"

"Got one in Haddonfield at a house. Another couple in clubs."

I'm delighted. I love to get jobs in clubs. "Super! Which ones?" I ask.

"One is at the Cadillac Grill on South Street. The other is at Roxy's, right around the corner, just off of South."

"That's bangin'," I say, beaming with satisfaction; been to both places before, and both are upbeat and fun to work.

"Look, Tommy, here's the thing…"

"Mitch," I cut him off, "Can I get the information from you later? I'm a little busy right now."

"Sure, Tom. Call when you get home tonight. I'll leave the information with Lisa."

"Okay," I confirm and then hang up. I don't want to take the information from Mitch at work. My terrific part-time job is slowly turning into a bustling full-time career. I've been a male exotic dancer since I dared to try it about two years ago.

"Why don't you do some work?" Janet says from her desk, jokingly. She, too, is a Personal Banker, but is classified as my leader. Sometimes we hang out and party after work and we're capable of being professional colleagues at work and close acquaintances off hours.

3:00 p.m.

Scheduled off earlier than usual, I grab my keys and lock my desk. I pick up my pending file, and in my rush it slips from my grasp, spilling paperwork all over the floor. Shit. Here comes Sue, our branch manager. She's very beautiful.

"Leaving already, Thomas?" Sue always calls me Thomas.

"Yes, I'm done for the day," I confirm for her. "Unless…Is there anything else you need before I go?" I ask, kneeling before her to pick up my paperwork.

Sue takes the stuffed pending file that I just managed to put back together and begins leafing through it. She asks, "Is this up-to-date? Have you made all your sales calls?"

"Yes and yes," I lie knowing that there is no way she could have made heads or tails of the jumbled file.

"Well, then, you can scoot," she permits cordially.

Outside, I get in my black 1985 Ford Thunderbird and head home. While driving, I subject myself to cassette tape after cassette tape of songs that remind me of Nadine. Nadine is my wife, and we're getting divorced. Only a week ago, I picked her up from the airport after she had finished an extended medical training program with the Army. She was coming home, and the plan was that I would resign from the bank and we'd go together to her first assignment – wherever in the world that was to be. Instead of a warm homecoming and the continuation of our relationship, she told me that we were through. Our songs, our memories, and our entire four-year relationship all stream through my mind. I love her like crazy and miss her terribly, but we had both been unfaithful to each other during this summer of separation. I'd grown so close to her that she has been my once-in-a-lifetime love, and she made it so easy to share my truths; so easy that I was honest about my most intimate homosexual desires and indiscretions. In return, she told me that I have to explore the part of me that's sexually attracted to men: I need to find out what truly makes me happy.

I tell myself, She's right — wash away thoughts of what will never be. I have to go on and be strong; there will be happy times ahead. But try as I might, I can't stop the pain. It's only been a week since she left. I also never meant to hurt my baby and I worry what this is doing to her.

I pull into the driveway at home in Wrightstown. It's the house where I live with my Mom, Dad and little brother Danny — the house and home I most desperately loathe right now. The house I was supposed to be leaving in two weeks to start my own married and independent life. I can't stop feeling like the rug has been pulled out from under me. I was raised as a military brat, and the prospect of a future life in a military family carried an appeal of familiarity and warmth that I'd decided I wanted and needed to be happy.

Sullenly, I walk to my bedroom and collapse on the bed. Thoughts keep racing through my mind. I need to reinvent myself. Where in the hell am I going? I want something to look forward to, to depend upon, but now the world is topsy-turvy. Uncertainty and excitement coalesce in my thoughts and I cannot wrap my mind around anything so I leave to hit the gym. A good long workout will help; it always does.

Friday, August 26, 1988

Having just finished a gig in my tux, I'm feeling really good as I fly down the Atlantic City Expressway going about 85 mph, listening to Terence Trent D'Arby singing "Sign Your Name." I have all the windows down and the wind is racing through my hair. I'm dressed to kill, looking and feeling a bit like a young James Bond, sporting a white dinner jacket over a white tux shirt and black bowtie. It's such a high to go on these expeditions. Upon arrival at the Golden Nugget Hotel & Casino, I walk up to the reservations desk in the glitzy lobby. There are several attendants standing around looking pretty. A cute male receptionist smiles my way and asks if he can help.

"I'm here for the Bellas Bachelorette Party in room…"

He cuts me off, "I… just one minute." I lift my chin proudly, knowing he must've figured out I'm the dancer. He walks over to a tall blonde woman, says something, and they both look over at me. He comes back and picks up the phone.

"Mr. Jones, please…" There's a pause and he continues, "Yes, it's Michael. The guy for the entertainment is here for the Bellas." He turns slowly while nodding his head and looking me up and down. "Uh, yes." Suddenly, he just hangs up the phone. I turn my glance to the casino entrance and act like I could care less what he's doing. I feel his eyes on me, and I can instinctively sense he's gay.

"Excuse me," he starts, "You can wait here until Mr. Jones, our host, comes down for you." I feel the butterflies coming to life in my gut. "You can go over to the bar and get a drink if you want," he offers, pointing in the direction of the bar.

Shit, I'm happy. I can use a cocktail. Doesn't matter how many times I do it, I always get nervous right before a gig. I strut into the sparsely-filled bar and grab a seat next to an elderly couple nursing drinks with umbrellas. The female bartender comes up and retreats several times. Finally, she asks me what I will have.

"Manhattan, please," I say, handing her a twenty. She returns with my libation and change. I'm trying to remain calm, reminding myself that the whole gig is a maximum of 20 minutes and only feels like five minutes. No sweat.

A large man walks up to me and asks, "You the stripper?"

I smile and nod.

He shakes his head, grinning, and motions for me to follow him. "Bring your drink," he says.

I pick up my boom box, throw my black leather gym bag over my shoulder, and follow him to the elevator. Off the elevator, he leads me to a room with the designation "CLUB" on it. Inside the abandoned suite, there's a small dance floor where a table and chairs are set up. There are opened gifts lying around, and some sexy undergarments draped over chairs.

"The ladies are downstairs in the casino. They requested that you do the job in here."

"Sure. Is there somewhere to change?"

"You can go in that room over there until your music starts."

I look around and see an empty DJ booth.

"Should I set up my music?"

"No, the DJ will be in with the girls. Here's a pad and pen. Jot down the music you want."

I take a second to scribble down my songs and hand the pad and pen back.

I barely have time to change into the football player uniform they requested for this gig when I hear voices, then music, slowly fill the room. The women sound pretty tanked. The girl's name is Jessica, and she's getting married. I think Mitch told me she's around 24.

I hear the prelude to my first song. Showtime. I get up, heart pounding, and walk out. There are a dozen women, and they start whistling and screaming right away. Jessica sits in a chair with balloons attached; the girls are sitting in a circle of chairs around her, and the table has been moved out of the way. They're all dressed up, very boisterous. I walk sensually around the girls, deliberately away from Jessica, but keeping my stare locked on her. The first rule of the business is to remember who you're there for, and not to get carried away being everyone else's toy. No grandstanding. After all, this isn't about me; this is about Jessica. A lot of dancers allow the attention of the group to go to their heads, and forget about the individual they're performing for.

I walk around the women continually, not touching anyone but maintaining a constant stare at Jessica. The prelude blends into the first words of the song, and I lunge through two girls' chairs in a snake-like jump onto the floor in the middle of the group. I pull myself up and remove my shirt. Screams rise, and I throw the DJ a look and smile. As adrenaline pumps through me, I begin feeling the natural high that accompanies this work. The floor and these women are mine. All eyes are on me. I'll never see any of them again, but I can, for 20 minutes, be the man of their attention and dreams. I will always be engraved in their minds as the stripper they saw at this party. Some will go home tonight and think about me while their men are making love to them.

I walk by the girls and feel their shoulders, letting them run their hands up and down my legs and ass. When I catch my reflection in the mirror on the other wall, I like what I see: five feet eleven of taut masculinity, without an ounce of fat. Tight pecs, rippling six-pack abs, and a line of soft dark brown hair below my belly button. When I unbutton my football pants I reveal the very top of my pubic hair over my jockstrap. They can't keep their eyes off my impressive crotch bulge.

I walk around the chairs with my chest sticking out, and stop at one woman who has a pack of cigs and a lighter on her lap. I reach down and pick them up. I start packing the cigs while walking around the group. I shake one cig loose from the pack and pick it loose with my lips. I light up, take a drag for a slow moment, then hand it to the woman I took them from. I do another jump, landing on the floor in a sexy position. I sprawl across the floor and reach for the bottle of champagne I brought with me. I bounce up on my feet and hand it to Jessica, along with a small kiss on the cheek. I jump up on Jessica's chair and loosen my pants. I dive onto the floor, and as I dive, my pants fly off of me and are hanging on the ends of my feet. I lie on the floor with my feet up toward Jessica, and kick my feet with the pants attached.

One of her friends snaps a picture while Jessica rips the pants off me. I get back up on Jessica's chair and slide slowly onto her lap. Holding back so she doesn't have to feel my full weight, I place my body in a sexy position, giving the illusion that I'm sitting on her lap. The girls are now going totally crazy. Pictures are being snapped, girls are coming up and shoving money in my g-string, and everyone's having a great time. Jessica is laughing and appears to be quite pleased. The songs finish and I end up on the floor, again, in another interesting pose. I get up, wave, and start heading back into the powder room wearing only my black cleats and g-string.

One of the girls helps me collect my clothes and any tips that fell as I walk back to the little powder room.

I say my farewells and I'm outta there. One more job to do, and I'm going clubbing.

1:30 a.m.

When I finish the last gig of the evening, I'm alone with my thoughts as I drive. Oddly, the hardest part of being apart from Nadine is that I miss my friend. Right now, my heart, my head and my soul are in such turmoil. It's hard to be caught up in something this intense, something you don't even understand. I feel like I'm being dealt a strong blow, and I have to deal with it all by myself. I wish I had her in my life, if only to talk to during this time of despair and loneliness. Trying to navigate in a strange new place of unknown certainties, I wish I had a "how-to" manual or pamphlet with an "answers to frequently asked questions" section.

I know people are capable of hating me just because I'm gay, and my parents are sure to lose all respect for me at the very least once they find out; more likely they'll disown me. I wish I could make them all understand what this feeling is like. I've been totally submerged in Roman Catholic culture and teachings all my life, so I struggle with some doubt and guilt as to whether being gay jeopardizes my relationship with God. I'm certain there's more to this gay thing than just the sexual urges.

It's late when I get downtown, so I decide to head to the after-hours club *The Two-Four*. In the parking lot, I check out my reflection in the rear view mirror. I'm wearing plain blue jeans and a white tank top. I pull a red football shirt out of my gym bag and pull it on over my tank.

I show my membership card to the doorman and proceed through the cool lobby of the club, which is encased in long, maroon drapes billowing against wall mirrors. A fancy glass chandelier casts a dim glow over the entire room. I enter another door and push my way through a crowd of people standing around the dance area until finally arriving at the back bar. I can't believe how crowded it is. I decide to add to the ton of smoke in the air by sparking up my own cigarette, and order a Manhattan. I usually don't smoke; it's been something of a nasty little release lately.

I quickly scan the room and crown myself most beautiful. Vanity is such a wonderful thing. Impressed at the speed with which the bartender brings my drink, I plunk down a couple bucks for a tip. Feels good to relax. After another drink, I begin making goo-goo eyes with one of the best-looking muscle guys standing across the bar. He takes the hint and makes his way over to me, instantly offering to buy me another drink. He's pretty decent looking, probably in his late 20s.

I offer a handshake, saying, "Hey Chief, I'm Tom. What's shakin'?"

He shakes my hand firmly and introduces himself. "Kevin. Not too much, man," he says, nodding and maintaining eye contact with me.

Kevin must know the bartender, because they're chatting and then Kevin says, "Tend your bar, man!" I can't hear the rest of their conversation over the loud dance music. The bartender picks up a towel and starts wiping some glasses, smiling and shaking his head. Kevin says to me, "I've seen you in here before, and never had the courage to come up to you."

He continues to fire a barrage of questions my way. I feel drunk. He must suspect this and asks, "Another drink?" Diabolical.

"No thanks, I gotta drive home tonight. I think I'll just let this one wear off," I say, pointing to my empty glass.

"How old are you?" he asks.

"Twenty-one."

"Do you live with your parents or on your own?"

Frustrated with the game, I sit back and ask, "What are all these questions for?" I think but don't say, *I'll have sex with you, just forego this useless formality.*

"I don't see any harm in asking questions when you want to get to know someone better." He's really being nice.

"Jeez, okay. I live at home with my parents. I work in a bank. I'm from Earth, I'm a person, and I find you very attractive." The alcohol is impeding my ability to filter my impatience and buffer him from my boredom with this or any conversation. My interest lies in fucking him.

"You're hot," he says. I smile. He smiles. He continues, "You know, you don't have to drive home tonight. I can let you stay over at my place, so you don't get in an accident."

He slides the key into the lock and opens the door, stepping aside to let me enter. The kitchen's nice, and as the lights come on I notice that it's very clean. The apartment is old; the paint isn't the greatest, but it's quite a bit bigger than I expected. There are hardwood floors with burgundy rugs, and the Venetian blinds match the kitchen décor perfectly. It's not as if the kitchen or even the entire apartment is big, it's just that he's made good use of space. A white shag carpet covers the floor of the living room, which is equipped with a white leather couch and loveseat. There's a large pillar aquarium and a pool table.

"Kick back," Kevin says. I walk over to the large windows and take in the spectacular view, then practically fall into his leather couch and take off my sneaks.

"Your place is awesome."

"Thanks. Want something to drink? Coffee?"

I shake my head. "No, but thanks."

Kevin comes over and sits next to me. We hold hands, and I can feel my dick stir. He has a boyish face and soft, brown hair that feels good as I rub my fingers through it. His scent is not offending, but not perfumed. I move in to initiate, engage and execute. He tugs my underwear off and I get a charge when I see him toss my white jockeys on the floor. Despite the fact that we have sex in almost complete silence, it's sensational. We enjoy each other. Exhausted, we fall asleep next to each other after sharing a warm, wet washcloth to clean up.

Falling asleep is easy. I'm satisfied and relaxed.

Saturday, August 27, 1988

I wake to the smell of something delicious penetrating my aching head. I walk into the kitchen and find Kevin cooking breakfast, wearing only cut-off jean shorts.

I sit at his small kitchen table, and he places a plate of food in front of me. We eat and then he says, "Let's get a shower."

Once in the shower together, he kisses me more passionately than I recalled from last night and places his hands on my waist. He begins caressing my shoulders; my heart races as I get more and more excited by his touch.

I say, "Hold on...do you have any mouthwash?" He reaches up to a small medicine cabinet and hands me the bottle. I swish some of the minty mouthwash around and gargle. I rinse my mouth out and turn back to face him. All the while, he's rubbing my body, and my heart races even more as I get more excited by his touch. He's gentle, and since I know this is headed nowhere, I can be the pig I want to be. All inhibitions gone, I look into his eyes while he rubs his body on me. I can feel his heart beating as he pulls me close to him. I bury my face in his chest and snuggle as close to him as I can get. It feels good. I adore the affection and close-ness. It's like medicine, healing me from all the detachment and self-defeat inside.

He starts kissing my neck and licking it softly with his tongue; it's driving me mad. He buries his face into my neck, and the tickling, tender sensation of his whiskers and tongue makes me pulsate. I push his face away, then grab the hair on the back of his head and shove his face back into my neck and try to take it as long as I can. I feel him throbbing against me. It's incredible. We adjust the water, so it's really hot, and I seize the soap and completely lather up. Our bodies, naked and wet, are so erotic. We pull close, and the feel of our lathered, soapy young bodies together fills me with excitement.

When I get home, I find Mom has made her own birthday cake. The first thing that crosses my mind is a memory of last year, when Nadine and I bought her an ice-cream cake. This year I bought her a couple of pairs of clip-on earrings. I keep nagging her to get her ears pierced, but she won't hear of it. While Mom, Dad, Danny and I sit at the dining room table and eat cake, Danny regales us with highlights of his last high school football game, and I fight back memories of Nadine that hurt to recall.

Monday, August 29, 1988
At the gym I make my way to the weight room and get busy with my usual routine. I start with crunches. My stomach is pretty tight now. After 50 crunches, I move on to the bench press. This area is full of heavy weights. I remember that when I first came to the gym, I'd pass this room, somewhat intimidated by all the beefy, brawny men and big weights, all looking so unattainable. Now I jump right in, and start by spotting a guy who's bench-pressing on the other side of the room.

I know the guy. His name is Chaz, and he goes to my church. He has a football-player chiseled build and a handsome masculine face with a square jaw and dimpled chin. His short blond hair, goatee, and huge ass are so tantalizing. I stand behind him and assist in placing the heavy weight back into its place on the rack as he completes each set. He grunts as he hoists the weight up again, and down it goes against his rock hard chest. He's sporting a Penn State shirt with his left shoulder protruding from a large hole, making him even more scrumptious to behold. I find a considerable comfort in the presence of his rugged manner and appearance. He completes the set, sits up, and reveals his firm V-shaped torso by removing the shirt from his sweat-drenched body. The sight of his chest gives me such a rush.

I get on the weight bench and lie down. I take in a deep breath and sigh for a moment before gripping the barbell. With all my strength, I grab the bar and lift it up. I lift and lower the weight six times. Chaz stands above, spotting me. I stare up at his face while I'm in the heat of pain, and he glares down at me, further igniting my inner desires. After completing three sets on the weight bench, my body feels weary but well worked.

As I start jumping rope, my thoughts float to Nadine as one of our songs comes on over the loudspeakers. I suppose as time goes by, the songs we considered "ours" won't be played as much over the radio, and these feelings of longing for her will eventually fade. She was here with me so many times.

I must be deranged. I can't stop thinking about her. I finish with the rope and hit the track to jog 30 minutes, finishing with a stress and worry crushing sprint.

I walk into the locker room and jump on the scale. I push the little black weights to the right… to the right… to the left… until I determine I'm 172 pounds. As I continue to play with the scale, Chaz walks into the locker room. I turn and nod at him, and he plays upon my nod with a friendly smile — a smile that somehow signals a persuasion aligned with my own.

He has to be at least 26 or 27 years old. He seems to be in here every time I am. I've seen him naked before in the showers and in the steam rooms. I've used those images in my head to beat off to. Previously, I tagged him as totally straight. Something's different today, and I feel brave enough to shower with him. I think, *what the hell, I'm gonna go for it* — the memory of a shower with him will supply a lifetime of incredible jack-off fuel.

My heart is almost beating out of my chest as I walk out to the office and sign out a towel. A hot GI is manning the office, and he hands me a miniature bar of soap tucked inside a flimsy white towel. I walk back into the locker room and stand near Chaz, now in his underwear on the scale. I open an empty locker and begin undressing. Totally naked, I pick up the white towel and place it around me. He walks into the shower area, and I follow, full of excitement and anticipation. There are benches adjacent to the showers and Chaz, still in his jockeys, tosses his towel down on the bench. He makes small talk with me about the workout, and I mention how cool it was when I went out for a run.

A feeling comes over me while I watch and listen to him, a new sense somehow enabling me to detect sexual interest. Sensing that my gut feeling is picking up on something beyond my own desire and fantasy, I feel butterflies in my stomach as I'm filled with mixed emotions combining the nervousness and excitement of being on the prowl. I release the towel from my waist and it falls to the floor. Never having been naked in front of him adds to the thrill. I quickly bend down and pick up the towel. I throw it on the bench and it lands back on the floor. Chaz reaches down and picks it up this time, placing it on top of his own towel. I walk toward the shower, saying, "Thanks." Careful to appear inconspicuous, I keep an eye on him as he peels off his underwear, revealing his well-shaped cock and huge gorgeous ass. My fucking dick immediately starts filling! I quickly switch on the cold water and begin soaping up.

Chaz asks, "Are you taking a cold shower?"

Not looking up, feeling my face turn red, I answer, "Yeah, I like 'em after a long workout."

In an open shower bay of eight nozzles, he pulls up right next to me and turns the water on. I guess this hunch is on target. He begins soaping up his unbelievable body.

I'm excited, but manage to keep my dick in check. I take a chance and glance over in his direction. He looks right at me and gives a big smile. His body is even more attractive when wet. I purposely close my eyes and put my head under the shower, letting the water rush down my face until suddenly, I feel his naked body press against mine! I open my eyes as he begins hugging me.

He grabs my cock and squeezes it with his husky hands. He says, "Let's get outta here and finish this somewhere else."

I'm astounded by his aggressiveness but welcome it, still in shock. After our shower, we race to get dressed. Eager with anticipation, part of me is disappointed because he doesn't seem like boyfriend material. Jumping into sex like this turns off my interest in pursuing him for anything more than for sex. I'll be the first one to say that I'm going to take a test drive before buying a car, but there's an element of romance that's necessary to begin a relationship. Maybe I have to start thinking differently and learn how to open my mind to accept the fact that having sex first doesn't diminish the possibility for romance or the beginning of a relationship.

Maybe that's just a quirk that I have.

We're completely quiet as we drive in his black Corvette to his apartment about 10 minutes from the gym. I follow him into the apartment, and as soon as we get inside, in a couple of seasoned moves long since mastered by habit, we're sharing great sex.

As soon as it's over, Chaz says, "Get dressed and I'll drive you back to your car."

Not too romantic. From his tone and body language, I get the idea he feels guilty that he gave in to his real needs, and probably doesn't want to have any reminder of it around.

"Yeah, sure," I say, pulling my clothes on over my sweat-drenched body. Within an hour of starting, we're back at the gym. He doesn't even look my way as I get out of the car. I turn to say goodbye, and he jumps right in, saying, "Later man," and takes off.

I'm not disappointed. I feel elated that at least I got a great orgasm out of it. Tossing my head back to gaze up at the stars, I wink toward Heaven and think of how eventful this Monday evening has turned out. I'm grateful. I thank God for every experience, confident the Higher Power wants me to savor every bit of life.

I think Chaz wants sex with men as badly as I do, but I sense he despises his desire for man sex. Like many others, I surmise he wears the mask of a straight boy until he finds a playmate with whom he can reach his ultimate satisfaction. Chaz probably feels the way I do. The mere thought of embracing this lifestyle is a struggle, given that we're brought up to hate it, surrounded by a world that not only doesn't condone it, but considers it vile and repulsive.

Tuesday, August 30, 1988

I'm at Gatsby's with Billy, the head teller at First Commercial in our Cherry Hill office. Billy doesn't pry into my sexual exploits or relationships; I like the fact that our friendship is light. We gawk at guys, talk about work, people, TV shows, movies and music. He introduces me to another one of his friends, this cute little Puerto Rican dude called Ozzie, who's been eyeballing me since I walked in. Ozzie and Billy used to work together at another bank. I'm impressed when I hear that Ozzie is an Assistant Branch Manager at age 22.

"Did you sleep with him?" I ask Billy when Ozzie steps away.

"No. He's a bottom like me." I drop my eyebrows and shake my head at Billy. Ozzie keeps looking at me and smiling from where he stands at the bar. I go to the bathroom, and when I return Billy says, "Ozzie likes you."

"Really," I say, sarcastically. Ozzie reappears and produces a mug of beer for me. I take it, smiling, and say "Thanks, man."

"You want to dance?" he asks.

"Sure," I say.

Gatsby's has a great aura. Formerly a country-western club, you can't help but love this place. Neon and mirrors surround the dance floor area; there's a main bar section and a separate game room. It all makes you feel comfortable and laid back. The DJ is enclosed in a little room off the dance floor. There's a piano bar upstairs, where mostly older dudes hang. When I say older, I mean it seems that anyone past 30 in this lifestyle is relegated to "daddy" status. I love dancing, and Ozzie turns out to be pretty good at it as we tear it up on the floor when DJ Michael finally plays "Prove Your Love" by my favorite singer, Taylor Dayne.

Friday, September 2, 1988

Out again, Billy and I are drunk off our asses. Ozzie is a good dance partner and he keeps buying me drinks. He won't let me return the favor, which I find odd. We hang out until the club is about to close around 2:30.

"I can't drive like this," I tell Billy, who has found his hookup for the evening — a guy with a pick stuck in his Afro. I try to reason with Billy to share a cab with me to his place, which is only about 10 minutes from the club. I plead with him for a moment, but he insists on going home with the trick he's found.

"Can you drive?" I ask Ozzie.

"Of course!" The one saving grace this boy has is his own apartment.

"Can I crash over at your place?" I ask. He seems elated by the fact that I'm coming home with him, given my drunken state.

After dark, the ballsy, reckless side of my personality — the one that takes almost everything off in front of strangers — takes control of my brain. I shudder to think what my daylight conservative banker would think of his car being driven by a stranger to his apartment in Camden. On top of everything else, it's fucking Friday night, and I have to work tomorrow! We stop for some barbecue at a take-out joint.

His apartment is a loft-type flat with huge windows. We sit on the floor and eat the barbecue chicken and ribs. It's tasty. I haven't eaten for hours and it's nice. After eating, Ozzie busts out with a joint and we share it, talking about banking. I tell him about my dancing, and he thinks it's cool. My dick is hard, despite the food, alcohol and pot. Now I'm ready for sex.

I kneel down and start kissing him. No games, no BS; let's get this going. "I'm ready for bed," I whisper in his ear.

Ozzie's bedroom is sizeable and he has a king-size bed. I lunge onto it and stretch out. He puts on music, and I heat up hearing the simulated orgasms of Donna Summer singing "Love to Love You Baby." Ozzie walks back and begins kissing my stomach.

"Can we get a shower?" I ask.

"Together?" he asks back, smiling. I nod and reach for his hand as we walk to the bathroom. As we undress, he notices my chest. "Nice," he says, rubbing it. "It's so hard."

I feel good about sharing it, knowing how hard I've been working on it. We're naked and staring at each other's bodies. As we lather up, I feel his smooth body, so soft to the touch yet hard to the squeeze. He has a nice cinnamon-colored butt, and I get down on all fours to pay it homage. There is something exciting about being with a Latin man.

After our long shower, we jump on the big bed and we have good sex together. I enjoy his smooth and silky body and he's full of compliments over mine. After sex, I'm beyond tired and dizzy from the alcohol and pot.

"Who's Rita?" I ask, pointing to the tattoo on Ozzie's arm.

"Ree-Tah? Is my Mom."

"My Mom's name is Rita, too," I announce. We talk some more before falling asleep. Ozzie tries to hold me while we sleep, but I push him away, enjoying the huge bed and all the space I don't usually have at home on my little twin size.

Tuesday, September 6, 1988

Right as I'm about to walk out the door, Janet shouts after me, "Tom, your WIFE is on the phone!" Damn. My heart shoots up to my throat as I retrieve the call.

"This is Tom."

"It's me. I wanted to remind you that I need the ID card back. When can I get it?" I'm instantly put off by her brash tone, cold as ice and right to the point, without even asking, *"How are you?"* She continues, after not hearing a response, "My C.O. is hounding me about it."

"Is that all you called for? Do you miss me at all? How are you doing?"

She fires off one-word answers, "No. Fine. I can't really talk, I'm in a hurry."

Fucking bitch. Bitter memories flash in my mind: thoughts of a scene that occurred just a month ago, when she took a call from her lover in Texas in front of me. Right before the call she said, "I tell him I love him. I hope you won't be offended by that." It burned so bad. It reminded me of her cheating in the past. I keep trying to recognize that she isn't hurting me; I'm hurting myself. I need to shake it off. I crash back to reality and finish the dry phone call with her. I walk out into faint drizzle toward my car and once inside immediately turn on the radio. I feel tears welling up inside of me, and don't want anyone to see me cry. The rain on my face helps disguise my tears. Everything seems so fucked up.

Friday, September 9, 1988: 8:45 p.m.

I arrive at Riccardo's Italian Restaurant in Oaklyn, a large, white box-like building without any windows. I feel euphoric. It had been raining out earlier, but it's cleared up to be a nice, warm evening. The parking lot is half full.

I enter and encounter two large mobster-type dudes who greet me with Jersey Boy smiles. I follow their instructions and sit down, parking my boom box and gym bag on the floor. This job is for a bride-to-be, and her family has rented the entire restaurant for what's supposed to be a bachelorette party. These guys must be members of the family because they're all into this, acting excited, like hyper kids ready to pull a prank on someone.

Through a glass partition I stare at the crowd inside. It looks like the entire families of both the bride and groom are here.

One of the two goons returns and takes my cassette tape, saying, "When you hear your music start, you can come in and do your thing."

He runs back, leaving me wondering if I've ever seen a bigger neck on a human being. Suddenly, I hear my tape playing. He has it on the wrong side, and in the middle! Unbelievable! I had it all rewound and ready to go. Any moron could have figured it out. How could he fuck it up so fast? Luckily, I remember how much time I have on that side of the tape and have a fair idea of the music, so I bolt out to the cleared dance floor and begin to perform. I don't know the girl I'm supposed to be dancing for. Mitch told me they would bring her to me from the crowd. I just dance and play the room, allowing the natural confidence that comes with erotic dancing to take over.

When you're thrust into something as different as stripping off your clothes in public, surprisingly, you just do it and don't think about it. I do, anyway. It's like working with all the cash in the bank; after a while it's not real money to you, just a somewhat transparent part of your routine. I don't think about the fact that there are several really good-looking men in the room, or that I'm going to undress in front of some grandmothers and kids. I just do it.

A woman drags a chair onto the dance floor. I continue my routine, and then a beautiful woman emerges with some coaxing from the crowd. She stands in front of the chair, looking at me. I stop dancing, walk up to her and reach for her hand. She's one of the most ravishing women I've ever performed for. I bring her hand up to my lips and gently kiss it. Her face lights up, revealing a radiant smile. She's absolutely exquisite. I continue dancing, and her bright eyes beam as they meet mine. Her friendliness and the fact that she's so receptive empower me to provide an outstanding performance.

I approach and touch her hand very gently, then run my fingers up the side of her arm to her hair and down again. The group enjoys the show, and is loud and wild. A bunch of them are pretty drunk, teasing the bridegroom-to-be. It should make me nervous, but I've got a safe and solid feeling, confident my performance is respectable and delightful. The future groom is a very good sport. He's of average looks, but has a charming smile. They make a dynamite couple. There's no hostility here. I begin to really enjoy this job as my act unfolds into another song, and more clothes come off.

I grab a carafe of wine on a nearby checkered-cloth table and pour some in her hand. I bend and drink it from her palm. The group loves it, screaming and applauding. After a few jumps and spins they start chanting "Maria, Maria, Maria!" I return to the bride-to-be and begin pumping my hips into a frenzy, swinging my head around and around.

I pick her up and enjoy that she's playful. I swing her round and round and she locks her legs around my waist and lets her head fly back. For a moment, I'm a bit taken aback and unprepared by her energy and antics, and I almost lose my footing on the slippery wine-soaked floor. I'm enjoying this job incredibly, and as the last song comes on, I let her down and strip down to my g-string. A woman, dressed impeccably, comes up with some money and sticks a $5 bill in her mouth, throws her arms around my neck, and starts dancing with me for just a few seconds. She puts the fiver in my g-string. This prompts almost every woman in the place to line up for a dance with me during my last song. Each of them smells so good, and each kisses my cheeks. Feeling it proper behavior or good manners, I kiss them back. The much older women turn their faces to offer me a cheek to kiss.

I find myself surrounded by beautiful women all yapping and smiling. Everyone seems so happy. I incorporate it all into my act, and I have a sense of safety, contentment and warmth. The sense of safety is beyond fear of pain; it's a feeling of belonging. As if in a dream, the whole group jumps on the dance floor and starts dancing. I get lost in the crowd of 80 or more people. I didn't realize there were so many people until now, when they're all up dancing. I feel several pinches and a young guy walks by and pats my ass.

After the tape finishes, the DJ puts on his own music and the crowd migrates back to their tables. A few of the women say, laughing, "Aren't you going to take off the g-string? Take it all off!"

I shake my head, but they persist. I keep shaking my head, but they're such a fun group. I shout, "You want me to?" Some of the mothers get a bit nervous with the teenage girls roaming around. They try to hush the brave ones, but they won't be silenced.

"How 'bout a private show?" I offer, wondering what I'm saying myself.

"Okay, come on…" one of the rabble-rousers yells. I walk around the corner toward my clothes, and dammit if a crowd of them doesn't follow, all laughing and daring each other. I wait a moment for any that may be trying to be bashful by showing up late and then tease, "You wanna see it all?"

"Yeah!"

"Yeah!"

"Yeah!" For a moment, I think about flashing them my dick, but wave it off and get dressed. I usually bolt after a gig, but I'm having so much fun. I'm drenched in sweat and asphyxiating in the smell of all the aftershave and perfume in the air. After I get dressed, a line of women assists me with a towel, drinks, food and more food. The food is delicious. The crowd is all on the dance floor. The DJ plays the other side of my tape and jumps on the dance floor with the crowd. The pretty bachelorette makes her way to me, holding hands with her future husband, and we introduce ourselves. Not my type, but handsome with dark eyes, fit, he has a sexy, thick black moustache. She has a Madonna-like appearance with a perfectly oval face and short brown hair sculpted to her head. Her hairstyle is something out of the '40s, but quite flattering. The two of them seem so much in love. I wish them the best of luck and happiness.

"Do you live in the area? Did you come far?" Same round of questions. The father of the bride stands up on a chair and toasts the couple. Everyone claps and starts talking again. I'm feeling good. Actually, thoughts of me and my life are so far from my mind. In a situation like this, you can't help but be totally absorbed by everyone around you — such merry folks. The father of the bride stands up on a chair and everyone turns to face him. He says something in Italian, and everyone laughs.

As I gather my things and say goodbye to everyone, one of the women who ordered me offers to walk me out. At the door, she hands me an envelope with the cash for the job. I thank her and extend my hand to shake hers.

She holds my hand and pulls me close to say, "Not so fast! You were fantastic. Much better than when I saw you at *Shadows*. Thank you for coming. You're a really nice guy."

I smile and lean in to kiss her on the cheek. She prefers to kiss me on the mouth. Having met her husband earlier, I instinctively scan the view behind her. Still holding my hand, she turns it around and places a mound of folded cash squarely into my palm, saying, "This is from all of us." I bid her farewell and leave. Feeling high over such a great evening, I can't but help think that I would have paid them to do this gig.

I get in the car and open my palm. Three $100 bills! I feel my jaw drop and immediately reach for the door handle, intent on going back in to return the tip. I feel guilty having had such a wonderful time, eating their food, drinking their liquor, and here they tip me $300 above and beyond the $85 I earned from Mitch for doing it! I open the door and then shut it. *It's my money,* I think. *I've earned it.*

Later

I'm speeding down Route 130 going close to 75 mph with the windows down, the radio blaring, enjoying the after-gig high. Highs like this are unmatchable. I want to share it; everyone should have an opportunity to feel this good. The feeling of being in the "spotlight" — of being young, well-built, handsome, and admired, combined with a warm sense of accomplishment, mixed with all the hope of the future, creates a raging wind in my sails.

GB's parking lot is jam-packed as I arrive just after 1:00 a.m. Inside, I find Ozzie, his friend — oddly, another guy named Ozzie — and Billy.

My Ozzie asks, "Billy said you used to strip here. Why did you quit?"

I shrug. "About a year ago I got in a fight, and the former assistant manager, Jason, fired me because of it. As I recall, two straight dancers were making fun of gay guys. I couldn't understand why. Here they were in a gay club, dancing practically naked for men, and these bigoted assholes were talking shit about 'queers.' It brought me back to my high school days when I earned the unfortunate nickname 'Rubin' and 'Rubin the Cuban' because I resembled a cute Argentinean exchange student who had the misfortune of being openly gay."

My Ozzie pipes in flamboyantly, "Was this Rubin appetizing?"

"Never met him, but I was told he was tormented so much, he packed up and headed back to Argentina before the end of the term. So even though I wasn't really out to myself yet, I wasn't going to stand by and allow those pretentious dancers to talk shit. I spoke up in defense of the clientele and they ganged up on me. After a couple exchanges of "Fuck you," "Asshole," "Faggot," and a good fight, I got thrown down the stairs and bought myself a bloody nose. After which Jason tells me, 'Tom, listen, we know you're good, but they're better... better built... and that brings in more people...' Can you fucking believe that?"

"Want another beer?" Ozzie asks. As Ozzie returns with my beer, and the conversation moves to another topic, I don't really participate, still reflecting on my high school days while watching people fill the dance floor now vacated by the strippers.

"Want to dance?" Ozzie's voice breaks my daze.

I have an incredible buzz going on from the drinks I've had tonight.

"I can't believe I finished this already!" I say, closing my eyes and momentarily pressing the neck of the beer bottle to my nose.

Ozzie says, "You're acting weird tonight. I'm going to dance with Billy." Whatever. John comes up to say hello. He was my first sexual experience with a guy. He's in his mid-thirties, handsome, wealthy and very gentle. I have a lot of respect for him; he made my entrée into the gay lifestyle one I will never forget. He gives my nipple a gentle squeeze though my tank top and flashes me a smile.

John, still smiling, says, "How you been, Champ?" We exchange some pleasantries and he moves on.

Ozzie catches sight of me chatting with John and glares at me from the dance floor.

I turn back to my beer, and all of a sudden Ozzie is right in my face shouting, "You're fucking drunk!" *Keep cool, Tom*, I think to myself, gritting my teeth. I look over at Billy and the others now staring at me. I turn and walk away.

I find a support beam on the side of the dance floor, and lean against it with my beer resting on my leg. I focus on the mass of men dancing on the floor. As I get even drunker, I believe they all want me. I can have any of them. My confidence rises, and I catch the eye of a tall and well-built hottie on the dance floor. He's dancing with another guy who has a moustache and beard, but I get a feeling they aren't lovers. As the song finishes, the two of them start departing the dance floor. I daringly walk up to them and grab the arm of the cute guy with whom I made eye contact.

"I guess I'm dancing!" he yells back to his friend, and he throws his muscular arms around me as we start dancing. The music is blaring, Ozzie and Billy are glaring, and I'm pumping my hips to the song.

The song ends, and we move back to the support beam by the dance floor. Without thought, I'm kissing this guy and he's fondling me right in front of everyone. I face the dance floor with him behind me and his hands are inching their way into my jeans. He has an incredibly full and sexy black beard. His pal has a flowery-type button-down shirt on. With control yet no restraint, I blab out, "My, what a gay shirt you have on there, Chief."

He glares and says, "They are... chrysanthemums."

I notice the dude behind me has my pants unzipped and his hands on my penis. I mumble the word *chrysanthemums*, and they both get some chuckles out of it. I feel cutesy, but recognize I probably look slutty. Several people catch the show we're putting on, and I like being the center of attention. My white jockeys are covering everything, but his hands are obviously inside and busily massaging and caressing my genitals. I like the fact that I've turned over control to him; he can do what he wants to with my body. It's exciting having everyone watch.

We take our act outside to a black Porsche in the parking lot. "I'd be afraid to park this here," I say.

We undress completely right in the car in the dimly-lit parking lot and begin fondling each other. Kissing, hugging, touching all begins, and all I can wish is that this is for real. It's so fast, so empty and unfulfilling. Rain starts falling, and I open my eyes to watch the droplets cover the windshield as his head moves down my body. It's dark and I feel weak. I give in to the pleasure and allow my thoughts to escape. I think, *let yourself enjoy it.* Learn to lean back and relax. Tension fades.

"I want you to fuck me," he says. He's practically hairless, with a small square of neatly-trimmed light brown pubic hair that is an incredible turn-on. I kiss his belly and he pushes me up, saying again, "I want you to fuck me." I'm not too keen on the idea.

"It's kind of cramped in here. Do you have a condom?" He nods, reaching for one in his wallet. I can't help but imagine we are lovers, and that tomorrow he loves me as much as he does now. I want to tell him I can fall in love with him. But I know I should concentrate on the pleasure, and forget my desire to make this more than it is.

All the way home, I smell him on me, and experience a sense of euphoria and unmatched satisfaction. Despite its casualness, I feel grown up and very free. It feels like I've satisfied an insatiable craving.

Saturday Night, September 10, 1988, Gatsby's

I'm feeling no pain tonight, especially after downing my second Manhattan. Billy walks over and offers a forced smile. "Hi, Tom."

"Hey, Bill."

"You're so predictable. Manhattan or Bloody Mary. Why not try something different?"

I turn to him and quip, "Hmmm. Different friends?"

"I'm sorry about the whole Ozzie thing," he says.

I look back into Billy's light blue eyes and shrug it off with, "Don't sweat it." My body language and tone of voice reflect a dismissive attitude, and I hate myself for acting this way when he's trying to apologize. I force a tough act, but feel like embracing him.

I walk into the game room and lean up against another support beam. It certainly is great to be young and good-looking, and to turn so many heads as I walk across a room. The alcohol-induced high intensifies my vivacity. Watching two women shoot pool, I absorb the beat of the music, which is now forcing me to move with it. Within minutes, a tall, good-looking admirer is staring at me from across the room. He's in a group of similar cookie-cutter preppy-type friends. He's a good-looking dark-haired guy, and we lock our sights on each other, exchanging inviting smiles. I grin as he approaches.

He stands next to me and says, "Hi."

I smile, offering a handshake, saying, "Hey. I'm Tom."

"I know. You used to strip here."

"Yeah," I say, looking forward now, feeling cautious.

"My name is Chris. Chris Donahue."

"You don't look Irish," I say, still looking forward, now wondering what exactly he remembered of my body.

"I am."

"What?" I ask, lost in thought.

"Irish. One hundred percent."

"Your hair and eyes are black, and I thought you were Jewish."

"What's the big deal anyway?" he asks. I keep my stare toward the dance floor, hoping he goes away. "I mean, if you like someone, it doesn't matter what they are." He continues, despite my obvious non-interest, "Are you Jewish? I mean, if you're looking for another Jewish guy, I suppose I understand."

My interest is renewed by his persistence. "No, no. I...I don't care," I reply, sounding like I'm hearing and speech challenged.

"I'm here with friends from the Haddonfield Playhouse. I act and sing in my free time."

What a fag. "Yeah?" I ask, not giving a shit.

"Yes. I must say I'm quite good at it, too. We have a loyal following. We're working on a play right now. You've heard of *La Cage*?"

"Huh?" I ask, this time trying to sound like an imbecile.

"La Cage Aux Folles."

"Oh, yeah. Great." I tell myself, *Just excuse yourself and go to the bathroom. Then you can leave, and…* Shit. He'll see me here again one night. He's talking. About what? I couldn't care less. He is kind of cute. The music is fantastic tonight. He has nice, curly, jet-black hair. I continue to nod my head and say, "Oh, yes. Mmmm-hmmm."

He asks if I wanted another beer. *Now, that's a good idea — make yourself useful.* When he gets up, I check out his ass. Okay, it's decent. It's uncanny how I know I'm going to have sex with someone; within a few moments, I've decided the future. Little does he know, walking to the bar, that he's going to have me in him tonight. I've decided. Little does he realize it's non-negotiable, and he has no choice.

We dance a few times and he surprises me with, "I'm heading out. I gotta go. Tomorrow, I'm going to the Eagles game. You interested in going with me?" I hate football, but being there in person might be okay.

"Sure. Here's my number." I hand him a piece of paper with my name and number. I always carry one with me in the club, so I don't have to ask for a pencil and paper at the bar. I walk him to his car with his friends. The introductions are meaningless to me. They're all nerdy losers. I stand out like a bullet in the group. Chris must think I'm going home, too.

"Bye. I'll call you tomorrow and let you know when I'll pick you up. The game starts at around 3:30." I wave to them as they drive off in a big hunk-of-shit car Chris calls "Marcy."

I re-enter the club, greeting the doorman: "Hey, Joe." He winks at me as I walk by. I get another beer from the main bar, and head to the perch in front of the dance floor. Ozzie and Billy are dancing together. As I look around, it seems like everyone is dancing so I join in as a dance hit, "S.O.S. Fire in the Sky" comes on. Out of no-where, a slim, cable repairman/UPS delivery type dude with Army fatigue pants and a white Marlboro T-shirt dances up to me.

"Are you as fucked up as I am?" he asks.

"Oh yeah," I say, laughing, totally into his style of dancing. He runs his hand up my arm and over my pecs.

"You're hot."

"Thanks." We dance seductively with each other as the song rolls into another one of my favorite funky tunes, "Midas Touch" by the group Midnight Star. He turns and bends down; I grab his hips and pump my body into his. We dance well together, and I like the fact that he's playful and no-nonsense. He grabs my arms and swings me around in a twirl. I am buzzed out of my mind, praying I don't look like an idiot as we almost lose our footing in one move, but catch and hold on to each other with a strange sense of familiarity that comes from years of dancing with one partner. I hear one fag mutter, "He's a slut," as I fly by him in a rhythmic dance that bedazzles me. *Was that directed toward this dude, or me? Who cares? Who gives a fuck?* If I were any higher, I'd probably start my exotic dancing routine right here and now. We finally stop dancing, and I can hardly catch my breath when he grabs my hand and takes me to the back bathroom in the game room. It's dark in all the bathrooms in the club, and I'm drunk off my ass, but it's pitch black in here, reeking of pot.

"I'm Dave Ritter," he says.

Strangely unaffected by the fact that I can't see this guy holding my hand and that there's an unknown number of guys in here, waiting in practically perfect silence, I gasp for air and exclaim, "You sure dance like a motherfucker!" He laughs. "Tom," I continue. My eyes adjust to the limited light, and I see Dave pull out a joint and get a light from one of the guys in the crowd around us.

"So this is what happens to all those fucking weirdos who hang out till the bar closes," I blurt out. They all laugh, thankfully. I don't know if it's the alcohol or the darkness, but I feel so confident. I practically suck down his entire joint, staring at the DRUGS WILL NOT BE TOLERATED sign on the wall that I can now just barely make out. We don't talk, just stand and stare at each other. Words aren't too important anyway.

"C'mon," he says finally. We exit the men's room, and I follow him up to two well-dressed, good-looking men.

"Tom, this is my brother Michael."

The gorgeous man extends his hand, "Mike, Mike," he says twice, like a parrot, correcting his brother. He's extremely bearish and has dashing, mature good looks. His bulge is outstanding. I gaze at Mike's friend, awaiting an introduction, but Dave and Mike don't waste time introducing the friend. Mike says to his friend, "I see Dave's found their toy for the night."

We proceed to another group of men and Dave introduces me to his boyfriend. "Tom, this is my lover, John." I get daggers thrown at me from John as he eyes me up and down. The other men standing with him all chime in the same time, "You're Flash."

"Flash."

"Flash." Yeah; they all knew me by my dancing name. I say, "You can call me Tom." I can tell by his expression that John isn't impressed. I find John to be pretty damned handsome. Dave and John whisper something, and all of a sudden Dave takes me outside while John wraps up his conversation with their buds.

"We're getting ready to bolt. You wanna party with John and me?"

I just want to keep drinking and dancing. I want to keep having fun. I feel so fucking good. Dave pulls me into their 1976 Nova and offers me another joint. We smoke it and sip some warm Orange Jubilee Mad Dog 20/20 he has stashed in the glove compartment.

Dave starts rubbing my knee, saying, "You're a knockout, man. Full knockout."

I look up at him, gushing in my half-conscious state, "And you are involved with a good-lookin' man."

He says, "Don't you think *I'm* good-looking?"

"Absolutely," I say, offering up the bottle in a toast, and continue, "Yeah, man, you're one awesome guy. I'm really impressed. John and you are lucky to have each other. Bet you have hot sex together."

"So you think John's hot?"

I reply in the affirmative. "Hell yeah. I like his ass."

"Who do you think is better looking?"

I laugh, and manage to verbalize a direct, unedited honest thought: "Have to see you both naked to judge *that* one."

Dave says, "From the look of that package, I bet you got a ten-foot pole." His breath reeks of alcohol and cigarettes.

"What were you drinking all night?" I ask.

He starts kissing my neck and doesn't answer. I seize his hand and move it up to my crotch. It's so exciting to put his hand here. He grabs my erection through my pants and lifts his eyebrows. He's got the face of a little boy, with a faint moustache that looks like it's growing in for the first time.

I grin as I close my eyes and reach for his cock. We start making out and are interrupted by voices coming toward the car. We hear John saying goodnight to a few people. When he gets to the car, Dave tells John he invited me to party with them.

"Sure. Got a car?" John asks me.

"Yeah."

"Got a place we can go to party?"

"No," I say.

I suppose my one-word answers are what prompt John to chuckle and say to Dave, "He sounds like a real intellectual," devoid of any concern that I'm sitting right here. He assumes I'm too drunk to care about his insult.

John gets in the driver's seat and says, "Go get your car and follow us."

I run to my car, completely drunk off my ass, and start it. I'm so fucking blitzed. My body is relaxed, and I have a warm feeling inside. Nadine is miles away from my thoughts, and for once I feel good. I've got somewhere to go and something to do. These guys want to party with me. I'm busy, I don't need her attention. She can't hurt me now. I pull up beside them and Dave shoots me a smile.

"This is for the road!" he yells, tossing me the bottle of Orange Mad Dog.

"Thanks!" I shout back, as I barely catch it. Clumsy with everything else, I manage fine when liquor is thrown my way. We pull out of Gatsby's parking lot and onto Route 70.

After a half-hour drive, we arrive at an apartment complex and John says, "We're going to see this guy who was Dave's old high school principal. We can party with him."

I feel uneasy while Dave bangs and bangs on the door. John also seems disturbed by it. He says, "Let's go. He's probably not here."

Dave is persistent. "His car is here. He's probably in bed."

I notice my buzz wearing off. I feel pain in my legs from dancing and standing all night. I don't recall sitting that much over the last eight hours.

I say, "I'm leaving. I don't think we should be doing this." John agrees, nodding.

Dave says, "Wait one minute. He'll answer."

We wait. Dave knocks. We wait. Suddenly, a fat old man in a purple robe opens the door. "Dave, what's up?" he says. Dave pushes his way in and we wait outside. Soon after, Dave pops his head out and invites us in. As I walk past the older gentleman, Dave introduces him to me as Russell, and he looks me up and down. Dave snickers at a disapproving John. We all sit on the couch and Russell turns on the TV and finds MTV. Dave invites me into the kitchen where he's preparing a drink.

"Would you care for a cocktail?"

"Why, sure," I say. We make ourselves comfortable in this man's kitchen as I throw a shot back before helping Dave make everyone a cocktail. I arrange the drinks on a tray Dave locates from memory. I can't imagine how Dave and this former principal discovered an informal friendship like this.

A porno is on when we return to the living room. My refreshed buzz demolishes my inhibitions and eliminates any remaining discomfort. It isn't long before Dave and John start fooling around on the floor, and I join in the performance for an audience of one.

After a few hours of what turns out to be some of the best sex I've had, we get up and head for the bathroom. I follow Dave into the bathroom and John shuts the door behind us in Russell's face, locking it.

"I hate that creep," John says loudly.

"At least he let us use his place," Dave answers, defending Russell.

John doesn't care, saying, "I still detest him. I don't like him watching."

Dave says, "I thought it was kind of exciting." I can tell John doesn't like that remark, because he gives him a lingering expressionless look.

The shower is equally enjoyable for all of us. "You could be in a soap commercial," John says as I soap up my chest. I smile as we rub our smooth, wet and soapy bodies together. It's outstanding. Dave is tall and lean with a smooth bubble butt and sexy thick cock. John is shorter and beefy with an even more amazing smooth muscular ass. It's tight and sexy and it's electrifying to fuck him again. This time I bend Dave over and plug him as well.

We take our time, each savoring a second semi-private orgasm with each other.

When I get to my car, Dave asks me to hang on a second. I get the car running, waiting for him. Dave comes over and hands me a folded piece of paper and says, "We're getting our own place. Here's our new address. Maybe we could get together sometime? I sure would love to be with you again." I smile as he turns to get in his car and shove the address in my wallet.

Sunday, September 11, 1988: 8:00 p.m.

After Chris and I watch the Eagles lose to the Cincinnati Bengals 28-24 at Veterans Stadium, we head over to Gatsby's.

When we pull into GB's parking lot, several cars are already there. Inside, we meet up with several of Chris's friends; they all seem to belong to this small community playhouse in Haddonfield and are performing in the play. It's semi-interesting listening to them, watching them and observing their personal habits. Chris introduces his buddies one by one, but I only hear, "Tom, this is Brian."

"Hi, man."

"Hey," I answer, as the dude eyes me up and down. Chris is talking non-stop, and the group is engrossed in his wit and knowledge of gay actors and actresses. I snatch a red stirrer from the bar and begin to swirl it in my Manhattan. I gaze into the glass, and watch the cherry swirl around in the caramel-colored liquor.

Brian nudges me and asks, "Want to play pool?" Nodding as I look over at Chris, who hasn't stopped jabbering to his buds, I follow Brian into the game room. We square up the balls and take on a lesbian couple at a game. We play till I start swaying from the damn liquor — I'm now up to my third Manhattan. The only way I can tell how many drinks I've had is by counting the number of empty glasses I've turned upside down on the shelf next to the pool table.

Chris and entourage come over and watch us finish winning the game. From where I stand, I see Nick dart in and out of the game room. Nick is in Branch Administration at First Commercial. The branch I work in was just built in April, so Nick and I met in April, when he was around for the set up and grand opening. I had a fling with him over the summer. It lasted all of three months. Nick keeps glaring at me. He was crushed when I ended it, but I was poised to begin my life with Nadine; and even though he's only 30, I didn't think we had too much in common.

Chris leans his head on my shoulder and announces, "I'm going to dance."

His buddy Brian and I finish playing pool and move to the bar. He offers to buy me another Manhattan, but I reject it, feeling fucked up.

"Just a ginger ale," I say. He laughs and directs the bartender to give me the ginger ale and to "Throw some whiskey and club in with it." I smile and turn away, feeling myself dig him.

"What time is it?" Brian asks.

I check out my watch, "It's only 11:00." We finish our drinks, watching Chris and their friends dancing with our backs up against the bar.

I turn and notice Brian noticing me.

"Oh come on," I say, taking him by the hand. We find our way to the back bathroom and go into a stall. Inside we start kissing and dropping our pants. I push his head downward, and the door to the stall bursts open as he drops to his knees. He turns to shut the door and returns to sucking my cock. I lean back and close my eyes, enjoying. I lift him up and turn him around and kiss his hair, his neck and work my way down. He's got a sweet blonde body and a sexy hairless bubble butt. I begin pounding his ass. Just as I'm about to unload into the condom, we hear Chris enter the bathroom, saying to one of their other buds, "Do you want to go home?"

"Well, I'm still not feeling well and I'm kind of tired."

We stop and quickly reset our pants. Brian's eyes widen, and I shake my head as if to silence him. Chris finishes his piss with their pal and they exit. We depart one at a time and return to the group.

After another hour of bullshit, Chris is ready to go.

We get in the car and Chris suggests, "I'd like to take you somewhere and make love." The *make love* part is irritating, since I associate and reserve the term "lovemaking" with Nadine and women in general. Sex with guys is exactly that. I don't associate intimacy or love with men.

"Sure," I answer, eager for sex. "I'll follow you," I say, and walk back to my T-Bird. I follow Chris out of GB's and across Route 70. There's a notorious park across 70 surrounding Cooper River that's known for promiscuous sexual liaisons. We drive up a winding road leading to a deserted large parking lot for the local Jewish Community Center. Chris jumps out of his car and walks over to my window.

"Wanna go in the wooded area over there?" he asks, pointing toward a tuft of woods surrounding the lake. It's a river, but looks more like a lake.

"Hell no! I don't want bugs up my ass."

Chris laughs. "Well, where?" With both of us living with our parents, it's a difficult thing to find a place to fuck. Despite having lots of cash to burn, I'm not about to sink any into paying for a motel room for a 20-minute fuck, so I don't even suggest it.

"My car."

Chris runs around to the passenger door and hops in. I tune the radio to DJ Frank Cerami's Quiet Storm on Power 99 and we start making out. We have our arms around each other and after 20 or so minutes of making out, I notice the windows are all fogged up. He's whispering in my ear, trying to make the moment romantic.

"Don't ever leave me," he whispers while grabbing at my crotch. By the light of the moon, we undress in the close quarters while remaining lip-locked. His body is lean, but his chest and arms are muscular. Sex with Chris isn't bad. He's got a small, tight ass and we find it easy to fit together. I rip the condom open with my teeth and struggle a sec to shove it on my cock. Within moments, I'm deep inside him and it isn't long before we're done. He has a notion that we're going to sit and revel in the moment.

After sex, I get dressed quickly and he echoes my movements instinctively but reluctantly. I reach for the ignition and turn the key. *Click, click, click.* Nothing. Fuck! I turn it again. Nothing. Fuck again. I turn and look at Chris.

He grins saying, "Try it again." I turn the ignition. The lights in the dash glow but nothing budges. Shit. *What am I going to do?* I wonder.

"Now what?" Chris asks.

I pop the hood and get out to look. Chris joins me, and after what seems like an eternity of poking around, we determine I need a jump.

"Do you have jumper cables?"

"Yeah."

We attempt to jumpstart the engine. It's unsuccessful, probably because his rust-bucket car doesn't have enough juice to spare.

"Goddammit! I better get a cab!"

Chris holds my hand and says, "Don't worry. Look, it's ten of two. I'll drive you home."

"But I live in Wrightstown near Fort Dix."

"Yeah, so, what's that? A half-hour from here?"

"Well, yeah, more hour than half."

"I don't care. What am I going to do? Leave you stranded?"

"Aw, this is so cool of you!" I say, going with it.

Reality bursts back in later, as he kisses me on the cheek as we stop in front of the house. "Call me."

"Yeah. Thanks again, Chris."

Monday, September 12, 1988

"And so my Dad and I went to get the car and when I told him I made out in the Jewish Community Center parking lot with a nice Italian girl, he was pleased," I say to Billy over the phone.

"You're kidding!" he responds.

"Nope. Swear to Christ. Dad and I jumped the car this morning, and I was only an hour late."

"You're lucky, man," he says.

"I know, I know."

"Did you tell Chris yet?"

"No, not yet. So how was your weekend?"

"We ended up at the Crestway." The Crestway is a dingy motel on Route 130 in Pennsauken. "We had…"

Billy pauses, then says, "Gotta run, that bitch is calling me," referring to Letitia, his manager. Lucky for him, she's being reassigned to a new branch soon. He's often bitched about her. His experience with Letitia is totally different than Janet's experience. Janet and Letitia have been friends since Janet worked with her in the Kings Highway branch. We hang up.

He called me this morning, cautiously trying to get back on speaking terms with me. I can't hold a grudge; I love talking to him. He's the only one I can really talk to about the gay experience in my life. It's fun chatting about our weekend exploits.

Friday, September 23, 1988

Mitch had a job for me in DC last Friday, so I decided to make a mini-vacation out of it. I spent some of the wad of cash I've been making on a puddle-jumper flight from Philly to the capital, rented a brand new red Mazda RX7 — my dream car — and after partying in DC on Friday, I drove back, stopping in Baltimore to party on Saturday night.

The DC job was for some cheap affluent bitches. They didn't tip, but it didn't matter; I made $400 on the job, given mileage. Mitch had several jobs waiting for me on Sunday. It's cool to make money faster than I can spend it. I remember busting my teenage ass cutting an acre of grass for twenty bucks.

I don't have any dancing jobs this weekend, so I'm taking another puddle-jumper from Philly to NYC. Flying up is such a disgusting waste of money. The flight, the taxi, the hotel; it's all so decadent and imprudent. My parents would be appalled. I reserve a $200-a-night room at the Grand Hyatt.

Wednesday, October 5, 1988

"Hi Mitch," I say when he answers. I just called him after not hearing from him for a full week.

"Hey, Tombo."

"What's on this weekend?"

"Kind of slow lately. Only got one for you, but it's for next weekend — Saturday the 15th. It's for some frat girls at Trenton State College." I'm silent for a long time. "Tom, you there?"

"Yeah, Mitch, go ahead with the info."

"Well, here's the thing. It's an easy hundred bucks for you. I got you twenty more for mileage."

"Thanks."

"It's up in Trenton, of course. Wear casual clothes — nothing hard. Easy money. I tried to sell them the pizza delivery, but they wouldn't. It's C.O.D. — that means you get the money first."

I've done dozens of jobs for him, and he always tells me C.O.D. means collecting the money before doing the job. "Ordered by Sheryl Kaytes. That's Sheryl with an S. She's ordering it for Crystal Lee. Twenty-first birthday for Crystal — hold on, Tom, hold on, hold on. I've another call coming through." I could hear Mitch pick up the other line and then start yelling, "Marie, Marie! You got line 2? Marie! Lisa! Hey! Line 2 is ringing. Entertainment, this is Mitch, can I help you? What? Hold on... No, we don't do them. No, we don't do sex shows. What? Hold on, hold on...Lisa!"

"What?"

"Call on Line 2! Tom, I'm back. You there?"

"Yeah, Mitch, I'm here."

"Oy, where was I?"

One thing that irritates me about Mitch is that he gives the driving directions really fast and expects me to automatically know where I'm going. If he gets interrupted, which is often, he gets back on the line and tries to rush through the remainder of the directions. Mitch promises to call back if something comes up.

I've had so much work from him and made some amazing money, socking away thousands in the bank. Mitch has sent me on jobs from Harrisburg to the Atlantic and from NYC to Baltimore and DC. Still, despite all that I've made, I heard another agency located here in New Jersey pays their male dancers more per job.

I have a meeting set up with Dory, the owner of the other agency, tomorrow at 4:30.

Thursday, October 6, 1988, 4:20 p.m.

I enter the Riverside-based agency and find it decorated in a contemporary style, with curving chic couches and winding walls leading to a receptionist's desk. I tell the receptionist why I'm here, and she points to a station with teas, coffee and lemon water. She tells me to help myself while I wait. I pour some water into a stylish glass and pick up a magazine.

After a few moments, she takes me to the back room and introduces me to Dory. Dory is gorgeous, with a magnificent figure, greeting me when I look her way. She's well-built, a handsome woman in her early 40s. She doesn't have the washed-out stripper look so many women in the business have. She's fresh and glamorous.

"Why, you must be Tom." Her voice is clear and direct, and she possesses a welcoming smile.

"Yes, I'm Tom," I manage.

Dory walks up, extending her hand.

"Come with me," she says, leading me into another room, holding my hand. She smoothly grabs my other hand, and now we face each other, holding hands. She holds them up and looks me up and down.

"You're striking. Mind if I smoke?" I don't mind, still smitten with her compliment. "Would you care for a drink?"

"Sure," I answer. Dory steps behind a large black bar in the corner of the room.

"Scotch?" I remain silent, but smile and nod. She pours a drink and walks it over to me and hands me the glass. I take a drink and smile again; I smile out of nervousness. For a moment, we remain silent, looking at each other, sipping our drinks.

She sits down on the hunter green leather couch. "Sit, please." I sit next to her and feel my face get hot.

"Tom, I run a really great place. We keep to ourselves and we expect our dancers to do the same. I don't want my dancers associating with each other or with clients."

I sit, nodding, sneaking peeks at the cleavage exposed by the red business suit she's wearing.

"Customers are always calling saying, 'Dory, the guy you sent us was so good. He made us feel comfortable.' I love those calls, and I like my clients. We have a great many regulars. Do you have a regular clientele where you're working?"

"Yes, I've had some call-backs and referrals."

"I see. I want to see you dance. Are you okay with that?"

"Sure. I brought one of my tapes."

She takes it, gets up to put it in her audio system and comes to sit back down with a remote in her hand. "All I have to do is push Play, so whenever you're ready."

"Let's go," I say, prepared for it. I take a deep breath, and I begin when I hear the sounds of my first song, "Midas Touch" by Midnight Star. I'm careful to keep my moves to the beat and end the song with a snake-like landing, chest supported by my hands, allowing my midsection and legs to come down ever so slowly, demonstrating the upper body strength I've worked so hard to achieve.

The dance I do, I do for me. I feel my spirit fly, happy and pleased with my performance. Have to say it's one of my best. My moves are right; everything feels smooth and well done. I'm confident about my performance. The second song on the tape is "He Wants My Body" by Starpoint.

The rhythm, the beat, and the words of former pals Choon-yei and Bryan, who taught me how to dance, are all over my head, all over my body. I close my eyes and visualize Janet Jackson and emulate her moves, her passion for her music. Dory sits back and watches without expression, clearly thinking more like a businessperson than a woman. I jam, pump, and bounce. With a burst of energy, I surge forward and my pants swoop down around my ankles. I roll them around in front of me so they dangle from my feet. Lying on my back, I edge toward Dory, kicking my feet to visually entice her to remove my pants.

"Don't involve me," she shouts over the music. Totally into what I'm doing, I ignore her behest and relay a playful yet sexy pout, thrusting my legs toward her. Exuding an emotionless resolve, Dory pulls my pants off, tossing them across the floor like they're rags. She crosses her arms over her chest as a pleasant grin spreads across her face. I stand up, then immediately jump back on the floor, crawling on my hands up to her feet. I remove one of her shoes, and run the high heel down my chest slowly as I lay at her feet. She parts her lips and I see her chest rise as she takes a deep breath. I replace the shoe and lie back, bring my knees up to my chest and use the weight of my lower body to propel me back up to my feet as I thrust my feet out and upward until I'm standing upright. It's a move I've been working on for some time and I'm elated it's perfected. I finish with a bow. I sit down on the floor, wearing only my black g-string.

She's quiet, then says, "Don't bow when you're done, Tom. It's tacky."

I nod, letting the coaching land, eager for some praise.

She says, "Kind of different ... it's good."

I stand and ask if there's anything else she wants to see before I get dressed. She shakes her head and turns away quickly. Once dressed, I sit back down on the couch with her. "I'm ready to give you a try," she tells me. "Are you interested?"

"Oh, cool, thanks," I say, anxious to hear the pay rate.

"I have a job to fill next Saturday night." She rises to retrieve a book and a pair of glasses from the bar. She goes over the date and details of the job.

"What will you pay?" I ask.

Dory turns to me and says, "Thirty bucks."

That offer sucks, and we both know it. I'm wasting my time. She makes it worse with her next comment: "If — and I do mean if — my customer likes you, I'll invite you back for more work. I am prepared to offer you $50 per job."

I get up and go for my bag. "May I have my tape please?" I ask.

Dory asks, "Don't you have any questions?"

I have no questions. I'd never be back. I'll do this job for the $30, since it's easy, but that's it.

"The job is paid. I'll mail you a check. Please call me if you have any questions later. Stop with Misty on your way out and get the details." She hands me my tape and I start walking out. Dory catches up with me and hands me a cassette.

"You'll be a nerd. You can do that, right?"

"Yes, of course," I say curtly.

Saturday, October 8, 1988

Chris calls and catches me right before I leave to hit the gym. He invites me to dinner. I'm not really interested in seeing him, but I'm suddenly consumed with the feeling that I owe him more than to dump him over the phone. He was nice to drive me home that night. I agree to meet him with the caveat that we go Dutch.

I have to explore this man fully before I flush it completely. It's worth one more look. I'm going to have a serious conversation with him today, and try to retain his friendship while ending this so-called relationship. I've never been any good at letting people go. I've balanced as many as five suitors at a time because I've struggled to let anyone go. I like the attention and affection these good looks bring. The experience with Nadine was a painful lesson and a wake-up call for me. In my egotistical delusion, I believed less-attractive people were unchallenging, uncomplicated, unable to earn my deepest love and would never leave me. The joke is on me.

I'm social to the extent that it results in something I need, but avoid socializing to gather friendships. There's something deep inside me that fears connecting to people. I think it's a fear of abandonment, as evidenced by how I'm dealing with this most recent break with Nadine. Being in control of relationships and being sought after overshadows any self-confidence. When you have everything and people come easy, it becomes simple to believe you have forever to avoid abandonment through the risk of any serious commitment.

We arrive at the Venture Inn. It's located on a street too small for cars; some of these old streets in Philly date back to Colonial days and are more like alleys. I realize I've been here before with Nick. The more I observe his motions, his looks and hear his voice, the more I dislike Chris — and that's unfair to Chris and to me. He could be perfect for someone. Someone else.

"Tom," he tells me, "I want to tell you how much I like you. I hope you can forgive me, but I've got a rehearsal tonight, so I've got to go to the playhouse. I wanted to see if we could get a room somewhere."

I have to tell him. I build up my courage to speak and what happens? "Would you care for a drink?" our server asks. Chris looks at me.

"A Manhattan, please," I say.

Chris, with eyes fixated on me, says, "Strawberry daiquiri."

"That's a nice cold drink and lots of fun," I say, acting fidgety.

Our drinks arrive and Chris says, "Tom, it would make me the happiest man in the world if we could commit to each other."

I look down and speak to my glass, avoiding eye contact with him, "Chris, I don't think I am ready to be..." I take a breath and continue, "...to commit to anyone right now."

Visibly distressed, Chris blasts me with, "What do you want? To continue in the bars like you have been? Slutting around like me and my friends have watched you do?"

That was loud. A couple at the table next to us, two polished lipstick lesbians, glance over. I'm more pissed than embarrassed and feel my face get hot. It's obvious Chris had been watching me before we met. What a freak.

I feel that Chris can sense my uneasiness. He says, "Sorry. That was wrong. Please forgive me. I don't know why I said that. You're just... I mean... I want to be with you."

I remain silent, thinking, trying to put on the most innocent puppy-dog face I can. He continues paying compliments, talking about "us" and his acting, which makes it easy to get through dinner because I can just nod and smile. While he gabs, I think about what I plan on doing the rest of the weekend.

We leave the restaurant, and it's pouring rain. We stand for a moment under the tarp of the restaurant. I met him at his parent's house in Jersey and we drove over here in his car, which is in a lot a few blocks away.

"Follow meeeeee!" Chris shouts, taking off into the rain, and I take a deep breath and follow him into the downpour. Within seconds, I'm completely drenched. We race through another alley and around the corner of another alley. Rounding the corner, I slip and land on the ground. Chris looks back and says, panting, "What kind of dancer are you?" We both laugh as he comes back to help me back on my feet. We stop for a moment in the rain and kiss. It's nice. I'm cold, yet warm inside. His black hair is more curly than usual. This is fun, but he's definitely not someone I'm interested in pursuing.

We reach a door that doesn't have a shelter from the rain. Chris bangs on the doorknocker. No answer. "My friend lives here."

"Knock again!" I yell. The door opens and a young, tall, very well-built man answers.

He eyes Chris and me and says, "Chris! Come in! Come in!"

We step into the narrow doorway and begin walking up a narrow staircase covered with Indian pottery and piles of books. Chris introduces me to the fine looking young man. "Tom, this is Chad."

Chad and I shake hands and exchange lusty looks. Walking upstairs, I notice framed pictures of Bette Davis, Joan Crawford, Billy Haines and other movie stars. Once upstairs Chris introduces me to Chad's lover, a man who has to be in his 60s. "And this is Benny."

Benny stands to shake my hand. He extends his hand palm down. He's heavyset with several rings on his fingers, and a gold necklace around his bull-like neck bearing the Star of David shimmering in the light.

"You sure have a hot one here, Chris," he says, not letting go of my hand.

"Let me get you guys some towels," Chad says, disappearing into one of the rooms. He returns with two large beach towels.

"Oh, thanks! We can share one of these!" I say, taking one and opening it. I give Chris half of the towel and rub my hair and head with the other half.

"Let me get you guys some coffee," Chad offers.

"No, it's okay. We can't stay," Chris says.

"It's made! Just take a sec," Chad answers.

I look around. Their place is large, filled with books and all sorts of movie memorabilia, matted posters of famous old movies, and a huge piano in the living room. "This is a great place," I begin. "How about I help you with the coffee and you give me a tour?" I direct my question toward Chad.

"Oh sure, cool," he says, "Follow me." I rise to follow him, as Chris and Benny are already engaged in conversation.

We go up another flight of stairs and within minutes, we're groping and kissing each other, acting on sheer animal instinct. We fall into a bed and I grunt out a whisper, "How the fuck did you get that piano up those narrow stairs?"

"It was here when I got here," he says, lifting his legs so I can position myself to enter him. He finds a condom in a nearby drawer along with some lube. I get the condom on and ram it in his perfect perky butt. After a few pumps, the condom comes off and I keep pumping him without it. I empty a load into Chad just after he shoots a load from the big wide dick he's been whacking off. We quickly pull ourselves together as we climb back downstairs and into the kitchen. Coffee is already made, so I fix myself a cup and follow Chad out with the tray.

I sit sipping coffee, feeling my heart racing from the workout with Chad. I'm bored in seconds with Chris and Benny's conversation. Comfortable as it is, I'm ready to go in fifteen minutes. Chris tells them he has to get to rehearsal and we say our good-byes. Chad rises to shake my hand; Chris notices Chad's lingering stare, and hurries our exit down the stairs. We begin walking to the car. The rain stops and there are huge puddles everywhere.

Inside my head, I compare the rain to my relationship with Chris: It's over, and I couldn't care less. Well, that was fun. I'm going back home.

When we get to his house, I say, "Chris, we're not meant for each other. I think you're a great person and we've had us some great times, but I'm not interested."

Chris, unbelievably, shrugs it off and says, "Ehh, you just need time to settle down and get used to it. I'll catch you over at GB's tomorrow night."

TAKE-OFF

Sunday, October 9, 1988

I arrive at the job on Sunday at precisely 9:00. It's for a woman in her mid-30s, at The Shark Club in Delaware County, Pennsylvania. Right inside the entrance is a huge room with a dance floor surrounded by aquaria. Big white bubbles surrounding the dance floor light up in different colors. I love it. It's ultra-relaxing in here. The woman for whom I'm to perform is called Wendy; she's brought out to the dance floor with a chair. For a moment, it's kind of tacky having her sit out there waiting. I give the DJ my selections, and he says, "The songs you got here are all kind of slow."

I dislike his attitude. "You know what I need?" I ask bitterly. "A DJ who can just play my music."

He shrugs, saying, "Well, I can liven these songs up for you. Plus, I have the new one by Taylor Dayne you might like, called 'Willpower'." I'm cautious, but a bit embarrassed when he sounds like he's genuinely trying to help. After listening to the new song on his earphones, I'm sold on dancing to it without practice.

"Look, man, do what you can, as long as the entire gig doesn't go over 15 or 20 minutes," I tell him. He gives me a thumbs-up, and I lift my fist to him as if making a toast — to which he meets my fist with his in a gentle gesture of teamwork.

He introduces me as I pounce down the stairs of the DJ booth to the dance floor. Encircling the dance floor, I scope out the large crowd and walk up to Wendy. The

DJ plays a mix of one of my songs, "I Should Be So Lucky," that I haven't heard before. It's more energetic. Wendy is all smiles as I dance. This is fun. I walk to the crowd and grab a mug of beer that's nearly empty from one of the women who looks easygoing. I pour it on my chest and run my hand up through the suds, ending up doing a floor dance — twisting, pumping and humping the floor at her feet. The crowd is remarkably receptive and lively. I'm pleased with the DJ's work; the mix is right, and when I dance to "Willpower" I realize I have to adopt it into my future gigs. I end by going up to her and whispering, "Thanks for letting me dance for you, Wendy! You're very beautiful."

I always tell them they're beautiful. They love hearing it, and it's usually true. The crowd converges on the dance floor, and I make my narrow escape.

9:45 p.m.

I put on my favorite jeans, medium-blue and worn to perfection. I put on my standard classic black tank top. I pull on my black Pumas and head out. No need to check the mirror; I know it works. Within an hour I'm at Gatsby's and notice that it's packed for a Sunday night. I find a parking spot on the rear side of the club's lot, behind the pizza joint. A cute guy parks a few spaces down from me. I exit the car, and as I walk, I see that my shoe is untied. I bend to tie it. As I do, I notice the cute guy from the other car stop and smile at me. I smile back.

Once inside, I get a beer from one of bartenders I've always flirted with. He spoils me by giving me a beer in a huge frosted mug. I find a place to perch at a standing table near the dance floor, and my mind slips into memory again. I'm far away, reminiscing about the time Nadine and I danced here.

There's a menagerie of hot muscle boys on the floor. Among the crowd I see John and Dave dancing. Dave catches my stare and waves. Memories of our threesome come back and I feel my cock stir. Dave grabs his crotch while dancing, and makes frequent glances in my direction. I avoid further eye contact. He struts up to me with a grin on his face, all sweaty, gasping, "You're one of the hottest guys in here."

I take a sip from my jumbo mug of beer and wipe the foam from my lips to say, "What's shakin?"

Suddenly, I catch sight of a guy dancing by himself, looking at his own reflection in the wall mirror. I don't catch Dave's response, feeling something wonderful but strange in the pit of my stomach. Rather than ask him to repeat himself, I smile and nod. He walks backwards toward John, clapping and moving to the beat, raising and lowering his eyebrows, watching me. I look back at the guy dancing and feel it again: a peculiar feeling I've never experienced. I feel a tingly sensation inside my head, just looking at him. Normally any good-looking guy I'd look at would be just that: a good-looking guy. This man is definitely beyond being just another pretty face. He's beyond handsome, unusually suave and exciting. He continues dancing alone, gazing at his own reflection in the wall mirror by the dance floor.

I find I can't keep my eyes off him. He's absolutely stunning. His looks are pleasing to my eyes, not only in a sense of sexual curiosity but also from a stand-point of sheer admiration for the work of our Creator. He sways his hips and has one hand palm-down and open across his lower chest, the other hand extended outwards. He pumps to the beat and mouths the words to the song. I scope the room and notice that I'm not his only enthusiast. Other men have him on radar, observing his dancing.

I'm fixated on this figure now.

To my surprise, he's looking at me now, too. It hits me. This is the guy from the parking lot — the guy I thought was really hot! A guy I went to high school with, Jeff, starts dancing with this fine specimen. I look over, and Jeff leaves the guy dancing alone again. I'm surprised to see Jeff appear at my side. Maybe he's upset that I was staring at his catch. "Hey, what's shakin'?" I ask cautiously. He's sweat-ing profusely from all the wild unneeded dance moves he made on the floor. Jeff resembles a bug, with beady eyes under dark-rimmed glasses on a thin oval face.

"Tommy Boy, what's up, bro?" I immediately ask him where he met the hot guy. He tells me, "He's a friend of mine, and it's funny you say that — he noticed you staring at him. I told him I knew you…"

My heart jumps and I'm instantly excited. "He did? You did?" I say, cutting him off. Jeff smiles and takes a drink of my beer.

"Yeah, he likes you. You should go for it. He's a nice guy. Go get it. You two would make a great-looking couple."

Couple? I think to myself. He laughs and jumps back on the dance floor, danc-ing by himself to the title track to the motion picture *Footloose*. I look up and notice that the cute guy has disappeared. The DJ has fog covering the dance floor now, so I can't see a thing. I squint my eyes and scan the room, searching for him.

I walk back to lean against the wall next to the DJ booth, holding a beer in my hand. I find a great spot to stand, right on the edge of the dance floor. Chris walks in with his entourage and, without stopping, grabs my hand and starts pulling me to the dance floor, "Tom, hi, let's dance…" he says, feeling me tug back. I don't want to humiliate him in front of his friends, but I've already made it clear that I'm not interested.

"Look, Chief, I'm gonna sit this one out."

"What do you mean?"

"Chris, I told you I don't want to dance."

"Still want to be a slut?" he asks, heading to the dance floor alone.

"What?" I ask, unsure if I heard him correctly.

He makes a hand gesture like a gun shooting me and then gives me the middle finger and joins his friends on the dance floor. He's glaring at me, and I suspect he'll be back over here as soon as the song finishes. I turn around to leave and bump right into Jeff's friend, the dreamy guy.

"Ooops, pardon me," I say, feeling my heart jump again.

"Am I in the middle of something?" he responds, pointing to Chris and then me.

"Oh, no, no I...," I start to say something, realizing he must have observed that scene with Chris.

"He's cute. Are you sure you know what you're doing?"

I shake my head and take a drink of my beer, not overly prepared for that question.

"I'm Tom. I bought another beer for you."

I look down into my almost empty glass and take the mug from him."Thank you, my name's Tom too!" I shake his hand and he smiles brightly.

"That's one I won't forget," he says.

"Me, too," I say, immediately in awe, struck by his aura. I don't exactly know what it is, but he's so different from anyone I've ever met up to this point in my life. I start checking him out as we stand next to each other. He is so hot — even better-looking up close. I get deep sexual urges, longing to devour him completely. The space between us is filled with electricity.

He's wearing a thick black-and-white stitched wool sweater with leather shoulder pads, which looks so chic. I have a terrible habit of staring at people, and I like the fact that he stares back. "You have incredible eyes," he says.

I see he has a necklace on but it's inside his sweater, the gold chain gleaming around his sexy neck. I'm instantly smitten with him, and feel my body heat up from the proximity of his. He has the sweater tucked into good-looking dark blue jeans with black leather boots. He's wearing a gold watch on one wrist, and a gold bracelet on the other. His thick masculine bracelet is comprised of gold letters spelling "T-h-o-m-a-s." He brings his mug up to his lips, and I see a college or high school ring on one finger. He has a gold hoop earring in his left ear, and he smells so fucking good. He's about four inches taller than me and has a smooth, clean-cut boy-next-door look. He has clear skin with rosy cheeks, short brown hair, combed to the side — very neatly — without sideburns. He has piercing brown eyes with sexy thick eyebrows. I'm enraptured by his looks.

He smiles, and somehow I feel warmed inside because of it, warmed as if in some way he's renewed my hope and spirit with one smile. Just one smile provides a wave of more soothing comfort and relief than an hour on the massage table. It feels so fucking good. He just stands there and captivates me. He takes my hand and leads me across the dance floor. We put our beers down and he jumps up to sit on a large black speaker, and I face him, looking up into his handsome face. He grabs my shoulders and pulls me into him. With one swoop I kiss him gently on the lips. He meets my aggressiveness head-on and satisfies my lust for passion. The kiss ignites my desire for intimacy. He knows what he's doing in kissing and I love it. I observe, absorb and love his sensitive, gentle ways. He grins at me as I turn, placing his arms around my waist and holding me.

This is absolutely, without a doubt, one of the most phenomenal moments in my life. My spirit is lifted, knowing everyone can see what I've attracted with my looks: the best-looking man in the place has his arms around me. I feel safe, secure, confident, and very attractive. I feel a sense of fulfillment, an overwhelming comfort and connection I've not experienced in my life before. If this moment could only last forever… It's got to be a dream. I have to be dreaming. I strain to catch a look in the wall mirror next to me. When I do, I catch my reflection standing here in his arms. This tenderness is so natural, like a perfect fit.

Jeff pounces up upon us, singing his words, "Hey, look! It's Tom and Tom!" He smiles and continues; "It didn't take you two long."

Tom's words follow, opening a flood of emotion and excitement within my soul: "When you find the right person, it doesn't take long at all!"

Jeff walks back to the dance area and I turn to face Tom, saying, "That was… I mean, that's how I feel, too." He smiles at me, revealing a gorgeous set of teeth and a fabulous smile.

"Oh, I suppose it sounded kind of intense."

"How do you know Jeff?" I ask, hating my mouth for continuing to jabber. Why can't I stay quiet and just enjoy his arms around me?

He answers, "I know him from here. We talk from time to time."

"Did you two ever…?" I can't believe I just asked that. I'm so immature.

Tom makes a face, saying, "Uh, no. We're just friends."

I turn back and face the dance floor, regretting my question. I close my eyes and wonder what else will pour out of my mouth. I contemplate on whether he already knows me — or of me. I would have remembered if we'd fucked. Before my stupid brain can finish a thought, my stupid mouth blurts out, "Have you ever seen me in here?"

"Yes. I've seen you with Nick."

Nick, the 30-year-old dude in our Branch Administration Department at the bank. The guy I fucked all summer.

A million thoughts pour into my head, and it takes all my restraint to force my mouth to stay silent. Relax. Take a breath. You aren't in an interview.

To say Tom is extremely striking would be an understatement. His looks alone bring my eyes a pleasure equal to tasting a fine wine, or listening to great music. We watch people dance for a few songs, until a slow song, "Baby I Love Your Way" by Will To Power, comes on. Tom jumps down from the speaker and takes my hand, leading me to the dance floor.

Never in my life have I experienced such a high degree of wanting someone. We dance, holding each other so closely, and the feeling in this moment is a slice of heaven. We dance slowly and melt into each other, molding our bodies together. I can feel his body, even through his clothes, and it immerses me into a fierce pool of desire. I want him in ways I never imagined wanting a person.

I surmise this craving almost isn't a choice, since I can't think of what I'd be capable of if denied the luxury of owning him and being owned by him. Completely oblivious to where I am, I can only focus on knowing I'm in the right place at the right time. All my fears, sadness, and anxiety are gone. We hold each other tight, and I instinctively bury my face in his chest. He smells so fucking good. I want him so much. I look up into his eyes, and he smiles as the song breaks into an emotional part.

Unsatisfied with allowing chance to steal an unspoken sentiment, I say, "Tom, sometimes words can't express a feeling."

He closes his eyes and whispers in my ear, "I know. I feel good about this too."

I am enraptured by his softness, his tenderness. Everything that makes a man appealing to me is what he is — big, strong, unbreakable, and intelligent. No slow dance I've ever had compares to this. It's indescribable. As we dance, I feel his heartbeat. It feels robust and strong, and it makes me happy.

Maybe God has a purpose and a plan for me after all. I made a pact with God when I was a little boy. I told God I would be his instrument on Earth to make people happy. I was far too young to make such a promise, but I've never purposely reneged on it. I pledged to God that I was willing to do what he wanted me to do, so others could be happy. In my life, I've always sensed God's protection. I believe God took me up on the deal — and even though I've set my life loose in his hands, I'm still scared, still vulnerable to heartache, loneliness and pain.

I believe and trust in God, so I will sit back and enjoy the good times — like this — and recognize that my existence is entirely because of God. I stand by my decision to let him guide me to wherever I can somehow help others. If this is to be a new chapter in God's plan for me, though, I wonder what purpose I will serve. This certainly seems more like a gift for me.

"Were you the one I was staring at in the parking lot?" Tom asks.

"Parked a few cars down from you?" I answer his question with a question.

He smirks, saying, "I was thinking to myself, 'What a great looking guy!'"

His words elevate my already inflated ego. We hold each other closer and tighter as a snug feeling comes over me, one that says we're made for each other. Tom begins mouthing the words to the song. As it concludes, it's mixed into an up-beat tune and we continue dancing — checking out each other's moves and bodies, and absorbing more of each other's auras. Tom is a great dancer. I love the way he carries himself. There are so many things about him I'm enamored with: he's tall, sexy, and extremely sensual. His voice: calm, soft and collected. I find I'm attracted by the sheer energy he radiates.

The music finally stops, so the show can begin. Every Sunday night GB's has a male exotic dancer revue.

For some reason I feel that Tom — who is a cross between actors Jean Claude Van-Damme and the late great Jon-Erik Hexum with deep brown eyes as warm as a fireplace — is out of my league. I can't deserve this man with thick, luscious eye-brows and lashes. I'm not good enough to attract this man with such a terrific ass, so nice and round. My hand trembles as he holds it. While holding me in his arms while we danced, I was all into him. I love snuggling my face into his soft sweater on his husky chest, enjoying the scent of Obsession. I can't stop staring at him. My eyes are drawn to him like a magnet.

Tom gives the dancers a buck.

After the show ends, we dance on and on. I'm surprised by how many people Tom knows. Gatsby's is packed full for a Sunday night — probably because tomorrow is a holiday, Columbus Day, and a lot of people, like me, are off work.

"Would you like to go get some breakfast?" he asks. I feel the warmth of want inside me.

"Sure!" We chug down our beer and head for the coatroom.

When we reach Tom's car he says, "I want to take you for a drive before we go to Denny's."

You can drive me anywhere, I think. "Sure," I say.

We hop into his '85 Ford Lynx. As we drive, I barrage Tom with questions to which he answers, "I live in Glassboro; I'm going to Glassboro State for English; I want to be a teacher; my parents live over in Haddonfield; they pay for my education and my apartment; I've got one sister and she lives with her husband and daughter in Erial."

I'm impressed with his answers, but he could just sit there and say nothing, and I'd be impressed. Then it's my turn to answer some of his questions about me. I tell him where I'm from, where I grew up. I say, "I never really went to college. I started with a few courses at Burlington County College, though."

"So you have an Associate's degree?"

"No, I just took two or three courses there." We talk about what I do and where I work.

Tom says, "I manage the McDonald's in Glassboro."

I want to share more about me, but stay silent, absorbing everything he shares about his life. I like listening to him. There will be time for me to talk about my fabulous and tragic life. We arrive at an immense warehouse off Route 295 on the other side of Cherry Hill. The name outside the large blue edifice reads "Shaw." Tom pulls his black leather wallet from the inside pocket of his leather jacket. I read his name from the driver's license he hands me: *Thomas Shaw.* I point to the building without saying a word.

"My Dad owns the company," Tom says confidently.

"Oh, damn. We're not on the same playing field, brother," I say, now feeling Tom is even more out of my league.

"No worries," he says, "Let's get some grub." He smiles and we head back to Denny's in Cherry Hill on Route 70. Walking into Denny's, Tom asks me, "What's your last name?" When I tell him, he asks me if I'm Italian.

"I'm actually adopted. My birth father is English, and birth mother is Italian. I was adopted by an Italian Dad and French-Canadian Mom."

Tom lights up, saying, "My Dad's background is English, and my Mom's is Italian. We could be brothers!"

"Sounds like the making of a porno," I say, hoping he gets my attempt at bad humor. He instantly laughs. It's a wave of relief.

We walk into Denny's and are seated at a big corner table. Tom lights another cigarette and stares at me with a big smile. I start feeling my cheeks warm up.

"You're blushing," he says. I look down into my lap. Under the table he brushes his leg against mine. "Something interesting down there?" he asks. I look up quickly. His eyes are on my chest and he raises them to meet mine.

"What?" I ask.

"You're staring down at your..."

"Oh, yes. Uhh... no. I mean, I..." I just smile and shake my head.

He says, "I was like, 'Earth to Tom' for a minute there."

I look into his eyes and, though my heart is racing, I feel as calm as ever. My palms — which never sweat — are drenched. I feel like I'm floating and watching the interaction between us from the ceiling.

The waitress appears, breaking the spell, handing us menus and preparing place settings. Tom peeks over his menu at me and winks. She fills our water glasses and then disappears. Finally alone again, Tom says, "I think I'm having the Grand Slam breakfast."

I read from the menu — two eggs any style, two sausage links, two buttermilk pancakes, and two slices of bacon. "Sounds terrific." I'm going with the flow in this dream-like reality. I feel like I'm in a daze. I'm focused on wanting Tom badly. The waitress reappears and Tom and I don't break our stare this time. We gaze into each other's eyes.

Tom finally turns to order: "Two Grand Slams." She's immune to the fact that we're gay. The place is packed with lots of gays and straights making an exodus from the bars. She asks how we want our eggs, what we want to drink, and takes off.

Our staring resumes, esoteric thoughts communicated silently through our eyes. He reaches across the table and extends his hands. I place my hands in his — not even minding the fact that we're in a public place — and we hold each other's hands. It feels so good, and I feel proud being seen with him. This moment feels out of this world. Our food comes soon enough, and as we eat, we converse. I ask, "What about you?"

"What do you want to know?" he asks.

"Tell me something about you," I probe.

He confesses, "I've never slept with another Thomas."

"That makes one of us." I say. He loses his smile with my remark. I add to my statement, hoping to get his smile back, "There's just something about calling out your own name in ecstasy."

Tom looks down at his plate disapprovingly. I should be applauded at how much I can fuck things up. Now he probably thinks I'm a fucking slut.

"How old are you?" he asks.

"I'm 21," I answer and ask, "How old are you?"

"I'm 23. I'm a Taurus."

"April 15th. Aries."

His eyes light up and he says, "Wait until your birthday: I'm going to make you so happy."

His words inflate me with a sensation of reassurance, hope, and fulfillment. I believe he's capable of catapulting my heart to the stars. Eager to win him over, I read his mere mention of plans for my birthday as a sign he's interested in exploring and building a future together. Tom looks at me and once again, my heart fills with emotion.

As he eats, I notice Tom is a lefty. We finish eating and I fumble in my pocket to pull out some money.

"No. I got it," Tom says.

"No, let me give you something," I say, thinking we should split it.

Tom takes his wallet out from the inside pocket of his coat. He opens it and removes a $20 bill. I take notice of the wad of money inside the wallet. We walk up to the register together, pay and leave.

Tom holds my hand as we drive back to GB's. The comfort level he has in holding my hand astounds and delights me. I revel in the feeling of tenderness and affection. It's gotten cold out and I'm shivering. His hand is so warm, so soft and so big. I can't describe how perfect this feels. I realize I've never just held a man's hand before; what appeals to me most is that he's so big and strong, yet gentle and soft. I can get used to this.

Back at Gatsby's parking lot, we sit in his car for a moment and glance at each other. My mind is Jell-O. Tom leans in and kisses me slowly and softly. We open our lips and explore each other's mouth. His mouth tastes and feels so good. The kiss is very passionate, and I'm instantly erect. When he finishes the kiss, I give him another. Our faces come together and my lips find their way to his soft red cheeks. They feel so good to kiss — soft, yet hard and tight. I return to his mouth and we get lost in a sensual moment sharing another long kiss. When we finish, I swallow some of the saliva he left in my mouth while my heart pounds, and I'm convinced I've met the man with whom I'll spend the rest of my life. I ask matter-of-factly,

"Gotta work tomorrow?"

"Yes, I do," he replies, staring straightforward with a slight grin on his face. I want him in every way. *Can he feel the same?* I wonder.

"Can I give you a reason to call out tomorrow?" I ask without regret, fully comfortable I won't be rejected. Tom's face lights up.

"Sure!" We embrace and he says, "Follow me home."

I jump out of the car and walk over to mine. Once inside my car, I revel in feelings of happiness and excitement. The anticipation is ecstasy as I await the opportunity to sink my face into his luscious ass. We pull out of GB's parking lot and I follow Tom for a half an hour until we arrive at a remote adult bookstore — a nasty-looking blue shack with a dingy yellow sign reading *Aquarius.* In the middle of what seems like nowhere, two cars are parked in front of the place.

I get out of my car and ask, "Tom, why are we here?"

"I want to say hi to someone." He takes me by the hand and leads me inside. As we enter the dumpy establishment, Tom says, "Actually, I want to show you off." I feel myself blush. Inside is weird: On one side, the place is really bright with gleaming white lights shining on racks of porno magazines held up by strings tied across the wall. They must be going for the seedy look. Two guys standing at the tall glass counter look up as we enter. Tom approaches them while I stroll around looking at magazine covers. Tom calls me over. I approach the trio. The clerk looks vaguely familiar, but he recognizes me instantly. "Do I know you?" he asks. I'm glancing at the customer who also looks somewhat familiar.

I look back at the clerk who says, "Michael. Michael Ritter!"

I smile and shake his hand, "Tom Marino." I'm still fuzzy as to who he is; he must sense my bewilderment and says, "We met the other night at Gatsby's? You were with my brother Dave and his lover John?"

It's apparent he's annoyed that he wasn't memorable to me. Oh, shit. It's all coming back to me now. Could he know I had a threesome with them?

I smile at Michael and say, "Man, I was probably very drunk that night." The customer and Michael give a charity laugh and Tom leans forward on the counter, crossing his arms.

I keep glancing at the customer — extremely thin with his hair pulled back tightly into a ponytail. He finally says, "Do I know you?"

"I get the same feeling. Where from?"

"I'm Pat."

"Isn't your name really Pasquale?" I ask.

"Yeah," he snaps, adding, "I go by *Pat.*"

"You used to work at K-Mart with my ex-wife Nadine."

He looks disturbed that I've recalled something he already connected. I think it might be the fact that he worked at K-Mart, because Michael pipes in, "K-Mart?" and Pat says, "Oh yeah a while back — years ago. He looks me. "You married that bitch? You were only dating when I worked there."

Michael chimes in, "I never forget a pretty face. We were talking about you after you left that night. You used to be a stripper at Gatsby's."

"Yeah, I did," I say, smiling with my mouth closed tightly.

"You were Flash."

"Damn, how does everyone remember me? I wasn't that good, and I didn't dance there long."

"You were good. I liked you. Always wondered what happened to you."

I take a closer look at Michael, a dashingly handsome man firing compliments at me like bullets.

Tom asks, "Can I talk to you a sec?" Tom practically drags me by the hand to an unlighted section of the bookstore with black wooden private viewing booths. I can only imagine what goes on inside the booths. I hope Tom doesn't think we're going to have any kind of sex back here. It's very dark except for a purple ultraviolet light and the glow of the bright lights in the other section. Tom looks at me seriously, "Did you fuck Michael?"

I shake my head, saying, "No".

"Did he fuck you?"

"No!"

He continues, "I take you down here and you say you've never been in this area — you say you're from up in Mid-Jersey. And now you know both the people in this bookstore?"

I say, "Coincidence, I guess," smitten with my unexpected popularity, still shaken by the barrage of compliments from the very handsome Michael. Tom doesn't appear amused. I restate the fact that I just met Michael the other night and know Pat from K-Mart where Nadine had worked.

"What's up?" I ask, using a deeper tone in my voice. He looks at me again and comes really close to my face. I naturally back up. He places his hands on my shoulders and looks into my eyes and slowly says, "Did. You. Fuck. Michael."

It isn't a question. I get the meaning. My face suddenly gets hot and I feel weak. I start to tremble. I feel so fucking stupid, and for the first time in my life, I really feel like a slut. I start to speak, "Tom, I..." He moves in close to me. I can feel his breath on my face. He holds me close in his arms and I whisper to him in his ear, "Tom, I slept with his brother and his brother's lover."

I feel Tom let out a sigh of relief. Shit, I fucking blew it. He's probably turned off now. Shit. Shit. Shit.

Tom says, "Let's jet." He nods to Pat and Michael, and I shake their hands, saying, "Later."

We exit the place, and outside Tom lights a cigarette, takes a drag and says softly, "I'm glad you were honest with me. Michael has had AIDS for a couple years now. Over the past few months, he's been getting worse."

I fall back against the wall of the bookstore. Tom reaches over and pulls me from the wall into his arms. I'm horrified hearing it verbalized. Tom puts his arm around me and says, "Let's go home."

We get in our cars and leave the parking lot. I see signs indicating we're on the way to Glassboro, where Tom says he lives. Going through my mind is the mass of dildos and sex toys on the wall of the bookstore... how healthy, strong and robust Michael looks. What bothers me is that I would have slept with him, had I not known. I never realized how close I was to the virus. It was always something I heard about. A feeling of gloom comes over me as I reflect on my past sexual deeds. I take a deep breath. I crush the gloomy thoughts and give in to the growing sense of euphoria in meeting Tom and eagerly follow him down a long, dark road.

We arrive in Glassboro, a South Jersey college town. We pass the University, the College Town Shopping Center, and an after-hours bar called The Library. There are still lots of college kids our age walking around at this late hour. I envy them — being able to attend school full time, trying to build a sound foundation for their lives. I feel like I just drift through life on autopilot most of the time. With the exception of working out, dancing and trying to get promoted at the bank, life is pretty lackluster. I think for a moment about the money I have saved in the bank as a symbol of accomplishment, and relax a bit on the self-destruction.

We arrive at the apartment complex where Tom lives. It's called The Crossings. We get out and I stretch my legs. I follow him though a wide brick hallway into the courtyard to his apartment. Inside, the first thing that hits me is the smell of aromatic candles. I walk past a large brass coat rack. Tom takes his radar detector out from under his coat and puts it on the kitchen table; then we bump into each other as he steps back to hang up his coat.

"Can I have your coat?" he asks. I hand him my light blue windbreaker with

"Tom" sewn on the front. As I do, he reaches for my shoulders and pulls me into his lips for a long kiss.

As we walk into his living room I notice his apartment is kind of small, but very cozy. I get a warm feeling as I sink into his cushy, tan, loveseat. Tom has such exceptional, mature taste for someone his age. His décor is contemporary and sophisticated. "Can I get you something to drink?" he asks.

"Oh, no thanks. By the way, thanks again for breakfast."

He smiles and turns the stereo on. "Amy Grant?" I ask. Tom nods, mouthing the words to "Find a Way." When the song finishes, Tom puts in another CD. "I want to know what you think of this one..." he continues to mouth the words to another song.

"Who is this?" I ask.

"This is me," he answers.

I'm not sure if he's trying to impress me or just joking. Tom places his hand on his stomach and outstretches the other hand as he dances with himself, lip-syncing the words.

Then he smiles and says, "It's 'Fear Not, My Child' by Carman." He comes over and sits adjacent from me. I have such a fixation on him.

With his eyes closed, he says, "What makes this song so great is the words." I can feel my heart beating as the soothing music sets an incredibly warm, comfortable mood. Unable to stop staring at him, I digest his mellow deep voice, clean-cut looks, long eyelashes. Tom opens his eyes and lights a cigarette.

He takes off his sweater, revealing a white T-shirt that's neatly tucked into his jeans. For a moment, we stare into each other's eyes. Tom says, "Come over here, you."

I get up and sit next to him. He starts tickling me, "Are you ticklish?" I laugh and tickle him back. We roll off the sofa and onto the floor. It's fun nibbling on each other's arms and necks as the tickling progresses into kissing and hugging. We wrestle playfully, grabbing each other's arms, trying to pin each other down. The playing gets me aroused, and I say, "Do you want to go to bed?"

Tom looks at me with bright eyes and says, "Oh yeah."

As we walk out of the living room, I notice in the small hallway that there are ceiling tiles that have brown water stains from some kind of leakage.

"How did this happen?" I ask Tom, pointing them out.

Tom says, "Water stains. Maintenance never takes care of this place. I've been meaning to fix that."

I immediately feel stupid for pointing out a flaw with his apartment. This is his home, after all, and it's ridiculous for me to verbalize my thoughts. I try to remedy my witlessness by saying, "Oh, cool. By the way, you have a great place."

We walk into his bedroom. It's superbly decorated, like the rest of the flat. A large king-sized oak-framed bed is made up with a masculine blue-lined bedspread. The oak headboard matches two huge oak bureaus — one of which carries an enormous mirror on it. He has an autographed picture of Amy Grant on the wall next to his bedroom door. As I stop to admire the photograph, he says, "I took that myself at one of her concerts."

"Great picture, man." The bathroom is a room within a room, as I find it inside the bedroom. "This is cool, having the bathroom right in the bedroom."

Tom says, "I don't care for it. When you have company, they have to go into your bedroom to use the bathroom."

When I emerge from freshening up in the bathroom, Tom is sitting on the bed. He stands and faces me. "I'm going to change the music. Do you have any requests?" I don't. As he turns his back to leave, I let out a sigh. I'm so nervous. I don't recall ever being nervous before sex. Excited, but not nervous.

He returns, and I say, "Thank you for taking me home. I'm having a fabulous time." I unbutton my shirt and take it off. As Tom removes his shirt, he gazes at me.

"You're really built. I love your chest," he says, walking up to touch it. He runs his hands over my shoulders and down my arms. "Jeez, you have really nice arms."

"Oh yeah, so you like my *guns*?" I ask, proud of the progress I've made in building them up.

He nods, smirking but keeping his eyes on them.

I finally get a chance to compliment him, saying, "Your fresh boy-next-door looks initiate dozens of fantasies in my head. You're beautiful." And he is.

I step up to him and look in his eyes. Time is suspended as we kiss. I taste his soft lips and tongue. I turn him around as I undress him. Tom has one of those bodacious butts that you could lose yourself in for days. Like a child opening a present, I pull his jockeys down to reveal it, and as I do so, my pulse quickens. It is beyond expectation. When we're done undressing, Tom showers me with compliments on my own ass as I simply tell him I don't have words to express my delight for his. Tom turns off the light and we creep into bed and get under the sheets. My eyes adjust as the light from the moon streams in to illuminate the room. We turn and face each other. Holding each other, we share another lasting kiss. I run my anxious hands through his soft neat hair as he caresses my shoulders, arms and chest.

"Do you work out a lot?" he asks.

My excitement is so high, I can only whisper a response, "Yes, I try." My mind is a thousand miles away from the base gym, from my job, dancing, and from Nadine. Tom and I embrace, and pulling each other close feels so good. Our hard cocks meet, to our mutual delight, and the feeling of his strong, strapping football player's build against my body fills my mouth with saliva in anticipation of tasting what I feel. We roll around and around, kissing and hugging, exploring the pleasure of our naked bodies together.

I smell his cologne on my skin, which has rubbed off from hugging. In the moonlight Tom's face is so beautiful. The scene is so erotic: here we are, two hot young men entwined in each other's arms. My heart feels like it is going to burst with feelings of excitement, lust and fondness for him. We kiss more than ever, exploring each other's mouths with our tongues and licking each other's faces. This experience delivers me to such a summit of emotional tenderness that tears begin to well up in and fall from my eyes.

Tom looks into my eyes and asks, "What's wrong?"

"I can't say. It's just — this is very intense. It's good. I'm very happy."

Tears stream down as I blink. There's no doubt in my mind that I'm achieving a new height in feeling absolute bliss and contentment. Tom rolls me over on my back and grasps my arms, pulling them up over my head until they reach the headboard. He seizes my hands and begins kissing my armpits, my sides, my chest — caressing and massaging my body with his nurturing lips and tongue. He gently licks and nibbles on my body until I'm completely relaxed. He rests his head on my chest, releasing the grip on my hands. We seamlessly assume a new position with me on top, letting my hands float around to his back to hold him close. I reach down to rub his luscious butt with both of my extended palms and then use my arms to part and hold his legs up as we continue. It's a warm sensation to feel wanted and cared about. Now I know I have never been this happy, or this content. When climax finally comes, it's magically together, with an explosive intensity I've never before attained. We relax and fall together in each other's arms, drenched in sweat.

I'm ready to sleep in the position we're lying in, but Tom rolls off me and reaches for a cigarette. Just when I think things can't possibly get better, he blows smoke out and dons a huge, strange grin. "What's up?" I ask.

"That was an incredible fuck. That's how legends are born." I'm beyond elated that he's so delighted with the experience. We're on the same plane. I was afraid it might not have been as intense for him as it was for me. And for him to verbalize it, for him to go first with the compliment, well — that's as sweet as it gets.

After sharing the cigarette, we take a long, romantic shower together. Seeing, and then feeling, his entire warm, wet, naked body in the bright bathroom light and then against mine is incredible. I almost fall asleep holding him under the hot steamy water.

Back in bed, he's asleep on my chest in minutes. It's been a perfect day, the best in my life. I notice he has a relaxing picture behind the headboard, above the bed — a picture of roses lying on piano keys. Under the picture is the word "Melody," barely visible in the moonlight. Tom stirs in his sleep, and pulls me close as I fall back to sleep. I wake again a few moments later and find him awake, staring at me. It makes me feel secure, warm and satisfied. I snuggle my face into his chest and it's his turn to hold me tight.

Monday, October 10, 1988

The morning light peeks into the bedroom through the curtains. The fragrance of his apartment fills my nostrils and I wake with a smile, feeling rested and unusually happy. This is the best Monday morning ever. I look over at my prince. He's sleeping, still and quiet. I stretch and softly roll over to absorb my surroundings in the daylight. This is all for real and not just a dream. The digital clock reads 12:20. Shit! It isn't morning after all; we slept right through it. I remember Tom saying he had to work today and now I feel terrible. I try to wake him by whispering in his ear, "Tom, you smell terrific." He shakes spasmodically and turns around, as if surprised and confused, squinting at me. He then goes limp when he recognizes me. I suppose he's not used to having anyone spend the night with him. That's a good thing.

A few more precious moments of peace pass until I try to wake him again. The fact that he has to work is nagging at me. "Tom, don't you have to call in to work?" Tom now stretches and rolls over on his stomach; then he opens his eyes and sits up. He starts to get out of bed and looks under the covers.

"I'm naked. Did you take advantage of me last night?" he says, smiling, leaning toward me for a kiss. He reaches for a comfortable-looking flannel robe on the bedside table and puts it on, then walks over to the bureau with the big mirror and looks at his reflection. He brushes his hair down and finds a cigarette. He lights it and sits on my side of the bed, running his free hand through my hair.

"That feels so good," I respond to his affectionate touch. Tom reaches for the phone, dials a number and waits.

"Cross your fingers," he says as he waits. Caught off guard by a speedy answer, Tom blows smoke out as he says, "Brett? It's Tom...hi...yes...my chest is still bothering me. Even after a long night's rest." He pauses, then continues, "Yeah, I've been taking Tylenol for the headache and…yes. Mmm hmmm. I know…it's…" Tom makes a fist and bangs it lightly against the bed. Sounds like he can't get a word in.

"Yes, okay, I…" another pause, then, "Thanks Brett, Bye."

Tom takes a drag of the cig, puts it out, and looks up in the air. Then, he turns to me saying, "I'm all yours!" I sit up against the headboard and give him a smile.

"That's good. I want *all* of you," I say.

He's somehow more beautiful today. I adore his gorgeous, bright young face with his intense, radiant eyes. He leans in and brushes his lips gently against my lips. We make love again, this time in the shower; soapy and wet, we find new ways to explore each other's qualities. I gaze into his beautiful face and soak in the pleasure of the sight of him. I wrap my arms around his strong hard body, with its sweet seamless blend of soft skin. As we exit the shower and as the fog clears from the mirror, we face our reflection; he stands behind, holding a warm towel around me in his arms. He lifts his hand to my cheek and gently says in a deep sexy voice, "You're really handsome, Tom. Look at how good-looking you are. Love that square jaw, that killer smile. Here, let me try something." He carefully shaves my face so as to leave the faintest shadow of a goatee just around my chin, fading as it reaches the corners of my mouth. "Look at how hot that looks."

I blush but inside I'm bursting with pride and love. "No moustache?" I ask.

"No, it's sexy like that," he says, touching it softly. I agree.

As I walk around his living room getting dressed, he asks lots of questions about me. Tom's interest in me, evidenced by his questions, is not only a turn-on, but an incredible compliment. I enjoy having the floor, given the opportunity to talk about my life. I share with him that I'm officially single for the first time in a long time, telling him about Nadine, how we met and how much I still love her. He offers, "All things are for a reason, and now you can live the life you were born to live."

Tom patiently listens as I answer his questions and interjects his feelings appropriately. I can't say whether it's his relaxed persona or his outstanding questioning technique, but I find it so easy to share some of the most personal things in my private life with this man. I find solace in hearing my story told; what I thought was dull and depressing actually sounds like a fascinating life.

"How do you take your coffee?" he asks. I walk into the kitchen, place my arms around his waist and kiss the back of his neck.

"I'll get it. How do you take yours?" I ask.

He turns slowly to face me and kisses me. I close my eyes and revel in the sensation of his soft masculine mouth. I don't budge — I don't want the kiss to stop, but Tom ends it and, as if in slow motion, his face backs away just inches from mine. In a slow, deep voice he says, "Little cream, couple spoons of sugar."

The toast is ready and Tom brings it out to the dining room table with the coffee on a perfectly appointed tray, complete with jams, jellies and little containers for milk and sugar. It's like a little tea party. He prods me to continue telling him about how I got into exotic dancing.

"Before we got married, Nadine cheated on me with this male stripper called Nick. I wasn't right after we got back together. The prospect of striking up a friendship out of the blue with the friends of the guy who'd just fucked my girlfriend was daunting, but something within me was determined to pursue it. I had to find out what she found so appealing about Nick. With Nadine as my uneasy guide to their hangouts, I found the courage to introduce myself into their circle. Surprisingly, assuming Nick's place as star of the clique wasn't as hard as I thought. Nick did everything halfway, and that extended to his relationships with people. I threw everything into the friendships, bodybuilding and dancing. This is where I really excelled at imitating him: I learned to turn my usual caring, sensitive and trustworthy nature into an act to get what I wanted. They took to me immediately, much faster than I would have imagined, and started training me to dance. My new buddies Choon-yei and Bryan were eager to teach, and I was anxious to learn how to perform in an exotic dancing troupe. I can't forget the couple months of training: I grew and changed more in those few months than I had in four years of high school. I did everything differently than before. My behaviors, my entire outlook on life, all changed. Things were less stressful because I learned to let a lot go. I got used to and learned to enjoy odd hours — staying up really late talking; staying over at people's houses; meeting new people, as well as all kinds of nasty new habits like drinking, getting into adult clubs illegally, smoking pot and constantly cheating on Nadine. When I finished my training I made my exotic dancing debut at this place called The Shed in Browns Mills."

I take a sip of coffee.

Tom asks, "How was it? Were you nervous the first time?"

"Surprisingly, no. I'd actually spent money to rent this caveman costume. I was having so much fun dancing for the crowd I forgot to start undressing! Choon-yei came up to me in the middle of the second song and gave me a dollar and a hug. When she hugged me, she nonchalantly reminded me to start undressing."

Tom reaches for my hand. He asks, "How did you and Nadine get married after all this?"

"Nadine wanted to study medicine. Without proper financial resources, prospects were bleak. She started talking to an Army recruiter and before you knew it, she was enlisted. That's when we decided to get married. She was making a sacrifice and I loved her. I didn't want to lose her again but while she was away in training, we both explored sexual horizons with others. When she got back, she ended it. I was crushed. I still am."

Tom looks confused. He asks, "If you were cheating on her and had mixed emotions about your sexuality, why are you so brokenhearted about her being out of your life?"

"Don't know. I discovered or gave into my secret gay identity while she was gone, and in my head I thought when she came back, we'd be whisked off to her first assignment and everything would be fine. I imagined married life would allow my sexual desire for men subside. Part of me was and still is fearful about being gay, and Nadine was my only link to leading the life I've always known to be the right path. Most of all, I miss my friend."

I finish talking, and we spend a moment looking at each other, holding hands. Tom leans over and kisses me gently.

"Thanks for sharing that with me." He gives me another gentle kiss and we sit in silence looking at each other. He leans back and crosses his arms over his chest, shaking his head, saying with a grin, "So...a married man in my bed, eh?"

I can't fathom why I just unloaded all this on some guy I just met, but it's the first time I've actually talked with someone about it all, and it feels like a release. We finish getting dressed. "What are you going to do today?" I ask, fervently anticipating his next move.

"You mean *we*. *We* have to go to Grossman's." Pointing at the water stains I carelessly mentioned last night, Tom says, "These ceiling tiles have to be replaced." It's obvious he takes a lot of pride in his apartment, and maybe he wants to make a good impression on me.

"Tom, I really don't think it looks bad," I say, regretfully.

Tom smiles again, revealing his great teeth. "Eh, don't sweat it. I've been meaning to get around to that mess for a while now. The maintenance in this place sucks."

Tom reaches up and pops the ceiling tiles out of their places. He takes them down and puts them on the living room floor. In the kitchen I open the drawer under the microwave and find a sort of "junk drawer" for all sorts of gadgets, tools and busted pencils. I find the tape measure and bring it to Tom. "Thank you, honey."

Honey. Honey? Honey! That sounds nice. I never had a man call me "honey" before. It fits and feels good. Tom starts measuring the ceiling drop tile. He tosses the tape measure back to me and gets up headed for the bedroom.

I replace the tape measure and follow him into the bedroom. Tom is in the bathroom. I sit on the bed and Tom opens the bathroom door and peeks out.

"Come here." I stand and walk over to him. "Let's shower together again." We undress and get under the steamy hot water. We rub each other's bodies up and down and I feel his hands exploring my private parts. It's a sexy, luscious, scrumptious scene as we play; but unlike other sexual sessions I've had, with Tom it's deeply intense in the way of passion. I try to take the flood of emotion out of it and drop to my knees to bury my face in his sexy football player's butt. Everything on him is sweet and tasty and I allow myself to get too wrapped up in his body to pay notice to what my heart is feeling.

We finish up, and Tom tells me he has to be alone in the bathroom for a moment. I get the point, kiss him, and exit the bathroom. I jump on the bed and roll around a couple times. The feeling inside me is outstanding — my heart and head are about to explode with joy. I just have to share my joy with someone or I think I'll burst. I reach for the phone and punch in Janet's home phone number.

"Hello..."

"Hi, Mrs. Bennett, is Janet there?"

"Tom, yes, she's in bed, but I think she's awake. Hang on, dear." I grab Tom's watch off the dresser and put it on; I hold my wrist up as I lay on my back, admiring it. I hear Janet's big mouth: "Mom, hang up, I got it, I got it." There's a click and a pause and then I make out the sound of Janet lighting a cigarette, taking a puff and blowing smoke. I can visualize her facial features.

"Janet, guess where I am?"

"Probably up some guy's ass?"

"That was earlier! I'm in Glassboro. I met this terrific guy."

"Glassboro? Are you in a college dorm?"

"Janet, no, he has his own place!"

Janet bangs the receiver against the wall. It's one of our inside jokes. "Tom, there's something wrong with my phone: I thought you said one of your butt buddies actually has his own place."

"He does. Hell, it's totally awesome too. I'm lying on his bed right now."

"Oh, goodbye!"

"Wait! I'm alone here."

"Tom, where'd you find that loser?"

"Gatsby's."

"What's he like?"

"Oh, he's coming out of the bathroom. Listen, I'll tell you later."

I hear her smack her lips in disgust and blow her smoke out. "See you tomorrow. Don't be fuckin' late."

"Whatever. Bye, bitch." We hang up.

In the bathroom, I put a bit of gel in my palm and rub it on my hair, giving myself the "wet look." Looking at my reflection in the mirror, I send a silent prayer of thanks to the Creator for what I see. It's redeeming to have attained the body I've worked so hard for. It feels good to be young, healthy, have money, a few decent jobs, and to have somebody to share it with. There's always been an invisible gap in my life and somehow I feel more complete today than ever before. I'm confident about Tom. He seems refined, dignified, polished. I just know this is the beginning of something great.

Tom walks out of the bathroom and sits on the bed behind me. He puts his arms around me and holds me. I close my eyes and allow myself to relax and enjoy it. He gently kisses my neck, giving me chills yet relaxing me all the more. I feel myself start to fade. Is this really happening? His skin is so bright in the sunlight coming in the window. It only adds to the attraction.

After we disengage I root through my gym bag and locate a new pair of black Adidas sweatpants with classic double white stripes on the sides, and rip the tags off. I grab a blue t-shirt and black baseball cap and toss them on the bed.

I'm ready in ten minutes, while he takes every bit of an hour to select the perfect outfit, iron his jeans and shirt, put on cologne and a belt, and fix his hair. He looks fabulous. He's wearing an untucked, long-sleeved pleated white linen shirt that instantly dresses up his black jeans. He puts on his "THOMAS" bracelet, his high school ring, and his gold necklace, and then he sprays on more Obsession — the familiar sexy scent from last night. He doesn't have a single hair out of place, yet his hair has the dry look.

As we walk to the parking lot, I feel a cool breeze hit my face. It feels and smells so invigorating. There's definitely something nostalgic in the air. Two attractive frat guys pass us and as I first look at them, a habitual shade of jealousy clouds my thoughts; then as fast as it comes, it's gone, as I realize I'm no less beautiful and desirable. That belief, coupled with the fact that I'm so proud to have Tom by my side, fills me with exhilaration. I love to toy with the notion that these straight frat guys could possibly think Tom and I are gay and sleeping together.

Grossman's is only five minutes away, in the Collegetown Shopping Center. On the way, Tom tells me there's a guy who works at Grossman's whom he "messed around" with.

"One of your exes?" I ask.

Tom taps my knee. "He was just a trick. Besides, he's married."

"Married?" Somehow the concept still sounds strange to me.

Tom glares at my confused look for a moment, then turns and faces the road and says, "Like you." In the store, Tom introduces him to me as Gary, who immediately says, "Wow, another Tom...Tom and Tom..." After being introduced, I don't make eye contact as they talk. I purposely act like I could care less, though it bothers me more than I can say that this guy was with Tom. What troubles me the most is that Tom sought him out to do business with while I'm with him. Is he showing off?

As we leave the section where Gary works, he extends his hand to me again. I shake it firmly while looking him right in the eyes. "Nice meeting you, man," he says, without smiling. I hide the fact that I'm feeling strangely uneasy, cautious and guarded in an alien world I'm unprepared for. For a second, I yearn for Nadine and for a role I'm comfortable with.

Tom and I turn to walk away and Gary throws another remark behind us: "I'm no stranger to guys named Tom." I turn and look at Tom, whose face has turned red. Almost instinctively, and easily back in the aggressive character I've assumed in the past year, I walk back to Gary and shove him back with both hands, saying, *"What?"* He falls back into a pile of boxes that were arranged in a neat little tower on a table next to him.

I turn to find Tom tugging at me: "Let's go, let's go."

In our wake Gary is lying on the floor, not budging, not saying a word. A customer shouts out, "HEY!"

A straight-faced, cool and collected Tom takes my arm to slow down my usual fast pace and guides me to the register, where he purchases the ceiling tiles with cash. We walk out and burst into laughter. "I can't believe you pushed him into that table and he fell over!" Tom says.

I just raise my eyebrows and grin, also wondering where it came from. When we get back to the apartment, I help Tom replace the ceiling tiles. When we're done he attaches the receipt for the new tiles to the old water-stained tiles, and writes a note to the apartment management explaining that he expects reimbursement for the work. Then we're off again, stopping briefly at the door to the manager's office to rest the tiles and note there. This time Tom is on a hunt for orange candles for Halloween.

These next few hours are the most wondrous in my entire life. We go from store to store, leisurely looking for orange candles. This is so simple and mindless — I'm so peaceful, so relaxed. He holds my hand while we drive around. I experience one of those rare moments when I feel a burst of sheer happiness and delight that lights me up and warms me from within. My eyes well up as I savor this moment: the sight of the last rays of sunlight on the horizon as I feel his big strong hand in mine. We're soon laughing about the fact that we can't locate the stupid orange candles anywhere. There are peach, red, black, pink and gray ones – but no *orange* candles. I don't know what it is that's making this mission so intensely refreshing. We decide, after a while, that we're hungry, so we go to Pizza Hut at Tom's suggestion.

While sitting and eating, I ask, "What town are we in?"

Tom smiles. I love his smile. It makes me crave his kiss. "We're in Woodbury." The setting, the moment, the season — everything surrounding us is perfect, the ideal ingredients for new love to blossom. The upcoming winter, the closeness, the union, the warmth…I can't explain it. It's magic.

I think I've found someone who's really right for me. After eating, we get back in his car and as we drive around, one song plays a few times on the radio: "Waiting for a Star to Fall" by the group Boy Meets Girl. It's a new song. It beautifully compliments the stage and occasion of my new relationship with Tom. There's something enchanting happening. A snug and cozy feeling of connection is drawing us closer. As every golden moment passes, I find myself eager for the next. I'm excited about what tomorrow and the future holds. He reaches down and squeezes my hand. As he unfolds more of his personality and heart, I drink in every drop.

After leaving another card store, where we finally find some orange candles, we stop at an ice cream place and get soft vanilla ice cream cones. We sit on a wooden bench in the plaza and I confess to Tom, "I'm glad we met."

Tom doesn't respond verbally; he places his arm around my shoulder, and rubs then pats me on the back. Tom rises to throw out our trash. His ass is so fine. He's so tall and dreamy looking. I find him standing in front of me looking down at me, as I sit and feel my heart beating fiercely inside me, as if it's going to burst out of my chest. I feel scared and nervous, excited and guarded all at once. I sense something peculiar in his eyes as they peer down at me.

Within an hour we're back at his apartment, with the mood set with soft music and orange candles, which provide all the light in the room. He's standing in front of me again, this time buck naked, and I'm sitting on the sofa completely dressed. I run my finger down his chest to his stomach and into his pubic hair. I pull him close to me and kiss his stomach and torso. He's so damn sexy, and smells good enough to eat. As I hold him close, he wraps his arms around me. He brings his hands up to my head and runs his fingers through my hair. It feels so good.

We get on the floor, kissing and hugging each other. I massage his back, his ass, his legs and his feet. He moans and grunts as I loosen up his muscles and gently kiss him all over. I love every inch of him. I get down and lie next to him.

He starts to speak. "About a month ago, I was so lonely. I thought I'd never find anyone who could truly be real. I think I've found that person in you."

His words, acknowledging a mutual admiration, are a welcome sound to my anxious ears. "I'm sure glad you feel that way," I tell him. "All day I've been feeling something in the air that lights me in a way I have never been before." Tom sits on my lap, and we kiss again as I lift his legs up and support his tall, strong body with my arms. I'm consumed with the thought, *I want you to need me like I need you,* as I explore his mouth with my tongue and let my fingers touch all his parts. I feel more masculine and in control of my role than I ever have before.

He smells so good, and his mouth is so hot and soft. His lips press against mine, and as we complete the kiss, we laugh from the joy of finding in each other something that feels so right. Tom gets up and goes into the kitchen, grabbing his robe off a chair on the way. "Dinner's ready," he announces. I jump up and sit down at the well-set dining room table. It's a romantic scene. Tom serves a pasta dish with a great salad. I compliment his table, his cooking, and his body.

"Italian dishes are my specialty," he admits.

After eating, we go into the bedroom where we begin having sex and end up making love. After, we shower and get dressed. I put my pants on and follow him into the living room with my shirt off. He lies on the sofa and falls asleep, while I sit on an adjacent chair watching him. I find a piece of paper in the kitchen and write him a note:

Tom,
Meeting you yesterday was exciting and … I hope you feel the same. If you–

I look at my words and trash the note, embarrassed at how desperate, gushy and needy I sound. Seeing it in writing makes feel embarrassed and makes me want to think differently. But I can't. I do feel myself falling for him. This isn't like me.

He's managed to crush the tough, live-for-fucking-around identity I've assumed.

I look at the pen still in my hand and shake my head. Me — writing a love note? You gotta be kidding. This is just a crush, I tell myself. I get a soda from his refrigerator and notice the time; it's already 11 p.m. Where has the day gone? We did get a very late start. I wake Tom to tell him I have to go but before I say anything, he says, "I have to work tonight."

"But, Tom, it's almost midnight." He explains that he's the closing manager at McDonald's, and his shift starts at midnight.

"Well, I have to go too. I have to work in the morning. Can you please give me the directions to get home?" I ask, rubbing my eyes.

Tom rises, and I follow him into the kitchen and then back to the living room, where he finds a little pink piece of paper to jot them down while he verbally explains them to me. As I put my coat on, he sits in the living room observing me. I say, "I really don't want to leave."

He says, "We both have jobs to attend to." As I walk to the door to leave, Tom gives me a lingering kiss.

"Can I have your phone number?" he asks, after the kiss.

"Yes. I want yours, too." Tom walks into the bedroom and returns with one of his personal business cards with his name, address and phone number. The card reads "Credit Management Associates." As I view it, the nervous, scary sensation I felt earlier causes my head to swim and my voice to crack as I ask, "What's this?"

"It's my company."

"You own it?"

"Yes."

I feel bewildered. Everything I've learned in banking about trusting gut feelings when making character judgments is telling me something isn't quite copasetic.

"What does your company do?" I ask.

Tom says, "I *am* the company. I correct mistakes on people's credit reports. It's a part-time thing. Something like your dancing." I choose to ignore my silly suspicions. I kiss him again. He hands me the pen and another little pink piece of paper. I clearly write down my name and phone number, and hand the paper and pen back; and as I do, he pulls me in for a warm hug. I bury my face in his chest and experience bliss wrapped in his arms. After a moment, he whispers in my ear, "I'll call you tomorrow." We part company, and when I walk outside, the cold air is shocking but exhilarating.

Just as his directions indicate, I find my way to the familiar territory of Route

295 and enjoy the ride home. Driving, I revel in the thoughts on our time together. Peace consumes my entire being and I welcome it. I also allow myself to relax, engaging in a prayer of thanks to God for this and all my gifts.

Tuesday, October 11, 1988

The very next day I wake up in a cloud and practically float around on it all day — at work I'm elated as hell all morning. There isn't a thing that can bother me. I get there early and knock out the pile of work on my desk and most of Janet's pile before she gets in. It's a good thing, because it's ferociously busy until noon. That's when Janet and I meet up in the kitchen to fill our coffee cups. She asks, "What gives with you today? You must've got it on with your butt buddy." I turn and lift Janet up, wrapping my arms around her waist, and place her on the table. She shouts, giggling, "STOP! Stop! Tom, Stop! Let me the hell down," she yells. I lean in and kiss her gently on the cheek.

"I'm so happy, Janet!"

She jumps down and walks out of the kitchen shaking her head, saying, "Christ, you're nuts!"

I jog up beside her and we walk behind the tellers discussing Tom. Our Head Teller, Nancy, whispers after me, "We don't run in the bank, Tom."

"Sorry," I say, slowing my pace. Back at Janet's desk, I continue telling her about the weekend.

"So which one of you is the top?" Janet asks, pursing her lips and widening her eyes. I roll my eyes. She continues, "Oh, I see, we haven't figured it out yet." I turn and scope the immediate area to see if anyone's around, embarrassed by Janet's words.

"What about Nadine?"

"What about her? I feel so much better now. That heartache I've been carrying went away."

"Well, that's cool. He sounds like a friend of mine. So powerful that he makes you forget your exes."

"What friend is that?" I ask.

She leans back in her chair and starts looking for something in her purse. "You know him — Jack."

"Jack? Jack who?"

"Jack Daniels." She cackles and continues looking through her purse.

"Janet, I mean it; this is a strange and beautiful experience for me. I always felt sexually attracted to guys, but never considered a man in a romantic way."

"Tom, this guy thing is all a stage you're going through. You'll meet a butt-buddy, get to realize that you can have a relationship with a man, and go on to your next female victim. It's okay to be bi."

It's busy as hell, since it's the day after the Columbus Day holiday, so I don't get a chance to call Tom until my lunch break.

His answering machine message comes on. "Hi, this is Tom. I can't come to the phone right now, but if you care to leave your name and number, I'll get back to you as soon as possible." There's background music behind his voice that sounds terrific — it's a new song, "Kissing a Fool" by George Michael, putting me back in my dreamy mood. When the beep comes for me to speak, I say, "Hey, stud! I think you're beautiful. You made my weekend."

We experience a temporary lull from the onslaught of customers pouring in, so I decide to call that Shaw Corporation Tom took me to. My mind keeps reviewing every inch of the entire experience of meeting him. I don't know why I'm calling the Shaw Corporation; I suppose part of me is intrigued by the thought of knowing someone so fucking rich, and part of me is suspicious. I dial directory assistance and retrieve the telephone number. I place the call.

"Shaw," a voice answers.

"Uh, yes, may I please speak with Mr. Shaw?"

There's a moment of silence, and then the voice on the other end says, "Mr. Shaw?"

"Yes," I answer, "the owner of the company." They advise me there is no Mr. Shaw. Shaw is just the name of the company.

Confused and somewhat disappointed, I hang up. Back to work.

After work, I hit the gym on base for a rigorous workout before going home. I get an unexpected treat as I'm showering alone in the locker room. Suddenly, a gang of two dozen or so young military dudes returning from some training bivouac invade, completely naked, and since there are only eight nozzles in the open bay shower stall, I share my nozzle with two other dudes. It's too hot for words and despite a desire to masturbate in the car on the way home I save it, hoping to see Tom. When I finally get home, there's a message from Tom. I pick up the phone and dial his number. He answers on the first ring: "Hello."

"Hi," I respond.

Tom says, "Hello, Tom. How was your day?" His deep dreamy voice is like medicine to my susceptible heart.

"Terrific! How was yours?" I answer, surprised by an intensely timorous feeling.

"Excellent. I've been in an extremely good mood since I met you."

"Me, too," I respond, feeling my eager heart rise.

Tom asks me to come over. I leave immediately.

On the road, I hear the song "Waiting for a Star to Fall" again. It elevates my already stellar mood. I mentally designate it as our song. I stop at a liquor store on the way, and select a bottle of orange Mad Dog 20/20 and a bottle of Red Bull Malt Beer — tastes remnant of my days with Choon-yei and Bryan. Some things never leave you. The cool autumn air hits my face as I leave the liquor store. The smell of burning wood in the air is terrific.

I find my way back to his front door, and after a series of knocks there's no answer. I noticed his car in the parking lot when I parked, so I know he's got to be home. A check on my watch shows five minutes have passed, which feels like an eternity given how anxious I am to see him. The door finally opens and Tom, looking half asleep, appears behind it. I feel the warmth of his apartment brush against my face and hands, "Hey," I say.

"Sorry, I was sleeping. Come here," he says, reaching out to pull me into a hug. He's warm and his arms feel amazing around me. As I enter, he takes my coat and leads me by the hand to the living room. Candles once again provide the only light, and soft Christian rock music is coming from the stereo. I feel an intense sexual craving and in seconds, my senses are rejuvenated in his atmosphere. He's wearing a white thermal shirt and faded loose jeans, looking so sexy and more beautiful than I remembered.

"I worked all night and all day today. I have to go back into work again tonight," he says. "Can I get you a drink?" I shake my head, and we exchange a look that conveys mutual desire. We start making out. It isn't long until we're on the floor, naked in each other's arms. We luxuriate in further discovery and exploration of having sex with each other. After what feels like a long, smooth slide down a waterfall of pleasure, I'm locked in his arms spent from pleasure. When I regain some strength, I realize he's dozed off. I don't budge for a good half hour, reveling in the moment of peace and love.

I lift him using all my might and gently place him on the sofa. I fix myself a drink and find a pen and paper in the kitchen and write him a note:

"T, I know we don't know that much about each other. The past few days have been special to me. I think I'm falling for you. I hope this doesn't scare you away. I'll just wait for you to catch up. — Tom."

I leave the note on the table in the kitchen and then go to his side and sit on the floor. At 11:00 p.m. I've got to leave. The time was good just being here with him. I wake him slowly, and he rises and leads me into the bedroom holding my hand. He throws me on the bed, lies next to me, and he whispers very gently, while looking into my eyes, "Thomas Marino, I think you and I are going to be together for a very long time."

My eyes fill with tears. We get up together and face each other. He kisses me. There is nothing I can say; my eyes are doing all the talking. My eyes reveal my heart. His words mean so much to me. He's nodding and says, "Yeah, this is right — let's run with this." I find my note in the kitchen and trash it before I leave his apartment, feeling more grounded in this — whatever this is.

Wednesday, October 12, 1988
Wednesday arrives and no sooner do I get to work than there's a call from Tom. "Good morning," he says robustly.

"Hello," I respond.

"How's your day going?"

"Not bad, just started. When do you have to go in to work?"

Tom responds, "Seven to closing."

"Well, that's not a bad shift."

Tom asks, "What are you doing tonight?"

I tell him, "Hitting the gym."

He says, "Sounds good — build them muscles up for me!" He knows just what to say to ignite a fire I already have raging inside for him. I tell him the weekend is coming up, and we can make plans to get together. We say goodbye, and I start thinking. I was proud of the fact that I didn't cave into his request to come over or be available tonight again. I need to let him know I'm not so desperate — need to set some kind of groundwork that I'm not sitting around waiting for him to call. I have a life, I have things to do. But then again I want to be with him. I swing my chair around and gaze out the window.

Suddenly a slam on my desk breaks my daze, so I roll my chair around. Sue is standing there. She's looking mighty good today, but none too happy.

"Did you collect that money from Jenkins yet?" This client owes the bank over $1,500, and I'm responsible for collecting it.

"No. But I haven't given up." Sue presses her lips together and scopes my desk — covered with work and the pile she just put on it. "You look really nice today," I say, continuing a flirt I've had going on with her since we met.

She just rolls her eyes, smirks, and walks off, saying, "Get busy, Mr. Marino. Get busy."

Janet's out today. After an hour of work, I can't concentrate, so I get up and walk over to Matt's desk. Matt is another Personal Banker like me.

"Matt, I need a favor this weekend."

"What favor?"

I explain that I'm going to be dancing for a new agency this weekend and that for some reason, I don't trust them. I explain how they seem strict and that I don't want anything said about me not doing the job. I want Matt to capture the entire gig on video. Matt is an electronics geek and has all kinds of equipment. I knew he wouldn't mind doing it for me. "Would you accept any money for it?" I ask him.

"No way! It would be way cool! Where's it at?"

"Copperfield's." Matt nods knowingly.

7:45p.m.

When I get home from the gym, I check myself out in the mirror and like what I see — but I know this infatuation with my looks can't be normal. I know people look at me and enjoy my looks. I turn and check out that nice butt again, and odd self-lusting thoughts cross my mind. I decide strong, self-centered thoughts build character and help me feel good about being me. I plop down on my bed, and I'm reading my mail when I hear the phone ring.

Mom shouts down, "Phone call! Who's Tom?"

I roll over to pick up the phone. It's Tom, sounding somber. "I won't be seeing you any longer," he says. My heart jumps.

"What?"

"I might be going to jail. I have to talk to you."

Without asking another question, I say, "Yes, of course, I'll be right there."

Tom says, "I'm at work, at the McDonald's in Glassboro. You know where it is?"

Full of sudden emotion, I say, "I'll be right there!" I immediately head out.

Mom's shouting out after me, "Who is Tom?"

"He's a guy I met at the bar the other night."

"I don't like it," she snaps.

"I don't care!"

Thoughts of Tom flood the gates of reason in my brain. I spark up a cigarette and begin puffing away in the car, affording me a small high. Acting purely on instinct, I go seventy miles an hour, bent only on delivering his rescue.

It takes almost an hour to get there but upon arrival, I notice Tom standing behind the counter in a manager's uniform, looking as delicious as can be. He makes eye contact with me immediately, and shoots me a soothing smile. I reach the counter and order a vanilla shake from the blonde cashier. Tom stands behind her and points in the direction of the seating area, saying, "Go sit on the side over there. I'll be right over."

A few minutes later Tom appears and sits down facing me.

"Mr. Shaw, I presume," I say, smiling to lighten what looks like gloom on his face. He lights a cigarette, pulls a business card out from inside his wallet, and tosses it down in front of me:

SARAH WHITMAN, SECURITY OFFICER
NATIONAL BANK OF SOUTH JERSEY

"My sister bought me a Camaro for my eighteenth birthday. It was stolen in May, right out in front of my apartment. The insurance company did investigate." He stops to take a long drag on his cigarette. He blows the smoke into the air and appears lost in thought for a moment. "They issued a check to me for the value of the car, $4,000, and I deposited it into my account. I then went into the bank a day or so later and asked if the check had cleared. The teller said the money was all clear in my account so I took it out. I took it out to buy the Lynx. Then the insurance company stopped payment on the check due to some pending investigation. This woman from the bank came in here a few hours ago to inform me what happened. She said by taking the money I committed a fraud. I told her the teller said the money was clear for me to take, but she said if I don't come up with the money to repay the bank, they're going to put me in jail."

"Tom, that wasn't intentional fraud — or even a fraud at all. The insurance company rejected payment on the check, that's all. You didn't intend to commit a fraud. Did you call the insurance company?"

"Yes. They said I should have a replacement check in about three months, when they complete their investigation. I know I have grounds to sue them."

I sit back, take a drink and then offer, "Did you ask your family for help?"

Tom leans forward and says, "I just met you and yet I feel so close to you. I…"

He's not telling me something. His handsome face shrouds my judgment like a good Manhattan on the rocks. This time the rocks are in my head. I know he doesn't want to tell me everything. I don't care. I know I'm being stupid. I don't really give a fuck. This feels like someone else's life I'm living; I feel no ownership or control over my actions, my thoughts, my words. Tom holds my hands over the table, not afraid of anyone seeing us. Holding hands in public with someone you care about should be a natural event. New to the gay world, admittedly, I feel a bit uncomfortable initially showing the world my sexuality. I fear what people think. Only a moment later, I am relaxed and absorbed in the pleasure of showing off; it feels good, and not only do I not care what people think, I like the fact that they can probably surmise the fact that I'm intimate with this beautiful man.

Tom continues, "My parents are dead."

Dead? I never thought dead. I thought maybe not rich, but not *dead*.

"Wow. Sorry to hear that. May I ask what happened?"

"Cancer. They both had it. My Dad died in '74 when I was 9 and Mom died in '78, when I was 13." I squeeze his hands tightly and gaze into his bright, tender eyes. I'm certain he's suffered a lot.

"Tom, the bank has to realize this wasn't your fault. I've seen this type of thing at work, and we usually make payment arrangements with people. The courts always rule favorably for people against the banks and insurance companies."

Tom looks up at me and says, "I'm really scared." I lean across the table and kiss him gently.

Feeling oddly elevated in status and much less apprehensive, I say, "You might as well know — I think I'm falling in love with you. You know, you're like that star in the song. I'm waiting for you to fall for me. You seem so untouchable. Now here you are, and I'm not about to give up my chance to keep you. I'm not letting anyone take you from me. I've got money in the bank. I'll pay for you to stay out of jail, and you know what? You can pay me back when you get the insurance check."

The words certainly sounded nice. I wonder if I have the balls to back them up.

Tom puts out his cigarette in the tiny gold tin ashtray and is making circles in the ashes with the butt. He looks up and grins at me, saying, "I can't let you do that!"

"Look, I want to. I know you'll pay me back. I know where you live; I know where to find you." I feel my heart racing. It's like we're on film — in an act. I'm playing out a part. "Saturday, I have to dance at Copperfield's, and Matt from work is going to be filming me. I'm dancing for another agency and I don't trust them. I want to get it on tape in case they say I didn't perform."

Tom nods, saying, "This business is kind of crazy."

"Yeah, tell me about it."

Tom smiles, saying, "Ooooh, good — then we can spend the weekend together. Do you mind if I tag along? I'd like to watch you in action."

Tom has to get back to work. He's off tomorrow and is going to stop by my work to see me. I'm elated to feel so close to him. He makes me feel so good.

"Do you want a refill for the ride home?" Tom asks, picking up my empty cup.

"Sure!" When Tom returns with the shake, he also produces a cassette tape entitled *All That Jazz*, by the English group Breathe.

"Pop that in on the ride home."

I fly down the interstate jamming to the music on the tape. Thoughts of the luscious scent of Tom's hair fill my head. I enjoy the smell and taste of him. For the first time in my life, I find myself fantasizing and indulging in daydreams about a current lover. Thoughts of his hot cock and sexy ass lead me to unzip my pants and begin masturbating while driving. The combination of driving and playing with myself is such a high. I think of Tom's beautiful looks, especially his smile and hair. His hair is a major turn-on for me. I want so much to be able to take him home and play with him in my own bed. I experience a marvelous orgasm and after shooting my load, I chase thoughts of my own avoidance of his obvious omission of the entire story. There is a huge looming gap in his story, in his life, and I know the questions I need answered but choose to refuse to ask them. I know I can get any guy in the sack, but I want him and I'm going to do what it takes. Am I buying his love and affection?

Thursday, October 13, 1988

Erotic thoughts about Tom continue today. I have a major erection while sitting here at work. Heaven forbid anyone needs me to get up suddenly for anything. Janet's sitting in one of the client chairs in front of my desk, going on about the club she went to last weekend, who was there and who wore what, while filing her nails.

Suddenly, my pulse quickens as Tom walks in and stands in the lobby looking at me. He lights up the room wearing a dashing blue dress shirt neatly tucked into tailored slacks. He walks over and I catch a glimpse of his bubble butt as I get up and walk behind him, after offering him a seat at my desk. It looks so delicious, like a baseball player's butt. I imagine it naked and I want to bend him over my desk. I introduce him to Janet and as she rises to leave she makes a kissing gesture behind his back.

As Tom leans in, my eyes go to what part of his chest I can view from the few buttons undone. He immediately says in a hushed tone, "I thought of something after we talked yesterday. You can get a loan against your money in the bank – a secured loan. Then I can pay that back and the interest. That way your money in the bank continues to earn interest." I lean back in my chair, impressed by his financial acumen.

"You're all business this morning," I say.

"Do you want to grab some lunch?" he asks. I look at my watch; it's 11:30.

"Sure!" I ask Janet, "Do you mind if I go to lunch now?"

Janet yells back, "No!" We all laugh and Tom and I get up and leave. Tom drives us to Pizza Hut, and orders a large pie.

"The bank would be more than happy to give me that kind of loan," I say, renewing our earlier conversation. "I'm sure the interest rate would be low, too."

Tom is excited about this. I could tell it was all he thought of last night. I smile to myself. "What are you grinning for?" he asks.

"Do you want to go to Gatsby's this weekend?"

Tom grimaces and says, "Sure, but where did that come from?"

I rest my head on my hand and smile again, saying, "You're something, Shaw, you know that?"

One of his trademark smiles bursts onto his gorgeous face as he says, "If you're not careful, I'll reach over this table and kiss you. You probably have people around here who are your customers, and they'll see, too!"

I don't care.

"Okay, down to business. First of all, I want to know how you know about all this banking shit."

He answers, "I used to work for Glendale National Bank in Haddon Heights."

"Really?"

"Yep. I was a teller," he says.

"I'm impressed. Why didn't you mention that before?"

"Thought I did."

"Nope."

"Another thing," I began. "I...called the Shaw Corporation. They said there is no Mr. Shaw. If you're going to let me lend you $4,000, you might as well tell me the truth about things. You already told me your father passed away. What's the story on the Shaw Corporation? Why did you say your Dad owned it?" I cringe inwardly, wondering what his reaction will be.

He looks out the window and says, "I'm sorry. I was just a little insecure about things. You're so handsome and doing so well for yourself, I feel embarrassed about my life and thought I needed something to impress you with."

I never expected that response. Amazed and delighted with this showing of brutal honesty, I say, "I hope you realize now that's not the case. I'm the one who feels a need to live up to walking beside you."

He laughs, saying, "Sorry, Tom, saying that to you — well, that was kind of stupid, wasn't it? I never cared about being alone before I met you. Now I'm very afraid of being alone. I crave you, Thomas Marino."

His revelation about not being related to the owner of that business creates additional questions in my mind, but I let it go for now. We've made significant strides today. It's quite a sum of money, but if I don't get it back, I'm young enough to go out and earn some more. "By the way, my money isn't at First Commercial. Do you think I want them to notice all the money coming in from dancing? They're my employer. I'm sure they'd get suspicious about where it's coming from. I'm also sure they wouldn't like the fact that one of their Personal Bankers is a male exotic dancer."

"Good thinking. What bank do you use?" Tom asks.

"Chemical in Manhattan."

"We should open a joint account at First Commercial. Especially if we're going to be together," Tom offers.

With that suggestion, I feel like he put another log on the fire of our romance and I'm proud and excited at this opportunity, immediately conceding to the idea as a way to further solidify our relationship, exclaiming, "Yes! Sure! Great!"

After lunch, we get in his car and drive to the bank parking lot.

"Esmeralda Chang is the woman I deal with at Chemical," I say, pulling her business card out of my wallet.

I give Tom the card as he circles back by my branch and says, "Can you please go get that Breathe tape out of your car?" I get back in his car with the cassette and Tom starts driving, while searching the tape for the song, "How Can I Fall?" Upon finding the song, Tom pauses the cassette until he finds a parking spot in the nearby lot of a business center under construction, then restarts it. He mouths the words to the song, without uttering a sound. We share some intimate kisses for several moments. I lift up his shirt, and lean down to kiss his stomach and rub my nose in the happy trail of hair leading from his navel downward. He pops the cassette, and the song "Baby I Love Your Way" by Will to Power comes forth. These songs create an astounding backdrop to our budding romance. We sit a few more moments looking into each other's eyes. Tom drives me back to the bank and comes in with me. We walk back to my desk and I call Chemical. I get Esmeralda on the phone.

After a few moments of coordinating how we can get this done without me having to take a day off from work, we come up with the following plan. Tom will have to go up to the city to get the paperwork, bring it down to me to sign, and bring it back up to the city to get the check — all in one day. I type a letter of authorization for Tom to take, as Esmeralda has dictated. Tom says he'll leave very early in the morning. He stays in the bank for a few more minutes to set up our new joint account, and then takes off and I get back to work.

About an hour later, I get a call from Tom. "Sorry I ran right out of there without saying much of anything. I was feeling that I had to leave, or you would see me cry."

"Cry?"

"No one has ever done anything like this for me. I can't believe you care about me so much. I don't know how to thank you."

Now I'm the one who's filled with emotion. "Hey, it's just a loan. I'm sure you'd do the same for me."

Tom says, "I would. I love you, Mr. Marino."

"I love you, too, Tom."

"By the way, I had to write a check on our new account for $63 for the homeowner's insurance — you know, renter's insurance. It's due now."

"Oh, of course. No problem," I say.

We finish our call and I sit back, reveling in his "I love you, Mr. Marino" comment. Mild thoughts of the negative implications of what might happen if he doesn't pay me back flash briefly through mind. I feel like being reckless. I feel like taking a risk. I feel like having an adventure.

Around 4:30, I get a call.

"Mr. Marino, this is Sarah Whitman at the National Bank of South Jersey. A client of yours, a Mr. Thomas Shaw, indicated to us that he's been approved for a $4,000 loan from your bank to pay the outstanding cash item he owes us. In order not to proceed with legal action, I need your verification that this is true."

I'm outraged that Tom assumed he could give her my name and work number and tell her that lie. Did he think she wouldn't call me? Did he think I would make a false representation using First Commercial Bank's name? I'm knocked right off my feet. I'm dumbfounded and can't find words. Clouds invade the short-lived period of basking in the sunshine of his love. I don't want to disclaim the loan, as she would probably have him locked up right on the spot, but I will never, ever misrepresent myself at the bank. There's more than my own reputation at stake. I have no business involving my employer.

I take a deep breath and say as calmly as possible, "Ahh, yes. That's approved and will be dispersed to him tomorrow. Mr. Shaw is borrowing the money from me personally. He and I are friends, and I applied for a secured loan from my bank."

Shit. I'm pissed that Tom gambled on the fact that I'd go along with his lie, and more so that he didn't tell me about it — but I instantly try to see the good in it. He probably made something up in the heat of the moment to get the bitch off his back. Maybe she just called him. I'm still upset he didn't call me instantly and tell me about it.

She doesn't respond to my words. I want a response, so I ask, "Tom told me that your bank would be pressing charges for this. Isn't that a bit harsh for a returned deposited item that he had nothing to do with?"

"I don't think so at all. Wouldn't your bank do the same?" I get a strange feeling inside, telling me to ask more questions, but my desire to connect with Tom outweighs and clouds my gut reaction to uncover what I fear.

"You'll get your money tomorrow," I say.

I get up and walk to the bathroom. I splash water on my face and stare at it in the mirror while it's wet, and think.

Friday, October 14, 1988: 11:45 a.m.

Tom comes into the branch and sits down in front of me. Beaming, he says, "Happy Friday!"

"You're back early!" I note.

"Well, I got to Manhattan by nine this morning. Met Esmeralda. She's cool."

"Find the bank all right?"

"Yes. You have to sign this." Tom produces a long collateral document with a few forms behind it. I scan it, take a moment to look up at him, and affix my signature to the document.

"Now you have to bring this back for the check?" I ask.

"Yes, I should be back before five."

I open my desk drawer and pull out a little yellow sticky note. I pencil on it:

I want to make mad passionate love with you all weekend.

I push the note toward him. He reads it and winks at me. When he winks, I feel chills go up and down my spine. Does he know the power I've given him over me?

I take him behind the teller area and lead him to our abandoned break room, where we share a quick, yet fiery kiss. Tom squeezes me close and I grow limp in his arms. I reach around and feel his ass, but the fear of the possibility of getting caught by someone walking in grows until we finally break our embrace, and sit for a moment to let our mutual erections deflate. After a cup of coffee, I walk him to his car. I can't believe he's going to make two trips up to New York in one day.

When Tom gets back from Manhattan at 4:30, the loan has gone through and I give him a check for $3,321.70 to pay off his debt. He heads out to take the check to Mrs. Whitman. I walk into the break room after he leaves, and spark up a cigarette. Matt is sitting in the break room reading the paper. He puts it down and looks at me. I jump up on the counter and sit facing him. He makes a face and asks, "Red Box Marlboro Man? How can you smoke them?"

I wave my smoke and his comment away with my hand and ask, "Are you ready for tomorrow night?"

Matt grins and looks back into his paper. "I'm not the one stripping." I jump back down and extinguish my cigarette in the ashtray. I unwrap a lemon lollipop and put it in my mouth.

Saturday, October 15, 1988

"First Commercial Bank, Tom Marino speaking…"

"It's me, Nadine."

"Yep. What's up?"

"Is everything okay?"

"Everything's great. What's up?" I say, knowing her attempt at cordiality is only a means to an end, and my usual attempt to return friendly banter is a fruitless pursuit of her affection.

"You have to turn in your ID card to me. I told you I was responsible for it."

"Nadine, you're not getting it. I'm not giving you that card until I get divorce papers. I mean it."

"You're going to be arrested, then. You'll be arrested the next time you use it. My company commander told me I have to get it from you. You have to surrender it."

"Are you threatening me?" The only reason I want to hold on to it now is to go to the base gym.

"You'll give it to my Mother. She'll arrange to meet with you," she snaps.

"No fucking way! You can fucking meet me your fucking self if you want the fucking card." Overhearing the conversation, Janet just bursts out laughing.

"I don't think that's necessary. Besides, I can't. I'm in school every day and can't get time off."

"Well then, too fucking bad," I say and hang up.

What's wrong with me? I may very well be gay. I'm happy with this guy Tom, and know I want to be with him now and maybe for the rest of my life.

Janet walks over and snaps her fingers in front of me, "You're lost in thought, dude." I grab her and start dancing with her right in the lobby. A few customers look over and we stop. Janet giggles as she walks back to the break room.

Jean shouts over from the teller line, "The inmates are running the asylum while the wardens are in a meeting!"

I sit and shuffle papers as thoughts of Nadine cross my mind again. I may be gay, but hell, I think I could still have had a life with her. We could work together and work through anything. We both made mistakes. She just wanted something or someone else. Maybe it was for the best. Why does it hurt so much?

I go home, and after a shower, I get dressed in my nerd costume, and place the pizza delivery costume in my gym bag. The nerd costume is my own creation and I like it a lot. I have these dark green high-water pants that I put on over two pairs of underwear – one pair of sexy bikini shorts with a Hawaiian design, and another pair of green army camouflage shorts, cover a sexy red g-string. I tuck in an ugly long-sleeved green shirt into the green high water pants. I wear a hideous tie, which is a potpourri of silvers, grays and yellows — it's the most mismatched possible tie for the shirt. I bring old nerdy glasses with thick black frames to wear. Instead of a belt, I wear white suspenders, and to top the outfit off, I don an itchy lime green Mr. Rogers-like sweater and two different colored socks. Finally, I put on red, multi-colored, laced high-top sneakers with holes in them.

On the way to Tom's, I stop and pick up the wine and roses for the girls. My second gig tonight is a pizza delivery getup. Tom is ready when I get to his place, and he gets a kick out of the nerd outfit. "Very creative," he says.

I go up to him, put my arms up and around his neck, and rest them on his shoulders, pulling him in for a hug.

"You smell terrific," I say, and help myself to a kiss while copping a feel of his nice butt.

I slide my hands under his shirt, feeling his warm body and wonderful skin, so smooth and soft, like silk. I run my hands over his chest, his ribs, and slowly pull his shirt off. Tom stares at me intently while unbuttoning my crazy looking green pants. I feel my cock inflate with excitement as he pulls down my fly. What starts as caressing and kissing progresses to a porn scene as I pull down my pants, looking at him as he does the same.

Tom places my hand on his underwear clad crotch. I yank them down and draw him in for another hug, bringing our naked bodies together. I kiss his chest, working my way from left to right, kissing his nipples and enjoying them. Tom runs his hands through my hair and pushes me down to his waist. I kneel down before him, kissing and licking his bellybutton, then move to his dick. I kiss it and watch it grow. With my eyes shut and hands on his hips for balance, I take him into my mouth. It feels so natural, clean and warm inside my mouth, as if it were meant to be there. I adore the taste and smell of him, but even more, I love being able to please him. Giving and receiving pleasure from someone you care about as well as whom you happen to be attracted to is indescribable. I stand and follow him to the bedroom.

I move up into position, both of us shivering with excitement. I find I can't stop trembling, given how anxious I am, how eager I am to unite with him. Despite worrying that the sex will not be as perfect as it has been, it is love that we make. The way he kisses me, the way he touches me, his passion and affection leave no doubt that this is love. I suspect my actions tell Tom the same thing.

Performing perverted but wonderful acts of pleasure ignites a thought as I look in his eyes, a thought that I'd do anything he would ask — not out of lust, but because he cares for me.

Later

We arrive at Copperfield's and when we go in I introduce Tom to the bouncer who, as luck would have it, is a cute customer from our Moorestown office that I once fucked, a guy named Dean.

He snickers as he looks me up and down saying, "You must be kidding — you can't be the stripper."

I don't bother explaining that I'm still working a "respectable" job at another branch of the same bank where he does business; I just nod, smile, and say nothing. We go to the bar and the bartender knows what I'm there for. Looking at my nerd costume, he jokingly says, "Your drink is on the house. Dressed like that, you probably can't afford it anyway." People around the bar are staring at me, and we can see the party of girls I'll be dancing for pointing at me from across the room.

They're gathered around the dance floor; some are dancing, and some are sitting at tables, but most of them look a little tipsy. Tom just orders a Coke and is taking in the sights while I, on the other hand, drink a Bloody Mary. The sunken dance floor is four steps below the club's floor and surrounded on three sides by windows. The lighting is marvelous.

Matt shows up and starts talking to me. I get a nice buzz from my drink and experience a feeling of euphoria. Things just can't get better than this.

Tom's more nervous than me. He leans over, saying, "How can you do this? I would be freaking out."

I respond, "I do this about five times a week, and sometimes I do get nervous just a bit. Tonight I'm not nervous at all. I can tell from the atmosphere it's gonna be cool and easy, my man. Besides, I want to perform for you tonight, Tom."

Dan brings the woman who ordered my performance over for introductions. "I'm Priscilla," she says as we shake hands.

"I'm Tom."

She says they're ready whenever I am. Right about then Matt comes back over and says, "I'm all set up."

Priscilla asks Matt, "Can I get a copy of the tape?"

Matt smiles and takes a walk with her. I finish my drink, walk over to the DJ booth, and slip inside inconspicuously. "Hey," I say.

He turns and says, "Hi. What songs would you like?" I ask him to play the tape from Dory with "Cool Jerk" followed by "What You See Is What You Get" by Brenda K. Starr, "Do You Want It Right Now" by Taylor Dayne, and finish up with "Together Forever" by Rick Astley. He smiles and says, "Great choices. I got 'em all."

"If you don't, I have a back-up tape."

He's very cool and I pass him a ten dollar bill. The dance floor is clear, and the girl who I'm to dance for is standing alone, looking very scared and embarrassed. Her friends scurry to get a chair on the dance floor for her. She's introduced to me as Becky, a very shy woman who obviously doesn't want anything to do with this. I turn to look at Matt, and he has the camera on me. The DJ hits the music right on time, starting with "Cool Jerk" as Dory suggested.

I like the idea after it starts, because it gives me a chance to act a bit with the nerd costume on. I dance up to Becky, now sitting with her legs and arms crossed, and she pushes me away, which I use to create a move to fall backwards onto the floor. She isn't playing along, which I find irritating, but nonetheless I continue to try and make her feel as comfortable as possible by smiling and dancing my best.

I get up and strut around the dance floor, which is surrounded by brass railings. I jump up on the railing and bend over it to kiss one of the onlookers on the cheek. As "Cool Jerk" concludes and is mixed into "What You See Is What You Get," I slow down and change my silly grin and bug eyed grimace to a serious sexy look.

As I undress, I pull off my suspenders, stretch them in my teeth. I go up to Becky and wrap the suspenders around her sideways, pulling her close to me. One of her friends watching stands up with a camera and snaps a picture. One of Becky's friends brings her a dollar bill and she hastily shoves it in my g-string after the DJ and her other friends prod her to do so.

I finish the act and slap my hand on my ass as I walk away from her – my way of saying "kiss my ass" to poor sports, tarts, or those who have a big sour puss during the show. In this case, she was all three. I sit on the dance floor and get dressed in minutes. Matt decides to stay longer at Copperfield's and socialize with the women in the group. He's earned some unexpected attention from the girls by being involved with the show. Priscilla and a couple of the women come up and thank me and compliment me. Tom and I collect my tip and escape out the side door. Tom stops outside and picks me right up off the ground, exhibiting strength I didn't think he had, giving me a huge hug.

"That was extraordinary," I say, as he places me gently back on Earth, both physically and mentally.

"You were extraordinary in there!" he says. It sure felt good to be held up and close in those strong arms. He really loves me.

I look up into his eyes, the moonlight shining on us from above in the cool autumn air, and say, "Hey, I love you."

He rocks his head back saying, "I love you, too." I grab his hand and pull him to the car.

"Come on, I don't want to be late for the next job. It's up in Trenton." Tom drives and I begin to undress.

"What are you doing?" he asks.

"I do this all the time."

"Get something on! Shit, here comes a truck, he'll see in the car! Shit!"

I look over at Tom and roll my eyes. He giggles. I pull a towel out and dry the sweat off me, then sit there naked with the towel over me for about a half hour with the window down. "Aren't you cold?" he asks.

"No, I'm enjoying the natural high that follows one of these gigs."

I put a lot of cologne on and began dressing in a different g-string. I pull a pair of new white jockeys out of a package I have in my bag and rip a small hole in the side of them.

"What are you doing that for?"

"You'll see."

"I know. You're going to rip them off you. I've seen that done before."

I smile and continue getting dressed. Once dressed, I brush my hair into place.

"How do you get ready when you're alone?"

"Same way. I just do it while I'm driving. It's pretty easy, and I'm used to it. Having you along is a treat."

I explain the whole Dory and Mitch story, as well as more dancing history and stories with him. Tom is very captivating. Without a doubt, he has all my affection.

"You want to move in with me?" Tom asks suddenly.

I hear but I don't believe. "Huh?"

"Do you want to move in with me?" he asks again. He starts talking again without waiting for me to answer. "I never thought I'd find anyone, and, well, I do owe you three grand. It just makes sense. I want you to feel comfortable. It's the least I can do."

I shake my head. I don't know what to make of his gesture. "I've only known you six days. Can I move in tonight?"

Tom and I laugh. This is coming so easily, so naturally.

As we drive, I probe Tom about his "side business" of repairing people's credit reports. He tells me about a large inheritance he received from his parents' estate when his mother passed away, and how his sister was guardian of his money until he was 21. He's opening up a bit more to me, and the information feels more reliable than it did when we first met.

Tom continues, "I lived with my sister Sandy in Erial after my Mom passed. When I turned 21, I got control of the money, but it was dispersed to me in various amounts at different times. I got a large amount at 21 and achieved excellent credit. This allowed me the ability to get gold cards; I bought an apartment complex down the shore. One of my tenants who lived at the complex fell and sued me, so I lost the building. I had to claim bankruptcy and lost all my credit. That gave me the idea of trying to help people repair their credit reports."

I'm confused about why he didn't fix his own credit, but something keeps me from questioning him about it. The inheritance bit sounds real; I'm not so sure about the shore house tale, but I love hearing him talk. I actually love being with another man — a good looking man, a man who loves me. My senses — all of them — are dulled.

He continues, "When I was 22, I decided to move out of Sandy's house. I'd been there since I was 13 when I lost my Mom. I got the apartment in the fall of last year, and furnished it with the money left over from the inheritance. I went out and bought a whole new wardrobe, too."

I contemplate the exchange of the sentiment of love between us. My thoughts are that he's my forbidden lover, and something about other peoples' perception that our lifestyle is illicit makes it all the more appealing. I'm not exactly sure if moving in with Tom is the right thing to do, since I'm technically still married to Nadine — but somehow logical thinking weighs far less than listening to my heart.

We find Trenton State College in no time, but finding the right dorm is another story. It takes us a while, since the buildings aren't numbered on the outside. We finally find the place. Inside several girls greet us, and we're led to the door of the dorm room where the party is. The gal who ordered it hands me an envelope with the money, which I open and check, then pass discreetly to Tom, who promptly slides it into the inside pocket of his beautiful leather jacket. Outside the door, I take a deep breath while Tom and a few of the girls stand back out of sight. I knock on the door with the pizza box resting on one hand. A girl opens the door and takes the box from me. She's pretty, with straight white teeth and long blonde hair. The entire party consists of a bunch of white girls with similar cookie-cutter smiles and hairdos. They appear to have been drinking and smoking pot which makes them fun and a lot more down-to-earth than they probably are. As she takes the box, from the expression on her face I can tell she immediately notices how light the box is, and she opens it to find a long stemmed red rose.

Before she can speak, I say, "Is your name Danielle?"

Her friends all roar with laughter and she starts backing away, putting the box down so she can cover her mouth with her hands. She lets out mouse-like squeal of delight as I put my hands on her shoulders and say, "Happy Birthday, Danielle."

Tom and the girls outside come in, and Tom automatically sets up the boom box without being prompted. The music starts and I have at it, despite there being hardly any room to dance in a small dorm room filled with 20 or more girls. I finish up with hoards of dollar tips in my g-string. The girls ask Tom who he is, which we didn't anticipate or come up with a response for. "I'm his bodyguard," Tom jumps right in and says. He crosses his arms over his chest; his tallness is accentuated by all the short girls.

One of the girls says, "Like I'm so sure he would care if a mob of girls tried to rape him," to which Tom replies, "We've been in situations where boyfriends or husbands didn't exactly approve."

All the girls laugh. I giggle myself at Tom's great comeback.

"Do you strip too?" I can tell he's eating this up, never having been asked that in his life.

"No, I don't do it anymore."

Back in the car, he's sitting there in the driver's seat shaking his head. I say, "Whatcha thinkin'?"

He shrugs and says, "Taking it all in." He continues, "I can see how this is a natural high and an ego trip for you. You're like a star to them, and it's so cool. I felt so important in there. I had mixed feelings, really. Part of me was jealous of you for being able to perform like that — to be so full of energy and uninhibited. Your spirit is so free, and you dance very well. You're so friendly and nice to them. Part of me is jealous that the man I love is showing off everything for the world to see — well, almost everything. Then there's a part of me that's gloating like a show-off, bursting with pride in what's mine. I'm so glad you're my man. I'm so proud to be yours. You're really something, Thomas."

We hold hands and head to my new home. On the way, "Baby I Love Your Way" by Will To Power comes on the radio.

"This is one of our songs," Tom says. I remember dancing together in Gatsby's to this song, holding hands. His big man-hand in mine feels so solid, so stable, so warm. "I think we ought to make a special guest appearance at GB's tonight," he says. I could swear he's reading my mind.

One of the headlights on my car went out about a week ago, and when another car with only one front headlight approaches us, Tom honks the horn.

"What did you honk for?"

"It's called a padoodle."

"What?"

"When two cars with one headlight pass each other, it's called a padoodle and you honk your horn." When he makes a sharp turn, he says, "Hold on to your laundry." I cast him a puzzled look. "It's just an expression," he explains.

I shake my head smiling, taking in all his ways. I love them all.

The rest of the weekend we share is amazing. We make love, dance, drink, make love, go shopping, make more love and on Sunday, I tell Tom I have to go back home, but I'll move in with him later in the week.

Sunday, October 16, 1988, 10:30 p.m.

Back at home in my own bed, I have time to reflect on the past week and think about Tom. He could very well make me happy in the role of my lover for life.

What do I care what people think? I do *wonder* what people think, yet I want to be happy. I want everything in life. There's not one reason why I can't have everything. Free to be me. I want to love who I want in every way. Can Tom be real? He seems too good to be real. The worn out feeling I get right before I slip into unconsciousness is awesome. It's like floating on a lake in the summer with every-thing still around you. I think about this past week — visions of his hand in mine; his nakedness close to mine. My bed actually feels cold and empty without him near me. I know now that this is what I am and this is what I need.

I feel myself falling asleep.

Monday, October 17, 1988

I feel relatively good while I dress in the morning sunlight after my shower. I'm thinking about my life and what I want when the phone rings. "Hello," I answer, and as I do, Mom answers from upstairs: "Hello." I hear Tom say, "Hi, It's me."

Mom hangs up. Tom asks, "Are we alone on the line?"

I'm elated to hear from him so early. I quickly answer, "Yes, we are!"

"Let's take the day off today and play hooky," he suggests.

I immediately love the idea, soaking in the glee of spontaneously blowing off Monday morning responsibility. "I'll be over in an hour."

I hang up with Tom and throw some play clothes on. I call Janet and tell her I can't come in today. "Shit, Tom," she tells me, "I had a long weekend too, but I'm dragging my ass in."

"I know, I know, but sometimes you just have to grab life and enjoy it. It's like I can't let life go by without having a good time."

"I'll make up an excuse for you to Sue. I'll tell her you're sick."

"Yeah — tell her I'm going to the doctor."

"Okay, you owe me, sucker."

"I know, I know. Thanks, J."

Within an hour, I'm in bed with Tom. He's holding me and we're kissing and hugging each other tightly, sharing all the passion I've ever known two people could share.

"I missed you last night," he says, to which I respond, "I missed you too, man." Until I met Tom, the romantic part between two men was always the piece I didn't think could fit. I could envision and enjoy great sex, but the actual lovey-dovey stuff seemed out of place. Now I have the most romance and affection I've ever experienced, and in truth it fits more than I could have ever imagined. The best part is the knowledge that he feels the same way I do. We thrash around the bed and I'm excited with the thought of two boys naked together like this.

"I could stay in bed with you forever," Tom says. The bed is so warm and smells so nice. After making love, we get into the shower together and begin soaping each other up. Feeling my body amorously rub up and down Tom's feels so exquisite. I love the way he feels.

I go to put on my sweats and T-shirt and Tom says, "You look good in that, but you can look better. Trust me on this, okay?"

"Okay," I say. Tom dresses me up in a nice pair of jeans with a white linen button-down shirt. He helps me put a dark navy wool pea-coat on over the jeans and shirt. He lets me wear a pair of his black shoes. We look at my reflection in the mirror. I look amazing in his clothes.

We stop at the alarm on the way out the door. "Do you remember the code?"

I nod, saying, "How do you think I got in here this morning?"

The day is amazing. We start by going to the mall for haircuts. Tom knows one of the guys who works at a big department store, and under Tom's direction he transforms my hair. I've always been one for having my hair parted and combed neatly, but finding it hard to manage for its length, I cave in to his recommendation to change direction. I give him free rein in exchange for a promise to keep the length, and when he's done my hair looks less severe, more relaxed and all forward. Looks good.

We stop at a locksmith to have a key made to his apartment, for me, then we go to a spa for manicures, a peppermint shower facial and body massages. As the masseur works, I consciously allow myself to relax and let the tension fade. I find myself drooling in a partially-unconscious state as the muscles that control my jaw give in to the leisure. My sinuses drain as my nose runs. My body feels light and refreshed; everything is calm. When we come out of the rooms in our white robes, drinking lemon water, Tom nods and smiles, clearly impressed.

Friday, October 21, 1988

The week blurs into Friday, and a telephone call from Janet wakes me before my alarm goes off. "Hey," I say, my voice as raspy as hers.

"My turn," she says, indicating she's taking off today.

"Why?"

"I'm beat. We went out to Concorde and I just got home an hour ago."

"Gotcha. Are you sick if someone we know asks?"

"Yeah, that'll do. I think Sue's off today."

"Just wanna make sure we get our lies in order."

"Yeah," she says, and we end our call. Anything for time off. We're such rascals.

It's been quite a week. Tom and I have done everything, from test driving a new Porsche and walking barefoot on the beach to feasting in the best restaurants in Philadelphia and drinking it up every night. Tom is bent on finding another apartment for us. He took me to tour this complex called Society Hill, among others.

I agonize about going into work this morning. Yesterday, Matt brought in the video tape from the gig last weekend. To my horror, I found him showing it to Sue and my co-workers in the break room after we closed. Even though I could have killed him, everyone was way cool about it, complimentary and supportive. I'm still not thrilled about it, and I'm wary of its effect on my future at the bank.

ASCENDING

Saturday, October 22, 1988, Noon

Some of us are working at the bank's booth at the Mount Holly Day event on Main Street today. It's a fun diversion and I feel amazingly comfortable and relaxed, enjoying the smells and sounds of fall in full bloom. It feels good to be alive. Crowds flock to booths and stands of local merchants, food vendors and people showing off various handiwork and crafts. There are large balloons and advertisements everywhere; it's very festive.

I didn't expect Tom to show up, so when I notice him walking toward the booth, my heart jumps into my throat. He looks incredible. On first sight, I don't believe he's actually mine. As it sinks in, an overwhelming sense of pride fills me. Totally the picture of an all-American jock, he's wearing a pale-blue faded jean jacket covered in pins, with jeans that match the jacket. The jeans do wonders for the contours of his hot, tight ass: he has the kind of buns you want to play with all night long. Around his sexy waist is a thick black belt with a shiny silver belt buckle. He's so stylish. His hair is combed back, neatly parted on the side, and his face is as bright and handsome as you can imagine. He smells terrific, and I'm bursting with joy to show him off as my mate.

"Thomas," I say as he approaches. "Are you a mirage?"

"Surprise!" he says, with everyone watching and listening attentively. I feel my face and neck turn red, and wink both eyes closed for a moment, then reopen them.

Tom does the same, in a way to mutually greet each other with sweet affection.

I take a moment and introduce him to some of my co-workers and my boss, Sue. I'm unsure if it's his friendly manner, his looks, or a combination of both, but no one can do exactly what he does. If my sense of euphoria was elevated before, it's through the roof now. I feel like I have someone on my side, someone for me in my life. He doesn't realize that he's more powerful than Mommy and Daddy and Wifey all rolled up into one. It's new and strange, having a boyfriend, and I'm not prepared for how people will react to me being obviously gay. Surprisingly, I am experiencing an awesome new sensation of pride and confidence, feeling more grown up than I ever have. I believe I'm encountering a connection to my inner self, on a brand new and higher level in celebrating my identity.

Sue allows me to take a break. Tom and I walk to a corner bistro, and sit at a table outside eating sandwiches. "What time do you get done here?" Tom asks.

"I'm not too sure. It's supposed to be wrapped up around 3:00 or so, but I gotta help take the shit back to the branch."

Tom glances at his watch. "It's almost 2:00 now, so it shouldn't be too long. I'm going to run an errand and I'll meet you back at your branch around 4:00," he tells me.

We go to the bathroom together, and in a cramped stall we share a hot kiss. "I want to suck that big fat monster cock of yours," Tom pants. I shove his head downward and enjoy the next two minutes immensely.

He rises all too soon, and I respond, "I'll see you at 4:00." We share an extended hug. My lips find his, and with eyes closed, we spend a calm moment feeling the warmth of our embrace.

Later

I find Tom waiting for me when I walk out of the bank. He's leaning up against his car, parked next to mine, his arms crossed over his chest. As I approach he says, "Got something for you in the trunk." I walk over to the rear of his car and he pops open the hatch, revealing a long, narrow white box with a red ribbon around it. I look up at Tom and he says, "What? Open it!"

I reach down into the well of the trunk and lift the box up closer to me, then set it on the trunk's ledge. I carefully remove the red ribbon surrounding the box and open it to discover twelve long-stemmed red roses. I feel my heart in my throat. This symbol, solidifying my bond with him, quells any concerns I've been harboring over recent monetary issues. It's a clear indication to me that he's in this for love. Tom takes his hand and gently lifts my chin. As our eyes meet, his trademark smile is all the approval I need. Ignoring the fact that we're in the bank parking lot, I begin kissing him deeply, our tongues performing an erotic dance on their own. I feel my cock rising, trying to find its way inside him. When we come up for air, I say, "They're beautiful, Tom. Thank you."

He shakes his head. I lift one rose to my nose and close my eyes as I enjoy the fragrance. When I open my eyes, I explain that I need to collect more clothes, and ask him if he would follow me back to my parent's house, adding, "You can meet my folks."

He nods, smiling.

As soon as we're in our cars, the sky opens up and rain pours down. Lost in a bubble of love, I don't mind the rain. Actually, I like it. Watching him follow behind me in his car, I can't help but pull over at a convenience store for another kiss. I dash inside and return with a coffee for each of us. I hand him the coffee and pass him another warm kiss. "Oh, perfect, thanks — but you're getting soaked!" he says.

Back on the road, I decide I want to give Tom my heart for the rest of my life. My dreams, my future, my plans — all have changed. I will go where he goes now. I ask God to give me the strength and wisdom to be a good lover to Tom, and to let this be right. I want it to be right because nothing has ever *felt* so right.

When we arrive at my parent's house, the rain has stopped, but Tom doesn't get out of his Lynx. I emerge from my T-Bird and walk over to him, asking, "Aren't you going to come in and meet my parents?"

He shakes his head. "I don't feel like it right now."

Strange response, but rather than explore it further, I leave it alone, go into the house, and quickly gather a bunch of clothes so we can get back on the road. I'm sure he has his reasons and when he's ready to meet them, I'll know.

Back at the apartment, I start putting my clothes away, then return to the living room and find Tom listening to music. "Hungry, Slugger?" he asks.

"Yeah, actually. Would you like me to make something?" I offer, half hoping he doesn't take me up on it. My cooking skills leave a lot to be desired.

"What do you say we go out for dinner? Then we make a guest appearance at GB's."

I smile and say, "That's cool. Do you know tomorrow is our second week anniversary?"

"Yes. It's been an amazing two weeks. I love you."

I turn to look him in the eyes. "What?" I ask, wanting to hear it again.

"I love you."

I ask him again, "What?"

He starts tickling me, saying, "You like hearing that, huh? I love you, I love you, I love you, I love you."

We feast on cheeseburgers and fries at a teen hang-out in the Deptford Mall. Once again admiring his jacket, I think how shabby my old black parka is in contrast. I say, "I'd like to get a new one for myself. Do you think we could find one similar to yours?"

Tom agrees, while scoping out a group of girls sitting at the table adjacent to us. Some of the girls are staring at Tom and me. When we finish our meal, and as we get up to leave, one of the girls comes over and asks if I went to Highland High School. Before I can answer, Tom says, "He went to Bordentown Regional." She smiles and walks back over to her table.

As we walk through the mall, I catch our reflection in various mirrors. We look hot together. As it turns out, the place where Tom bought his jacket no longer carries them; I feel annoyed and disappointed that I can't find one like his. Finally, Tom calls my attention to what I perceive as an ugly brown bomber jacket in Macy's. I walk over, inspect it, and, not really liking it, place it back on the hanger. Tom takes it off the hanger and holds it open for me to try on. I put it on and notice that the inside of the jacket is lined in white wool. It's heavy and very hot under the bright lights in the store. My facial expression shows my displeasure with it.

I'm about to take it off when Tom puts his arm around me and says, "Go look at it in the mirror. It suits you much better than my jacket does."

I pull it back over my shoulders and walk over to the full-length mirror on wall. As I approach, I'm taken aback by how the jacket looks on me. Once in front of the mirror, I really like the way it goes with my style. It's heavy and bulky, but the brown leather compliments my skin tone and hair. The jacket looks like it was made for me. Its huge, broad shoulders accentuate my own shape, and its cut and style are rugged and masculine. I develop a liking for it and decide to treat myself to it, despite the $325 price tag. Unfortunately, I don't have my Macy's card with me, but Tom suggests that we can go to the Customer Service desk upstairs to obtain a temporary card to make the purchase. We do that, and after the woman hands me the temporary card, we walk back to get the jacket.

"Can I see the temporary card?" Tom asks. I hand it to him. He looks at it momentarily and says, "Do you mind if I carry this?"

I don't think anything of it. I've already loaned him a bucket of cash and am practically living with him, so it's a non-event. I think of him as my partner. We buy the jacket and Tom takes out the temp card to make the purchase. He seems to enjoy paying with a credit card. We stop at Strawbridge & Clothier, and Tom browses through the dress shoes for a while before selecting a pair of really nice penny loafers.

"You have a Strawbridge's card?" Tom asks. Without a second thought, I take out my card and hand it to Tom. He makes the purchase and signs my name to the sales draft. I notice that Tom places my card in his wallet after the sale. I don't say anything.

Later

Tom takes us for a short ride to see where he grew up, and then where he went to high school. It's relaxing and somehow intriguing to learn more about him as a boy. My thoughts go to a time when I was a boy, when I used to wonder where my future wife was. How could I have ever imagined what lay in store?

At GB's, Tom and I dance the night away. I don't recall ever having as much fun. Tom and I tear up the dance floor, and I relish the numerous stares that come our way. Normally, I attract a fair share of stares, but coupled with Tom, we turn almost every head. It feels good basking in this, but the best part is his love.

Everyone crowds the two-tier bleacher-type seats lining one side of the dance floor as the show begins. I sit on the lower deck with Tom behind me on the top deck with his arms around me, showing everyone we are a couple. Before the drag show, the exotic dancers perform, and one of the straight dancers I used to perform with is first up. "Lee" jumps up and jiggles his pelvis in my face. He's hot, and I've engaged in many personal jack-off sessions fantasizing about his fantastic ass. He pulls his g-string down while he's in front of us and I reach behind him and shove a buck into it, after a enjoying a generous helping of ass groping.

Soon after the drag show, we decide to head out. We stop at Denny's for a bite and then drive back to the apartment. As soon as we arrive and get out of the car, Tom says, "Jump on my back. I want to give you a piggyback ride up to the door."

"No way, Chief, I'll break your back." He bends over and gestures to me to climb on. I take a few steps backwards to give myself a bit of a running start.

"You asked for it!" I shout as I jump on his back. He barely has me, and then all of a sudden he pulls me up with his powerful arms and carries me on his back. It's extraordinary, being carried by piggyback. Tom walks half the way to the apartment door, carrying me on his back, before he gives up. Now, this is impressive. Tom ignites a playful, pleasurable passion I've never experienced. In my usual competitive nature, I insist he jump on my back, intent on carrying him the remainder of the way. It's not as hard as I thought it would be, and supporting him completely on my back is exhilarating and fun. We begin undressing as we walk in, laughing like two boys up to no good, leaving a trail of our clothes all the way to the bedroom.

We fumble over getting out of our underwear as we enter the bathroom and fill up the tub. I soak up the sight of his sexy body as he sinks into the water with me. First, I lather up the soap and wash his beautiful back. Then I wash his hair, and begin kneading his shoulders and arms to wash away the stress. I save his sensitive parts until last, and he lets out soft groans of pleasure.

After a steamy hot session of mutual satisfaction, we drag ourselves to bed. Lying together in each other's arms, we continue our expression of love by whispering sweet words to each other as we drift to sleep.

He's so beautiful, and I love him so very much. I take a moment and look upward toward heaven and wink. *Thank you, God. Thank you, Mary. Thank you so much for this. I pray this will last forever.*

Sunday, October 23, 1988

We're entwined in a cocoon-like love hug as I wake. It's beautiful waking up on Sunday morning in each other's arms. I still hear the pumping music from last night in my head. Tom's sexy personal scent fills the bed, and I run my lips over his soft shoulders, aching to make love again. I pull away, out of our love hug, and stretch out on the bed for a while before dashing off to the bathroom. I gaze at myself in the mirror after my pee and think good things about what I see. The warmth of Tom's love accentuates the narcissism I feel. I brush my teeth and wash my hands and face. Back into the bedroom, I walk in to find my love sitting up in bed smoking a cigarette.

"Want some juice or coffee?" I ask.

"Why sure, coffee sounds great, my naked little flight attendant, you," he says, stretching and smiling at me. I chuckle and locate my jockeys. I pull them on and go into the kitchen to put the coffee on. When it's brewed, I bring our mugs into the bedroom.

"My aching head!" he laments.

"Me too," I say, suddenly feeling the effects of my own hang-over. I get up and locate some ibuprofen in the bathroom. I bring the bottle and hand Tom two pills, and he says, "Three," so I give him another and I also take three tablets.

"So when are you moving in here permanently?" he asks.

"You really want me here?" I ask, reeling with delight.

"I want you with me all the time. We should be together. I never felt this way about anyone. You feel the same, right?"

I lean over and kiss him. "Of course I do. It's gonna be a long drive to work every day, though."

Tom scratches his head, "Shit. Who cares? You're doing it now, and besides, can't you transfer to the First Commercial branch here in town? This should be your home. You belong with me. I want you here."

What can I say? This is what I want. I ask, "How about today?"

Totally out of character, yet playfully cute, Tom gets up and starts jumping up and down on the bed saying, "Great!"

That's it. It's decided. I don't have any doubt that this is the right thing to do. I feel confident, reassured by his reaction that he's excited about the idea, ready to be in a full-time homosexual relationship. I once questioned whether I had the guts to be openly gay, but my love for Tom and his love for me — honestly — has made me feel more certain and sure of this than anything before in my life. My entire life has been shaped and dictated by a strict Catholic and military blended code, ethical "standards" my two parents fostered. Although there are some merits to the values and environment they created in my childhood, things aren't always the way Mommy and Daddy said they would be.

Face-to-face with what I perceive to be Catholic-driven guilt, I ask myself questions like, *Will this hurt my parents? Will this upset my Lord? Do I have the strength to say "no" to Tom to avoid what my parents would abhor?* I hate myself for even thinking these questions, but they pop up — as if my brain has been conditioned to deny any deviation from some master blueprint already predetermined for my life. Then I consider my personal needs and desires. There exists a gap in my life, and a selfish need to be loved, wanted, and belong to someone I truly love, to build my own family and achieve my own happiness and fulfillment.

Tom gets up and walks into the bathroom. He turns and smiles at me as he closes the door behind him. Despite my resolution to finally be true to myself, I walk over and sit at the dining area table, continuing to assess my situation. If I live my life only for my parents, the way they want me to live, my youth will be gone, and they will be gone, and then what will I have? I want to be able to reflect back on my life and have no regrets, be able to say that despite everything, I did what I wanted to do. I took risks, win or lose; they were my decisions, and I sought out what brought me happiness and love.

Tom comes out of the bathroom and goes into the kitchen. He's cooking. Good. I'm hungry. I actually feel more comfortable in this apartment than in my parent's house. I don't feel out of place; it feels like I belong here. The atmosphere is peaceful and relaxed. It's noon already.

"Tom, I'm horny and hungry!" I sprawl out on the floor in front of the TV and turn it on.

"Hey, I'm cooking for you!"

"GOOD! I'm in the mood to eat with you and then eat you." We laugh.

"Why don't you watch TV?" he says, not realizing I already have it on. I flick through the channels until I find MTV. I turn it up.

Later

Driving to Fort Dix on the way to my parent's place, Tom asks what I want to do on Halloween night.

"Isn't it next Tuesday?"

"No," Tom answers, "it's next Monday, so Gatsby's will probably have a Halloween bash on Saturday night."

I smile and ask, "Are you asking me out on a date?" He reaches down and holds my hand while he drives. I say, "I always have jobs for Mitch on and around Halloween. It's unavoidable."

"That's okay, we'll do the jobs, then go out afterwards."

"Last year, on my last job, I was dressed as a cop and stopped into the Key West in my costume. It was great to be able to go to the club right after dancing without having to change. It was a lot of fun. Couple dudes asked to see my nightstick."

Tom smiles and says, "Uh huh."

Arriving at my parent's house, we find no one home. "I can't just move out without anyone here," I tell him, so we sit around waiting for my family to come home. I show Tom the house and my room, knowing my parents may freak out about him being in here without them being home. While we wait, I pack a ton of work clothes into Tom's car.

Mom and Dad get home and find us sitting in the living room watching TV. I introduce Tom to my parents, and am taken aback by how well they all immediately hit it off. Mom and Dad seem genuinely warm and sincere in their greeting and conversation, but I can detect their suspicion, resentment and phoniness. We sit there momentarily, chit-chatting about the latest Nadine bullshit, when Mom lights a cigarette and says, "Would you excuse me? I'm going out for a cigarette."

Tom asks her if she'd mind if he joined her for a smoke. "I don't like smoking inside — it smells up the house," he says.

"Me, too," Mom says. "Come on out with me."

Eager to join them, I don't budge, sitting still in my chair. I don't want it to seem like I'm following Tom around like a puppy. Dad changes the channel to the football game. "Where did you guys go?" I ask.

He responds, "CHURCH!" in his usual forceful, loud tone.

I nod nervously, and look around for the next question in an edgy attempt to make small talk. Since I can't find a question written on any of the walls, I remain silent and anticipate a remark about Tom. Dad is all into the game and not interested in talking, even after we haven't seen each other for over a week. Not a problem.

I get up and walk down to my room to go through the mail that has piled up. I can hear Mom and Tom talking up a storm in the backyard from my room. I crack open the window so I can tune into the dialog. They seem to be getting on fine. She asks Tom if I smoke and he says he hasn't seen me smoke. Gawd, I feel so embarrassed. Jeez, what should I expect a Mother to ask one of her son's "friends"? She asks him where we met, and Tom says he's a client at the bank where I work, and we've seen each other out and about. I close the window and go back to my mail.

Tom clears his throat in the doorway to my room after a few moments, and I jolt up in bed. I must have dozed off. There he is, the man of my dreams, standing in the doorway of my bedroom. So many nights I've spent locked in this room, alone, dreaming and fantasizing about a sexy guy like Tom alone in my room with me. I get up and walk toward him. He grabs me, pulls me close and we kiss right here in the doorway. This is the exact spot where, seven years earlier, I had my first kiss ever with a girl named Angela.

I turn and begin to show the man of my dreams the things in my life that I want to share with him. It excites me to the core to see him so interested in my history. He pores over the photo albums, pictures, keepsakes, letters, essays, and poems I've written, as well as clothes, records and things I've collected — all parts of me. It gives me undiluted pleasure to see him look and listen to my story with such attentiveness.

As we fan through my record collection and chat about each other's likes and dislikes, we end up lying on the floor kissing. Tom lifts the hooded gray high school logo sweatshirt I'm wearing and kisses my stomach. "Nice," he says, resting his head on my belly, rolling his face into it. He undoes my belt buckle and then the snap of my jeans slowly. He reaches in and cups my balls and massages them gently. I lose the battle of fighting the feeling of arousal as my cock inflates.

I hear Mom calling me. We walk upstairs and she introduces Tom to my brother Danny, who is a high school senior this year. I can tell Tom finds Danny attractive.

Dinner is good, and Tom is skilled at the art of conversation. We finish eating after what seems to be forever and not long afterward, Tom declares that we're leaving. Mom expresses her concern about me staying with Tom, inasmuch that I might be an imposition for him. Tom eloquently paints them a picture of perfect harmony with the arrangement, and we leave.

Tom says, "I'll drive," and I reply, "Thought we were taking two cars. I'm staying over with you, right?"

"Let's just go for a drive," he suggests, "and talk."

Tom drives around Fort Dix at my direction, and he seems to enjoy seeing all the young, hot military dudes walking the sidewalks. I explain that Fort Dix is a training site. Tom suggests offering one or more of the guys a ride to wherever they're walking. I tell him I'm not fond of the idea, so he doesn't.

After a few hours of casual driving and talking, we're back at my parent's house and Tom suggests, "It might be best if you stayed here tonight." I don't argue, though something inside of me resents any time away from him.

"I guess I'm not moving out today, eh, Bud?"

Tom nods and says, "Bud? We'll get you over; take it slow. I'm so tired, I don't feel like driving back tonight."

"Do you want to go get some coffee or something?"

"No, I'm all right."

"Do you want me to drive? Then I could just spend the night with you."

"No, you have to work tomorrow, you need your car."

I reluctantly accept it. Tom suggests that he's so tired, in fact, that, "I should spend the night in one of the hotels we passed on our drive."

"You can stay over with me here. My parents won't mind."

Tom shakes his head again and asks if he can use my American Express card to pay for a hotel room. I hand him the card, and it doesn't dawn on me until I'm out of the car watching him drive away that we didn't kiss goodnight. He'd mentioned that he would call me at work tomorrow. We've been spending almost every night together since meeting, so I'm saddened by the fact that I won't be in his arms tonight. For a second, I put together that the hotel he wants to stay in is directly across from a gay bookstore. Why a hotel room? I can't think on it too hard. I'm being ridiculous.

Monday, October 24, 1988

I arrive for work feeling refreshed, bright-eyed and bushy-tailed for the first time in ages. Sitting at my desk, I take out my pending file and begin to sort through my work. About an hour into working, I receive a call. "Tom, Mitch."

"Mitch, how are you?"

"Fine, just fine. Listen, I got a busy weekend for you with Halloween coming up. Can you take some of the information?"

"Sure," I say, giggling inwardly at how excited Mitch is over the hoard of money he's gonna make since it's Halloween. He's silent for a moment and I can hear him shuffling through paperwork. Finally, he goes over my itinerary. As he rolls through the conversation, I'm impatient and ready to get to the end of the pile of jobs. "The job sold for $100, just send me $30. That's $70 for you on that one!"

Like, no shit, I think to myself.

"I have a club in Ridley Township for you. It's Dellapolla's. You've been there before, haven't you?"

"Many times, Mitch," I say, wondering what planet he's on, since he sends me there almost every other week.

"The Della's job wants a tux. Get the tux ready and be ready to go on at 11:00. That means you can't fool around on the Fishtown job. You gotta get right out of there and to Ridley Township straight away. You'll make it. It's a done deal. You'll get a check for a hundred for the Della's job. Then, Saturday, you need to do a job in the club Wok-n-Roll in Cherry Hill. Know it?"

"Yes, I think it's on Cuthbert?"

"Yes, and you gotta get in street clothes for that also. It's their Halloween bash, and you go on at 11:00. It's a real easy one, Tommy. You have to get to another job by 12:30 right after. I know they're booked right on top of each other, but since they're so close, I figured you could get 'em both in there for us. The 12:30 is for a group of gay men. You cool with that?"

"I'm a trouper."

Mitch continues to provide me with all the details and information on the jobs. He mentions that I'll get more jobs as the week progresses. The orders he's giving me now were all placed last week. As it gets closer to Halloween, the last-minute gigs will be priced higher.

After work, I hit the base gym to work out a bit, and it makes me feel really good as my thoughts are all on Tom. I think about his handsome face as I walk around the track and bolt into a fast quarter-mile sprint. Surprisingly, I'm in and out of the locker room quickly; I rush through my shower and change, barely taking notice of any sights.

After the gym, I stop at a payphone and call Tom. "Hey, it's me. How ya doing?" I ask.

"Great! Where are you?"

"I just finished working out."

"You coming home?" he asks.

"Yes," I begin, my heart filling when I hear him say 'coming home.' "I didn't hear from you all day and was getting worried."

"Okay — I'll see you in an hour and five minutes then!"

"Okay."

On arrival we kiss and embrace. His hug is tight and hard; I sense he missed me.

Tuesday, October 25, 1988, 6:30 p.m.
Deptford Mall

Strolling through a mall with Tom is quickly becoming one of my favorite simple pleasures. I absolutely adore being in public with this beautiful man, because my ego is magnified by all the heads we turn. Almost as if in a mild trance, I soak in an intense sense of safety and pride having him beside me. I told him earlier that I wanted a watch like the one he has. I admire everything about him. I've never been much into wearing jewelry, but Tom's things are very masculine and attractive to me. We walk into Littman's, and in a matter of minutes the same gold Nicolet watch he owns is on my wrist.

"Do you have an account with us?" asks the saleswoman with a German accent, her gold hair tied up in a neat bun on her head.

"I love it. I can give you a check."

Tom interjects, "It might be a good idea to establish an account in case we want to buy some other things later."

I totally agree, staring at my new beautiful gold watch gleaming in the light. It has a square white face with black Roman numerals.

After a romantic dinner out, we head home and watch some TV. Lying in bed, as I snuggle close to Tom with my head on my chest, I whisper in his ear, "Hey Sport, I'm off at 2:00 tomorrow."

Tom looks up and smiles softly. "Okay, are you coming right home after work?"

"Yeah. When do you go in tomorrow?"

"I'm working the morning shift, and I'll be home before you get home. By the way, I had to write a check on our account for the electric bill. It was past due for $200."

"That's fine," I say. "We're caught up now with it, then?"

"Yes." It's Heaven staying up to the wee hours of the morning talking and enjoying each other, taking our sexual exploration and relationship to a place where there are no limits.

Wednesday, October 26, 1988

The next morning when I awake, I notice it's rather bright out for 6:00 AM. The next thought that comes to mind is that I got up with no alarm. I quickly shoot a glance at the clock and freak out when I read 8:30. FUCK! I sing a song of obscenities as I scramble to get to the phone. I call work, and luckily, Janet answers.

"Where are you?" she asks.

"I got up late."

"I figured. I'll tell her your car wouldn't start. Hurry up and get here."

"I'm on the way." We hang up, and I blow through the apartment getting ready for work like a bat out of hell.

Just when I need to rush, a night of freezing rain has produced roads covered in ice and there's a light dusting of snow on top, causing very slippery conditions. In no time I'm racing down the slick exit ramp onto Route 42, and my car slides as I gun it through the ramp at almost 40 miles an hour. I have an empty gas tank and my two back tires are kind of bald, which means I have no traction and my car weighs less than it could. I notice the wheels of the car don't turn as I turn the steering wheel, and that I've lost control of the car. It slides straight for the large curb, and my heart jumps up to my throat as I brace for impact.

"Fucking son-of-a-bitch," I mutter as the car collides into the curbing on the side of the ramp. My head bangs the windshield as the car jolts to a stop. After impact, other than seeing a few stars dance around my head, I'm fine. Cars begin queuing up as they slow down to gawk at me as they drive by. I get out of the car and stumble on my first step forward to view the mess. Both front tires are blown. A kind Samaritan in the form of a local trooper takes pity on me and pulls over to help. He tells me I broke one of the rear spindles that hold the wheel on, and broke a strut.

After the tow truck arrives and my car is loaded up, the driver hands me a business card for their garage. I turn and walk toward a diner just before the ramp. I try to think good thoughts, turning them to exquisite experiences I've shared with Tom — especially our nights under the covers.

Once in the diner, I drop coins in the pay phone. Tom answers the call on the second ring. "Honey, I was in an accident."

He's silent for a moment, and then asks, "Already?" I'm a bit taken back by his response, expecting his first reaction to be an inquiry as to my well-being.

"What?" I ask, fuming.

"I mean, you just left." Irritated by his lack of concern, I explain what happened and he says he's coming to get me.

My next call is to work. Sue answers. Eleven fucking employees there, and she has to answer. "Sue, it's Tom," I say and wait for a response.

"You're not coming in, right?"

I explain the accident to Sue. I play the martyr card, overdramatizing a headache from my head hitting the windshield, hoping to tug on her sense of compassion. Sue isn't totally thrilled, but she ends the call with a "Hope you feel better" comment. I think I dodged that bullet.

By the time Tom finally arrives, a full hour after I called, I've had three cups of coffee and I feel pretty wired. He's dressed and primped, complete with cologne and jewelry. Suddenly those things aren't very appealing to me. If the tables were turned and he'd called me saying he was in an accident, I would have run right over in PJ's and Pumas out of concern for him. On the ride home I consider asking Tom, *Was it necessary to grab a shower before leaving?* He's quiet, and his silence fuels my discontent.

We arrive home, and I follow Tom into the apartment.

"Are you okay?" Tom finally asks as we recline on the sofa with our feet up on the coffee table. He's obviously responding to my attention-seeking tactic of sitting with my hands covering my face.

"Yes, I'm good, thanks." The station where my car was towed calls and relates to Tom that they're willing to do the repair work. Since I'm in possession of an Exxon charge card, I ask Tom to tell them to just do it. In an attempt to bring a little levity to the situation, I tell Tom to instruct them to keep the bill under $10.

It's only Wednesday, and already my week is a shambles.

Thursday, October 27, 1988

Tom picks me up from work promptly at 5:00. I smile and kiss him, saying, "Hello, my man."

It seems perfectly natural to talk to him like my "other half," and being a novice in gay relationships, I take my lead from Tom. Initially, saying romantic, cutesy type stuff to another guy is a bit awkward, but the more I do it, the more natural it feels.

"Let's move you in with me," he says.

My smile grows wide as I say, "You mean, totally?" He reaches for my hand and brings it up to his lips, gently kissing it. I'm ready. Living in my folk's house, I've been surrounded with memories of Nadine. I feel happy with Tom, especially at night — in his bed, and in his arms. We both agree that it isn't a good idea to flat-out tell my parents about our true relationship. I'm just getting used to the idea myself, actually. I don't share this with Tom, but I consider this move an adventure, and part of my personal exploration and growth, as much as I consider doing it for love.

We reach my parent's house, and finding no one home, Tom follows me into the basement to my room. We move my clothes and some personal things into his car. As we leave the house and drive down the street, I see my parents heading right toward us, homeward-bound. Tom is driving, so he slows down and finally stops as we approach them on the street. Mom is driving, with Dad next to her. Mom's smile fades as she notices the car filled with my belongings. She quips, "I suppose this means you're moving out?" in a not-so-friendly tone, her eyes affixed on me.

Tom greets them as I answer, "Yeah, kind of."

They put on phony smiles.

"I need to get away from these memories," I say, sure that they know I'm referring to times with Nadine. Mom shoots me a disapproving grin and Dad just shakes his head and waves his hand at us in the air. They both force another smile.

I say, "We'll see you later."

They offer us dinner, and Tom lies, saying that we're going to his sister's house for dinner, but "Thank you, and we'd love to come over and have dinner another time."

Hearing the word "we" in Tom's response paints us as a couple. It's trivial, but that one word carries so much weight and feels so good. We get back to his apartment, which now feels more like home than ever before, and unload the car.

We decide to go to Gatsby's to celebrate my moving in with Tom. Surprisingly, it's semi-crowded for a Thursday night, probably since tonight is "Quarter Night," when the club sells beers and well drinks for 25 cents. We find a place to sit on the bleachers next to the dance floor, and I offer to walk up to the bar to get us a drink, but Tom says, "I got it."

As I watch him greet a few people he knows, I think about some of the contrasts between this relationship and ones I've been in with women. In any relationship, there are various differences I've expected to encounter; however, there are some unexpected distinctions in this one. For instance, it's out of character for me to not be the one driving the car when we go out together, or even something as simple as not being the one to go up and buy the drinks for us at the club. There are certain behaviors that are either engrained in us from childhood or else come naturally in association with our gender. With a female, I tend to assume the role of navigator, leader and provider. With Tom I find it odd to take a passive role in certain tasks initially. As I assume new positions in my gay relationship, I realize roles we fall into in any relationship should be based on mutual comfort and personal desire rather than predefined societal structures.

A former high school chum, Jeff, walks over and interrupts my meditation by saying, "You guys make a hot couple."

"Thanks. I finished moving in with him today."

"Cool," he says, offering his fist up in praise. I raise my fist to meet his. Jeff says, "Do you remember Beth Birney from school?"

Beth, a pretty albeit muscular blonde, was a tomboy in high school that everyone assumed was gay. We didn't associate until after high school, when she would frequent the pool where I was a lifeguard. She had a crush on me, and I recall Nadine being pissed over Beth's many advances toward me. I turn as Tom approaches with my beer in hand. Jeff points to the dance floor where Beth is dancing. She catches sight of us and shouts, "Rubin!" I cast a closed-mouth smile her way, nodding my head to acknowledge her, feeling a flood of anguish over the high school nickname. Beth approaches with arms wide, ready for a hug. I reluctantly put my beer down and get up to receive her hug. She introduces me to a beautiful woman whose name is Melanie — her current lover. After an hour of drinking and catching up, Beth is thrilled hearing about my escapades as a male exotic dancer and is eager to be a stripper, asking me to introduce her to Mitch.

Around midnight, we're all drunk, except for Tom, who's just a bit silly from the few drinks he had. He places his arm around me, pulling me close, and whispers in my ear, "I can't wait until we make love tonight. Your sweet, hard body has had me rock-hard all evening." Hearing his words and looking into his eyes, I feel my own cock swell in anticipation.

When we get home, there's a message on the answering machine from the garage, indicating that my car is repaired and can picked up tomorrow. Since the repair place opens when I have to be at work and closes before I finish, Tom offers to drop me off at work and then go pick up the car. He takes my credit card to pay for it and says he'll leave his car there, pick me up from work in my car, and we can go get his car later.

Friday, October 28, 1988

A call from Tom is transferred to me. "Hello, Champ," I answer.

"Bad news," he begins. "My car quit on me on the way to pick up your car and I had to have it towed to Exxon."

"You're fucking kidding me. What happened to it?" I ask, half laughing at the absurdity of our run of horrible luck.

"It just died on me at the light in town. I'm at the station now. The battery just gave out, so I'm having a new one put in. It should only be around a hundred bucks or so, so I'll put it on the card."

I'm totally committed to the idea that we're in a relationship and our finances are commingled, but it bothers me a bit that he just assumes that using my card is okay without asking first. Part of me wants him to relax and feel comfortable using my credit cards because, in some strange way, it strengthens the bond between us and somehow validates this unconventional marriage. I'm considering what we have a marriage, and in my mind, in a marriage you share everything.

I ask, "When do you get paid?"

Tom answers, "I get my check today. I'll put it in our account. I should only be here for about another half hour."

Tom arrives at 5:45, driving my repaired T-bird, which he's obviously taken to get washed. I get in the driver's seat and greet him with a kiss and hug. I missed him. "So what's the damage on the credit card?" I ask.

He smiles, "Minor. About $150 — don't worry, we'll pay it off."

I swallow hard and scan the invoices from the mechanic he hands me. One invoice is from a garage in Winslow, not Glassboro.

"Why did your car get towed to Winslow?"

"That's just where the tow truck came from."

I'm still not too familiar with the general surroundings of the area, but I recall the address of the Winslow Exxon as around the corner from the Aquarius adult bookstore. Odd coincidence, I suppose, trying to envision the distance from Glassboro to Winslow and whether there were any service stations that would be closer. I focus back on the invoices: Tom's is $173.58, and mine is $473.71. That comes to almost $650!

"Jesus H. Christ! This is a lot of money!"

"Don't worry, honey, we'll do it," he reiterates. "Besides, I have a surprise for you after dinner." The words are incredibly soothing to me. I dismiss the whole thing, cramming the invoices into the glove compartment.

We go to grab something to eat before the dancing gigs I have scheduled tonight. I'm not crazy about eating before dancing, but I'm so hungry, I feel too weak to perform. We stop at Bob's Big Boy on the Black Horse Pike in Audubon, since they've got an awesome all-you-can-eat special for $12 on Fridays, and play footsies under the table while we feast on cocktail shrimp from the bar. After eating, we sit in silence and I feel the pang of sexual desire rising in my pants. Tom winks at me as I smile widely.

"I'm suddenly ready for a blow job," he says.

His thoughts mirror my own. Tom, with his sexy eyes looking at me, enables my hard-on to gather momentum. I wonder if the people in this restaurant would mind if I slip under the table and suck his cock. My mind is focused on how willing and able I am to give him the best blow he's ever received. It feels good to find someone who meets my needs and matches my level of sexual energy and desire. I love being in his presence. I trust his love.

Our robust waitress arrives with our check. I give her cash for the check, along with a tip. She thanks me and we depart. Tom and I walk out to the car in the parking lot.

"Close your eyes," he says in a boyish way.

I comply with his request and close my eyes. I can hear him open the trunk. I try to peek without opening my eyes more than a crack, but I can't see a thing. I hear him lift something and close the trunk, then place it on the top of the trunk.

"Okay! Take a look!"

I open my eyes and focus in on what looks like a fireman's uniform.

"Is that...?" I start, but Tom jumps right in, "It's a fireman's outfit. I borrowed it from a friend who's a volunteer at the Clementon Volunteer Fire Department! Isn't it cool?"

I'm so elated, since this will be a major hit on my jobs; plus it makes doing them a lot more fun for me.

"You can wear it out for Halloween too!"

I grab him and hug him close, right here in the parking lot. I shower him with kisses all over his face until I find his lips. "I can't believe you did this, man! When did you get the time today?"

All my wondering and doubt melt away. I am so happy. I can't believe it. Only a shadow of a question remains in the back of my mind: *What friend at the Fire*

Department? I elect to leave it in the back of my mind. I'm just too happy. Besides, I don't really want to know the answer.

We stop at home and I jump in the shower. After showering, I dress in the bombdiggity fireman's outfit — with the extra large yellow pants into which I tuck in a white tank top. I pull on the red suspenders that hold up the pants, then the big yellow jacket. The hat and axe accentuate the look. I pull on the big black knee-high boots and check my look in the mirror. The sight of my reflection feeds my already inflated ego. The cherry on top is Tom's whistle when I come out of the bathroom.

"You look sensational in that," he says, his eyes wide open, his lips parted as he scopes me up and down. He rises and comes to me, now uninhibited. He puts his hands on my shoulders and then around my waist, pulling me in to kiss me fiercely. His eyes are closed and it's as if he's in a trance now as I undress him. We share a controlled fall to the floor, clutched in each other's arms, kissing and groping each other.

"You should have joined me in the shower," I say, voice deep and in character.

He pants, "I like that wicked smile you have there, Marino. Put your hands on my balls, take them in your fist, lock them in there, pull them up, squeeze them… that's it. Feels good, doesn't it?" His comments dictate where our fantasy goes and it's easy, playful and natural to fulfill the dominating role he's constructed for me.

We finish our steamy session and grab another shower, then sit on the sofa watching MTV. Tom has his head on my lap. I look at him, and think how very wonderful he is — because even without this beautiful and exciting lovemaking, he is all I could ever want. Somehow I know that I will be happy for the rest of my life, as long as we're together.

Later

One of the girls announces, "I've got a treat for the ladies tonight: a hot fireman." She starts clapping, and I find my way through the back of the room to join her at the front while everyone joins in the whistling and clapping. The house is packed. I'm not used to being introduced without my music. I stand there for a few awkward moments, grinning, taking in dirty looks from some of the guys in the crowd.

My music begins to play and it's like a wave of cool water rescuing me, allowing me to escape to that special place I adore. I asked a DJ who works for Mitch to compose a special mix of tunes for this Halloween, leading with "Love Is for Suckers" by Full Force. It's an immediate hit as soon as it starts. I walk around the room in a circle with a serious expression, looking at their faces. Some are smiling, some frowning, some laughing and whispering. I don't care. I'm deep into this and feel the smooth waves of energy flow through me as I peel off the uniform, revealing my gym worked body. The feeling is magnetic and self-gratifying.

As I tear off the tank top, some of the girls scream, further inflating my ego. As I perform, I notice a huge bean bag chair. I have visions as I dance and sometimes I make things up and take risks as I go. I signal to a guy in the hallway to come to me. He shakes his head, but his friends pull him over to me. I make a motion for him to make a foot stand with his fingers interlocked. He leans over and I put one foot in his cupped hands and jump up. With all my might, I push my feet over my head into a somersault that results in a semi-belly flop on the bean bag chair. It hurts like hell, but I smile and roll over as slowly and sexually as I can. They don't know I'm in pain, they only see it as a hot stunt that gains some respectable applause. My knees take a little beating on the landing and I begin to feel it as I rise and dance. A thought flashes in my head – of the dude who helped me with the somersault and how close I came to kicking him in the mouth when I flipped over. One can only imagine that scene – it makes me laugh out loud.

I can't do a mediocre job, I can't go half way — every part of me goes into the show. I want to give a great performance. I strut up to some of the girls and dance close to them, focused on thoughts which give me a natural euphoria. Finally, I'm out of my underwear and down to a black g-string. I continue to dance up to everyone — even some of the guys in a kidding-type way, faking belly punches to them when I approach.

Later

We get to Della's, and Tom is pumping with energy. "Is this a male stripper joint?"
"Pretty much."

We park in the lot across from the club. I'm supposed to wear a tux for this job, but I really like the fireman's uniform. "Maybe I should try and call the woman who ordered this at the club, and see if she wants me to use the fireman outfit?"

Tom says, "Don't worry about it. I got it for a couple weeks."

"Wow! That's cool. Who do you know at the Clementon Fire Department so well?" Somehow I don't want to know the answer; and not so surprisingly, I don't get one.

I grab my tuxedo out of the back seat where it's hanging and change into it in the car. Inside the club, Tom asks, "Where should I go? This place is wall-to-wall chicks."

I laugh and lightly punch him on the shoulder, saying, "Then I guess you'll fit right in!" and jolt ahead of him. He catches up and pinches my side, winking at me with his sexy eyes. I say, "Follow me. You can stand with the DJ."

I take Tom around to the back of the DJ booth. I introduce him to Mike, and Mike shakes Tom's hand with one hand, holding an earphone to his head with the other.

Mike sets up a line of five dance songs, so he can have a cigarette and talk for a moment. "Ever get drunk up here?" Tom asks him.

"Oh yeah," he says, blowing smoke out and silently catching a belch. "That's what makes the mixes even better. Do you spin? Want to take over?"

Tom's eyes widen in terror. He quickly chirps, "No."

Mike blows his cig smoke out in a chuckle, coughing the words, "Just kidding." I tell Mike I'm leaving Tom up there with him until I finish my gig.

"My check," I say, practically screaming to the familiar-looking old hag who usually pays me. We go to a corner and she tears through a bag looking for it. She produces two checks: one for this job, and one from the last time I worked here, about a month ago.

I'm the first dancer to go on for the evening of male dancers. I don't mind going on first; usually the crowd is fresh, and there's nothing they can compare you to that they've just finished watching. When I finish my show, I go over to the bar to get some orange juice. A pretty woman approaches me and hands me a red rose. I kiss her on the cheek, and as I turn to leave, she touches me on the back. I turn and she kisses me on my mouth. Usually a nice kiss is a crowd pleaser; however, with Tom watching, I tone it down and just peck her momentarily on the lips.

"I love your chest," she whispers, running her finger down to my belly button. "Nice pecs."

"Thanks, but it's still a work in progress," I say, smiling, and making a quick exit to depart with Tom.

Later that night — in bed

"How many women have you had sex with?"

I shake him gently, then squeeze him tightly. "What? C'mon..."

He cocks his head, apparently serious about getting an answer. "Tom, I never fucked anyone with this job," I snap, confident in sharing and revealing my truths, not reserving my secrets the way I know he does.

He smiles contently and closes his eyes, pulling the covers up to his chin. *This little bugger is in love with me.* I want to believe that the love Nadine and I shared was mutual, but I think she might have loved the "idea" of me. Perhaps she was in love with the idea of a husband. In Tom, I find the ultimate best sex, friendship and soul-mate combination. I feel he loves me completely. I start dreaming about him.

My dream turns to reality as I feel Tom kissing the back of my neck and his arms reaching around my body. Our hard bodies entwine as we pull each other close. My eyes are delicately sealed shut by my sleep state, and my sleepy head is gently brought back to consciousness as Tom brushes his lips over mine. I feel my heart beating faster as I turn over. He runs his fingers through my hair, then down to my arms and hands. He gently strokes my arms, and then grabs and squeezes my hand. The massaging motion of his hands has me experiencing a feeling of floating on water. I position myself on top of him, and we share a long, warm kiss. His tongue and mine dance together within our open lips. I run my hands down the side of his strong, naked body and up to his sexy face. Our petting and foreplay elevate me to a point where I can no longer restrain myself.

We engage in a hot steamy session of passionate lovemaking so intense it takes us both to teary eyes and, as our bodies became one, we declare how intensely we care for each other. As the sex continues, our bodies become drenched in sweet perspiration. His gentle touch brings me to a dream-like ecstasy unsurpassed by any experience I have ever had. This is true lovemaking. I realize this is the ultimate sexual experience of my life; Tom is perfect in every way — emotional balance, knowledge, body, personality, and sensitivity. Such extraordinary feelings race through my body. After a mutual climax, we fall limp against each other. We conclude our lovemaking session as we started it — with a long kiss.

Tom looks into my eyes and purrs, "I love you more than anyone I have ever known." He just met me - that just can't be the true. My head is clouded with suspicions, telling me to run as far away as I can, but I want so much to go with it. It feels so good to hear. I want to believe it.

He brushes my hair back with his hand and kisses my forehead. He picks up my hand, opens it, and turns it to him. He brings his finger to my palm and traces an invisible heart and kisses it.

Saturday, October 29, 1988

We get up early, make coffee and jump into action, charged with an unknown source of energy and enthusiasm. Tom takes on the difficult task of finding room for all my work clothes by moving his things around. He empties the jam-packed bedroom closet and completely overhauls it so everything fits neatly. The apartment is very sexy, cozy, tidy and organized, but in dire need of a good dusting and deep cleaning. While he helps get my personal stuff situated, I tackle scrubbing the toilet, sink and tub with bleach, then flush them out with vinegar. I vacuum, dust, and clean the windows inside and out. I attack the kitchen in my usual meticulous fashion. By 3:00, we've finished and the whole apartment is gleaming.

We get in the shower, acting giddy, laughing and being silly, punch drunk on sheer love. Tom soaps me up gently, giggling. He starts to tickle me, and I feel myself slipping on the surface of the newly scrubbed tub. All at once I lose my footing and fall. I extend my hands to shield me from the fall; the sensation of falling helplessly is a rush. One hand lands right on something sharp and I immediately experience a terrible pain. I swipe my hand away from the offending area and notice that it landed on the sharp side of a semi-broken metal drain cover. It slit my hand open, and now blood is pouring out. I'm trembling from the shock of the fall and Tom helps me to my feet and applies some hydrogen peroxide to the cut. He cleans the wound and puts a small dressing on my hand. I feel like a big baby, but soak up the attention and affection.

"Tetanus," Tom says.

"What?" I ask, knowing full well what he said.

"When was your last tetanus shot?"

I shake my head. "I can't remember. I should call my Mom and ask."

I walk over to the phone and call. I look at the clock, trying to fixate on where she is right now and what kind of mood she'll be in. She answers and is concerned about what happened. After checking my shot records on a little booklet she's always kept, she says I was 13 years old when I last got the shot — more than 8 years ago. She says I should go get another shot just in case. Tom insists she's right, and we plan to drive down to the hospital near my parent's house to get one. I think about having to perform tonight and try to call Mitch to see if I can cancel; however, as usual, there's no answer on the weekend. It's terribly annoying.

No such thing as calling out from a gig. The events are one-time occasions like birthdays or bachelorette parties that the customer could never reschedule, so the agency expects us to follow through on every assignment we accept. That means we have complete freedom to accept or decline any job when it's offered. I usually take everything, still clinging to the normal work concept that I can "call out" if anything arises. This isn't so in the case of dancing. It is virtually impossible to reassign a job to another dancer the same day. The schedules are so overlapping that it's just not feasible. Mitch's reputation is on the line, so cancellations are never an option.

I've done some weekends sick as a dog.

Mom suggests, "Since you're still married to Nadine, you can make use of your medical benefits by going right over to Walson. All you have to do is show your ID card."

So I go there and get my shot, and we head home. In the bathtub before the gig, I notice a bruise on my arm where I received the shot. Looks like I was shooting up.

I get out of the tub and sit on the bed. Tom comes into the bedroom and straddles my legs. He suggests we go to Gatsby's for their Halloween Bash after my assignments, and asks, "What costume are you going to wear to the club?"

"You have to ask?" I answer.

He smiles, fully aware of how excited I am about wearing the fireman's uniform. He comes in close and brushes his lips against mine. I have a towel wrapped around my waist. Tom kisses my chest and slowly moves over my body. He takes the towel off me and begins kissing me everywhere. He looks up and winks. It's a good moment.

After our fun, we get up and have a little picnic of light eats on the living room floor in an area Tom prepared for us. "Do you have a costume to bring along to wear when we go to GB's?" I ask.

Tom makes a grimace saying, "I don't like to wear costumes."

11:15 p.m.

When we arrive at Wok-n-Roll the parking lot is so full we have to park across the street at a bowling alley. We walk in and can hardly move. I look back at Tom and shake my head. It's loud as hell in here.

Tom leans over and yells in my ear, "You have to have some big ones if you're dancing in front of all these people." This is one of the larger straight clubs in the area, and is quite intimidating. There aren't many people dressed in costumes.

"I'll wait here by the door," Tom says. I nod and push my way through the crowd to the DJ booth.

White balloons semi-conceal the dance floor, which is elevated like a stage above the rest of the club.

As usual, my insides begin to quiver. Things are as they should be. The DJ finishes the last song and gets on the microphone and, while the dance floor clears, talks to the crowd about a Halloween costume party and contest on Monday night. Then he announces me. "Tonight we have a little trick-or-treat for the ladies. Welcome Fireman Tom to Wok-n-Roll!"

Everyone starts clapping as my first song, Jellybean's "Who Found Who?" belted out by Elisa Fiorillo, comes on. I strut around the now cleared, open dance floor with the big ax on my shoulder. I get several whistles and put the ax down, so I can unbutton the large jacket. Under the jacket, I have a white muscle shirt on under thick red suspenders. I catch a glimpse of Tom for a moment. His height allows him to see over much of the crowd. It's extremely invigorating to have the attention of everyone in this place. I climb up on top of a large black speaker and dive onto the floor, landing on my palms; using my arm muscles, I contort my body into a wave-like move in slow motion onto the floor. The weight of the coat and boots surprises me. I feel it in the landing. The second song is a slower song, which is unusual since I rarely include them in my routines. This is such an escape and, being fully into it, I mentally leave the planet for a short time. The crowd is responsive and fun. I enjoy the sudden rush of euphoria and pleasure I derive from performing.

Showing my body isn't something that gives me a sexual charge. It's the ego-inflating high of having everyone's attention — of showing off — that I crave. I finish the last song and exit the dance floor into the DJ's area behind a roar of applause and screams. After a moment, a cute bar-back brings in my clothes and asks, "Do you want to use the staff bathroom?"

"Sure, thanks…" The eager bar-back dude is exceptionally nice. I follow him through the "off limits" door through a huge kitchen to a bathroom complete with a shower.

"The shower isn't working," he says, opening the door. I sense he's gay. "Can I get you a drink?"

"No, thanks," I say, "I'm in a rush to get to my next job."

"Oh, I see. You want me to get your car and pull it up to the front entrance for you?" I quickly dress to avoid the temptations of his advances, perky butt, and another opportunity for sex.

As I walk back out into the club, many of the faces I pass have beaming eyes and raised eyebrows. Fingers point and heads turn toward me. It feels so good, as if I am moving in slow motion as I absorb every bit. Tom is leaning up against the doorway to the exit. He smiles when he sees me, and we walk out into the cool autumn air.

"You must be freezing!" Tom says, noticing that I'm wearing only a white tank top partially stuffed into jeans. The cold air that greets my sweat-covered face and chest feels refreshing.

"Nah — just a natural high." We still hear the music from inside the club pumping and Tom, with fingers in his ears, says, "I can't hear! Damn, the music is loud in that place!" We get inside the car and that's when I shiver, feeling a familiar chill come over my whole body. Tom starts the car and looks over at me. He leans into my face and we kiss.

"You were terrific. I can't believe how good you are. You must have danced in front of a couple hundred in there." I smile.

At 12:45 I'm due to dance for the group of Hispanic guys in Collingswood. I change into my cop costume — an actual Philadelphia policeman's uniform — and the directions are outstanding, making the address easy to find.

When we get to the door, we notice loud music coming from inside. Two dudes answer the door, and their eyes widen at the sight of us. They bring us in and we're escorted to the living room area, where a few couples are dancing to salsa music. The décor is rather stylish, with beads covering the entrance to the kitchen area and beautiful plants surrounding the living room. I am introduced to the birthday boy, Victor, and a couple of guys grab him and start teasing him with punches and back slaps. Surprisingly, they're a pretty quiet and tame group.

My music begins, and I jump right in, letting them have it. It's a pleasure dancing for these guys. They touch my legs and arms gently. As I play up to each one of them, they stare at my parts and caress my chest. I give some special attention to Victor, who is celebrating his 50th birthday. I don't catch a glimpse of Tom, but the thought that he might be jealous of me dancing for guys mildly crosses my mind. I wipe it from my thoughts and keep enjoying what I'm doing because it's terrific harmless fun. Gay men seem a bit more serious and less playful than the women I dance for. Some of the men have no expressions on their faces as I perform to a slow song. They catch my eye and wink and then return their gaze to my body. I crawl on top of Victor's lap with my stomach down and my ass out for him to pat. He slaps it gently, which draws some wailing from the group, but then softly caresses it. I roll off him and onto the floor. As I complete the third song, I rise to my feet and give Victor a kiss on the cheek that he reciprocates.

After dancing, I change back into the fireman's outfit as we drive to GB's.

I love being with Tom. He's fresh and tasty and ranks up there with vanilla wafers and green apples. He makes me feel so good about myself. Having an attractive guy like Tom with me validates my own self worth and appearance. He has the style, charisma and charm that makes heads turn as we walk into GB's. I walk holding my head high, wearing the fireman uniform, hand in hand with Tom, feeling a sense of power and prestige. I feel bigger than I ever have. I am at the top of my game. I sit down on the side of the dance floor and as friends come up to me and chat for a moment or linger by me, I feel like royalty. Slowly, even beautiful chicks find their way to our throne and before you know it, I'm meeting everyone. Everyone is anxious to know me. They look over, wondering who I am, probably knowing Tom. They want to meet me; they like to look; they stare, they gawk, they smile. It's incredible. I look around the room, daring anyone to match me.

Clearly, for probably this one and only time in this busy club, I am the best-looking, the most respected, and most popular man here. It feels damn good. I breathe it in. I absorb and suck up all the absolute joy one can get from being "that guy" everyone wants. I catch myself looking down, looking up, and knowing I'm being stared at. I enjoy the stares, the glares and the winks. We meet new people as a couple and it's sheer bliss to introduce and be introduced to people as each other's partner. How could one word carry so much weight in the way of love, honor and respect?

"Can I get you a drink?" I ask. Tom gives me a thumbs-up and I turn to head to the bar.

He catches up to me and says, "Sit. I'll go. Need to hit the john. You want a Bloody or Manhattan?" I nod and smile, then say, "How about a Miller Lite?" He smiles while his eyes give a look of disbelief. I shrug my shoulders and turn to return to my seat. It's Halloween, after all, time for celebrating and mixing it up a bit.

I affix my eyes to Tom's ass as he walks toward the bar. He's carrying the money I made tonight from dancing. I don't mind bankrolling our entertainment. We're definitely a couple, so does that matter? I'd be spending it on a hotel room or airfare for myself anyway. I'd rather spend it on someone I love.

The music is superb, and I'm enjoying looking at everyone dance in their costumes when Beth and Melodie approach. Beth is dressed up as a gypsy, and Melodie is a soldier. "Where did you get that cool costume?" Beth asks, admiring my fireman's get-up. We start talking about my dancing job for a bit. Tom returns and we all lift our drinks in a toast to nothing more than cheers, though inwardly I salute the Higher Power for the joy of this moment.

A song I requested, Siedah Garrett's version of "Do You Want It Right Now?" comes on and as we dance I feel so fucking good. Tom pulls me in for a kiss that's both powerful and soft. As if in a magical fantasy, it's beyond relaxing to love each other like this on the dance floor. As we dance, my surroundings fade from my peripheral vision, and I only see Tom's eyes. In my vision, we're alone, surrounded by candles. There's intense heat in this moment as my soul floats to indescribable heights of euphoria.

After dancing, I down my beer, dance again, and then swallow a Blue Hawaiian. The aquamarine color is more appealing than the taste. We dance again and I'm on to a tangy Long Island Iced Tea. I'm plenty blitzed when the same men I just danced for at the gig in Collingswood approach us. We all laugh for a second and share greetings and introductions to Beth and Melodie. I try to make conversation about our recent car mishaps, but Beth is so interested my dancing gigs. I tell her the place I work always needs help and that Mitch would probably like to meet her, thinking he'd probably give me a bonus for the referral.

As the night progresses the music seems to be getting louder and the liquor is intensifying the effect. At one point, practically everyone in the club is on the dance floor; what a blast!

My head is spinning and my heart is racing. The party is great and to top it all off, one of the Collingswood guys, dressed up in drag, enrobed in a marvelous gown, wins the best costume prize. The room is spinning, I'm here, I'm there, I'm talking to everyone. Soon everything's a blur. I'm in and out of the bathroom and each visit gets more daring. At one point, I'm shoving my hands down strange guy's pants in the dimly lit room. On another visit, one of my co-workers from the bank, Jon, pulls up at the urinal next to me. He's dressed up appropriately in a devil costume. I introduced him to Tom earlier and Tom found him as hot as I do. Jon's one of those men who makes your mouth water: he's dripping with masculinity, and I've always enjoyed flirting with him. He offers me some pill, but I politely decline. He expresses disappointment in me. I rest my drink on the sink so I can wash my hands. I feel my erection grow as I catch sight of his cute dimpled chin in the reflection of the mirror. Jon crushes the little pill with a key and sprinkles the dust in my drink. Feeling buzzed and eager to please him, I shrug my shoulders and just drink it down. There. "Happy now?" I ask him. I emerge from the bathroom, feeling soaking wet, and notice my shirt is drenched. I'm trying to think. Didn't I ask Tom to get me a bottle of water? I'm wondering where it is. Did I pour it on me? I remember pouring it on me, but I don't remember drinking any. I'm so fucked up. It feels incredible. I'm dizzy.

Sunday, October 30, 1988
Completely disoriented, I wake up in the car next to Tom. "What the hell?" I get up and look around to discover we are driving in the dark. The clock on the

dashboard reads 2:05. Tom puts his arm around me and pulls me close to kiss my head. I want to ask if I passed out, but don't want to know. I just shake my head and ask, "We going home?"

Tom chuckles and says, "Beth is behind us."

"What?"

"We're going to get something to eat," he says, as if I were already aware of this fact. I nod and roll down the window, eager for fresh air. The sky is unusually bright and clouds semi-mask the moonlight.

When we arrive at the PB's Diner in Glassboro, I ask Beth where Melodie is.

"She had to split. Lives with her parents and they're assholes."

Over our meal, she's full of questions about my dancing. I tell her about various themes I do, like pizza delivery, tux, cop, and construction worker.

"What do you wear for a costume when you do the construction gig?"

"Beat-up, tight light blue jeans, a white tank top, a tool belt and tan work boots."

That inspires her to talk about her job, working on a road construction site. How butch. After eating, we say our goodbyes and depart for home.

No sooner do we crawl into our apartment than the phone rings. It's Beth. Tom takes the call and relays the information to me. Her van has broken down about ten minutes from our apartment. Tom tells her we'll be right there. While changing into a pair of jeans and a sweatshirt, I suggest we let her stay with us overnight since it's so late. Tom insists that he doesn't want her over. I can't understand why, but don't push it. We throw our wet coats on and go to help. After we briefly look under the hood of her old white van, Tom tells Beth we'll drive her home.

"I'm up in Bordentown. It's far too long of a drive. I'll just call my grandfather, and he can come pick me up at your place."

I can't stay awake any longer. I would have much rather just gone back to our place and let her grandfather pick her up but Tom doesn't mind driving, so I support his decision and say, "Well, let's go. We can spend time driving instead of waiting. You and your granddad can come down here tomorrow and take care of it then."

Beth gets in the front seat with Tom and I climb in the back to pass out. I love sleeping in the car.

Tom nudges me when we arrive at Beth's place. It's almost 5:00. Beth says she can't thank us enough. I'm sure her Grandpa wouldn't have appreciated getting a call in the middle of the night to come fetch her in Glassboro. Tom had a good idea, but I would have just let her crash at our place. She asks us to wait a sec and she jogs up to her house and soon emerges with a bright orange construction worker vest and a white hard hat.

"Put these on when you do your construction gig. You can give them back later."

I adore the thought, but graciously resist her offer.

Resistance is futile. She insists, so I take the props and pull her in for a hug. She gives Tom a hug as I get in the front seat, resolved to stay awake and keep him company on the ride home. After we take off I'm fighting sleep. "Tired?" Tom asks, reaching for my hand.

"Yeah."

"Tomorrow will be a relaxing day for you. We just have to pick up my car when you get up. I'm working the late shift."

"I'll just hit the gym," I say.

"That's good. Work that hot bod for me," he replies, squeezing my hand. I smile back and he says, "Go ahead and pass out. I'll get you up when we get home."

Monday, October 31, 1988, Halloween

When I come home from work, I find Tom lying on the couch staring at the ceiling. He gets up and sits in the recliner facing me on the loveseat.

"I was let go," he announces.

I shake my head in disbelief and ask to confirm, "You lost your job at Mc-Donald's?"

"I got there at around 2:00 and Brett called me into the office. He was made the general manager. He said he was promoted during my absence and that he was tired of me being out all the time. Can you believe this shit?"

Even though I feel sorry he lost his job, I'm glad Tom is telling me everything. I have a feeling he doesn't confide in anyone, and it gives me a sense of importance in his life. I get up and turn off the TV and switch on the stereo to a smooth station. I move next to him and put my hand in his. Tom goes on to explain that Brett was previously a shift manager on the same level as Tom, and apparently had to work Tom's shifts when he called in sick. Tom had thought he had a good relationship with Brett. The thought of my relationship with Janet briefly crosses my mind, and I wonder how intact that really is. "Office politics," is all I offer, trying to be sensitive to how he's feeling.

We decide to go to the base gym. I tell him working out will help him release some frustration and maybe afford him the opportunity to change his thought patterns.

Tom wants to give me the play-by-play of the day's events on the hour drive to the gym so I sit quietly and listen. When he's got it all out I offer, "Don't sweat it, bro. I'm glad you're out of that shit hole. You've got a lot more potential than working there."

Tom reaches for my hand and holds it.

At the gym, as we walk on the basketball court I catch our reflection in the large mirror covering the wall on one side of the court. I stop and look at it. Tom turns and gives me a big smile. He has such an appealing smile, with bright white teeth. We continue walking into the workout area to the section with the free weights. There are a few brawny men inside the closed-off room; it has dusty old gray carpet on the floor, and it isn't as brightly lit as the rest of the gym. There are mirrors on the walls, and a platform area with the largest weights — huge hundred pound barbells. Tom follows me in hesitantly. I nod at one of the large guys who is familiar to me. I approach the medium-size weight bench and ask Tom to spot me. He shrugs.

"Stand behind me when I lift the weight onto my chest. If I choke and get stuck, help me get it back on the rack."

Tom stands behind me as I grunt out six sets with 180 pounds. I ask Tom if he wants to give it a go. He takes his coat off and lies down to attempt to lift the poundage. He gets it off the rack momentarily but drops it back in its place. I bring him to another bench where you can sit up to lift weights, thinking it will give him more leverage; I don't want to demoralize him. I give him two 35-pound barbells and he fares much better.

"There!" he grunts as he returns the weight to its place after performing the last of six sets. "That was easy; can I have more weight on there?"

"Don't you get a great sense of accomplishment from this?"

Tom completes another set.

I say, "You'll feel it tomorrow. Your arms will be sore."

For a fleeting moment, memories of Nadine and I working out in here flash in my head. Thoughts of Nadine spotting me to the amusement of all the big brawny guys in the gym; thoughts of her hair tied up in that cute pink mane, the laughs we shared, and her face. I remember her getting dolled up to work out, complete with pink lipstick. I block out thoughts of jogging beside her and racing her down the track. I try to forget about her pink gym outfit and smile. I block out thoughts of her curvaceous figure, of picking her up and running with her over my shoulder.

I look next to me and focus my sights on Tom. The boundaries that define friendship between lovers and friends are suddenly very clear to me. I miss the friend I had in Nadine. This thing with Tom is clearly different.

After our workout I hop on the scale in the locker room. I motion to Tom to step on the scale with me. He smiles and jumps on with me. We are fearless about putting our arms around each other to support our balance on the platform of the scale. Our combined weight is 355 pounds. We're giggling and a few of the airmen getting dressed look up at us. We jump off and act a bit more serious.

I say in a very low voice, "Allow me to give you a tour of my amusement park."

Tom follows me as we encircle the locker room. A few naked GIs walk right in front of us. We pass the shower area where several men are showering together.

"I'm going to grab a shower — want to join me?" I ask.

"No."

He walks with me to my locker and sits on the bench watching me strip. His eyes widen as I wrap the towel around my waist.

He says, "I'll wait for you in the car. Don't be too long. Don't fuck anyone."

I join a group of three young dudes in the midst of showering, and once I'm half done, I turn and catch Tom walking by checking us out.

In the parking lot, and finally alone, Tom asks me if I ever hooked up with any of the guys from the gym.

"I thought I told you about my experiences here?"

"Nope, I'm sure I would have remembered that!" Tom says with a big, curious-looking smile. There is a momentary silence as we get in the car and start driving.

"Well?" Tom asks. I understand the desire he has to hear about another guy's sexual experiences from a buddy-type standpoint, but it doesn't sit well with me from a lover's standpoint. I don't notice any sense of jealousy. I previously shared a few stories from my past to see if a sense of jealousy would be ignited, but he only absorbs the experiences as a friend would. I elect to share only one of the many trysts I've had in here.

"I once met a guy in here when I was 17 — this guy John. He was the first man I had sex with. I'm sure I told you about this."

"Yeah, I remember. You met him here? Didn't he have a lover in the Air Force?"

"Yep. John and I met, naked, in the sauna right in here. John was 34 and his partner, Doug, was 26. Doug was on assignment in Saudi when we met. John took me on an introductory tour of the gay life: a three week escapade, which I'll never forget. It was so erotic, enjoyable and uplifting. From our first meeting, sitting in the locker room talking about the heat outside, and how John was a builder, working on building a new house in Browns Mills, to rolling under the covers with him and then with him and Doug when Doug got back from Saudi in the loft-like bedroom of that gorgeous new house. It was all so gentle and beautiful, a very soft and pleasurable initiation to a new way of life."

We decide to stop by my parent's house. When they ask, Tom tells them his job is going fine. I suppose he doesn't want to invite a conversation about what happened and rehash it all again. I don't blame him. Plus, I don't want them asking me any questions around how Tom will support himself or pay his part of the bills. I don't need to raise any suspicions. After about an hour and a half of visiting, the first of the trick-or-treaters begins to arrive. My parents have bowls of candy ready. They really enjoy giving it out; I derive enjoyment from watching them get all excited over the kids coming to the door. Despite numerous terrible memories of my childhood, there are dozens of good times — mostly around the holidays and special days like Halloween and birthdays. My parents were usually decent about making them special. Mom wants to believe me when I tell her Tom is my friend, though I think she has to know there's more to it than that. Dad plays the avoidance and ignorance game, but I have no doubt he knows I'm gay. They're both quite perceptive, but I suppose with an unwanted reality, it's so much easier to avoid gut feelings and submerge into denial.

On the way home Tom wants to stop by J.C. Penney. "It's getting colder at nights and in the mornings. There's nothing better than flannel jammies in the winter."

"What's wrong with what I wear to bed now?" I ask, referring to my underwear.

"Oh, I can get your flannels off easy enough."

I take his hand in mine and squeeze.

Later

Back at home, as I get ready to climb into bed, I notice a card on my pillow while Tom is in the bathroom. I'm instantly warmed by his romantic gesture. Just when I think already he's the most wonderful man on earth, he goes and exceeds my expectations yet again. Clearly it's an example of how Tom makes life and this love so exciting; he continually surprises and delights me.

Inside he writes, "I want you to know just how deep my feelings are for you. These words convey my sentiments exactly." I read the touching words of the card and my heart fills with emotion.

Each part of the nest
is added with love and hope,
making it strong enough to protect
a treasure from the world,
but soft enough to cradle
the most delicate of dreams;
hidden to keep its secrets private,
but clearly seen by those who built it ...
... just like our love.

Tom exits the bathroom and says, "I'll be right back." I hear the sounds of soft romantic music come on. He returns with two glasses of wine. We toast our love and, after a drink, put our glasses down. He takes me into his arms in an envelope-like hug as we cuddle on the bed. As we embrace, the smell of his cologne fills me with passion while he whispers how much he loves me, gently, into my ear. The softness of his touch combined with his big manly hands and fingers arouse every sensation within me. I'm proud of our young, strong bodies, and that builds on the arousal. I close my eyes and we begin exploring and experimenting, pushing farther beyond the limits of sexual boundaries than we've ever gone. Trying new moves and assuming new identities expands our respect for each other as we expose our individual vulnerabilities.

After lovemaking and a shower, we dress each other in our new flannel PJ's and jump into bed. Tom gets us more wine. I offer him a full body massage, tenderly kneading his muscles. As I conclude, he says, "I love you. You're so attentive, so loving, and so hard to figure out."

I roll my head over on the pillow to look at him and ask, "How so?"

"You seem too good to be true. I wish I could paint, because I'd paint a picture of you holding me in your arms. You keep surprising me and coming up with new ways to please me."

Funny, that. I feel the same way about him. I remain quiet and allow my system to absorb the alcohol while I bask in the sensation of this moment, being snug, warm and loved. I don't want to say anything else. Tom holds my head in his arms and his touch is soft as he gently rubs my scalp while rocking me to sleep. I feel myself drifting as all my tension is soothed away.

Tuesday, November 1, 1988, 9:10 a.m.

My first call of the day is from Nadine's Mother. Janet looks over, and says, "It's your mother-in-law."

"She's going to ask me for the ID card," I tell Janet before picking up. I must be clairvoyant because that is exactly what she does. I set up a date and time to meet her, knowing full well I have no intention of showing up. Fuck it. I laugh when I get off the phone.

Later

I get home early and find Tom sitting in bed, watching TV and eating candy. We stare at each other for a moment.

Tom asks, "Want to catch a movie? It's something to do on a rainy day." We go to the Deptford Mall, and walk around before the movie starts. We see "License to Drive" with Corey Haim. The best part is sitting in the theater before the movie begins and being seen with Tom. In my mind, I know people think we're pals, but I want the world to know we are intimate, feeling proud of the sexy catch I landed.

The movie is funny and we have a good time. The combination of a movie on a rainy afternoon combined with popcorn turns out to be a fabulous concept. Tom holds my hand during most of the show, causing my spirit to float.

After the movie, Tom drives to the cemetery where his parents are buried next to each other. We walk up to their gravesites, marked by plaques, and bow our heads. I say a silent prayer, directed to them and the Higher Power in the universe that connects us all, offering thanks for Tom while asking for direction for the future.

"James and Elizabeth, I am standing here with your son. I want to thank you for making him. He's a beautiful man and I love him. I promise you, I will love him for the rest of my life and take care of him." I sense they hear me and are here with us. Tom bends down to clear the dirt and overgrown weeds from their plaques. He doesn't display emotion, just a serious look on his face as he looks up at the road and says, "My Dad died first. He'd always say he wanted to be buried by a highway or busy road, so we could beep our car horn when we passed by." I smile, now realizing Tom had done that whenever we passed this place on this road. It was something I never thought to ask at the time. Now it makes sense.

Directly across the street is a Chevrolet dealership. We elect to stop and take a look at the new cars. I've been telling Tom I want to dump the damn T-bird, and one of my dreams has always been to own a bright, shiny red sports car. We come upon a shiny blue 1989 Camaro with a tan interior. Tom says, "This is like the one

I had," referring to the one that was stolen. The one I just bailed him out on, with the repayment for the insurance check.

Looking beyond this car, I set my eyes upon one that's a gorgeous, bright fire-engine red. It's further illuminated under the brilliant dealership lights. I walk up to it and notice it's semi-covered in a tight plastic wrap with water dripping from it. It's love at first sight with me and the car.

A salesperson walks over and introduces himself to us: "I'm Tony." We take turns shaking hands and keep looking over the Camaro.

"You like this one?" Tom asks.

"I do."

"It's you. You'll look totally awesome behind the wheel," Tom offers, feeding my ego better than a salesperson ever could. My stomach and neck stiffen to a point that I am uncomfortable.

"Do you think we can afford it?" I ask.

"We'll do it!" he replies, his upbeat attitude overriding the sensible side of my brain. He puts his arm around me and whispers in my ear, "Stud, buy the car. It's what you want. I want you to have it."

"Wanna take it for a drive?" Tony asks.

"Sure," I answer.

"Please step inside so I can get a copy of your driver's license."

Tony the Salesman introduces us to his boss, Chad the Sales Manager, who in turn introduces us to Barry the Finance Manager. The handshaking and back slapping is all part of the phony niceties bestowed as part of the foreplay before you get fucked. You have to see through all this shit and keep your wits about you. Immediately I'm everyone's best buddy. They are all making remarks like, "Nice car." "Good choice." "Sporty." Suddenly I'm burst into a world of newfound friends, surrounded by porous feedback about how nice my jacket is, my choice in cars, smiles, smiles and more smiles. Everyone is happy as hell — but little do these fucks know that I'm a sure thing, already sold on the car. I am leaving here with that car, regardless of their ass kissing. When I want something, I go with my gut feeling and get it. Tony the Salesman leads us to a desk to do some paperwork and he asks me for some information.

"Who is buying the car?"

"We are," I state, proudly. "We're a couple."

He immediately looks down at his little contact information card, blushing.

"Which one of you will test-drive it? Are you — both going to be test-driving it?"

His uneasiness is evident, and Tom and I both sense it. "I'll be putting the car in my name, but we both want to test-drive it," I say. I look over at Tom, who is grinning ear to ear.

Tony hastily exits to make a photocopy of our licenses, saying, "Be right back."

Tom gets right up and follows him. He turns my way and throws me a little wink. He has an endless way of sending chills up and down my spine. It seems like an eternity, but it's Tom alone who returns with the keys.

"Let's go!" he says.

I jump up and follow him outside. Once outside, I ask, "How did you get them to let us take the car alone?" I'm delighted, but curious.

"I followed him back to the copier and asked him if he had a problem with us being gay."

"You came right out with that?"

"Sure I did. Wanted to see what he was thinking and he was fine with it. He said, 'I don't give a shit, I just want you to buy a car from me.' Then I asked the manager dudes – what're-their-names, Skippy and Chap — and they were cool with us taking it out alone."

I roar with laughter. "Chap? Skippy? …It's Chad and Barry!" We both burst out laughing. Tom produces a Gulf gas credit card with the dealership's name on it.

"What's this?" I ask.

Tom smiles and says they told him we could take the car out together if we would get the tank filled with gas and pick up some coffee for them. Tom pulls a $20 bill out of his pocket and says they gave him the cash for the coffee.

"How much coffee?"

"Six coffees. Six for $20."

"Does that mean keep the change?" I ask.

"Yep — he said 'Get whatever you guys want, too.'"

Tom is clearly amazing. His personality moves mountains. I'm glad we're able to be alone with the car, so we can discuss it. Tom goes to drive first, but I stop him, commanding, "Let me drive it first."

"Oh, sure!" he says, smiling and opening the door for me. I immediately notice I'm sitting really close to the ground and my legs are just about equal with my hips. It's very comfortable. Sitting behind the wheel, I notice the car has absolutely zero miles. The scent is terrific, and the interior looks like a cockpit, really sporty. Tom lets himself in the other side and tosses me the keys. They, in themselves, are different. They're smaller than other car keys I've seen and have a black plastic top on each key. There's also a metal slug on the ignition key.

"What's this?" I point it out to Tom.

"It's a special computer chip that works with the steering column to prevent theft."

"Interesting," I respond.

I start the car and the sound of the engine roaring is exciting. I look over at Tom, saying, "Excellent!" He's all smiles too. I find the lights and the dashboard lights up really cool, as does the center panel where the transmission shift is. The car is absolutely beautiful. The interior is a grayish color, but on close inspection, I see the strands the cloth is woven with are more aqua in color. It's flawless. Tom reaches over and grabs my hand.

"Oh, man," he says, "listen to the sound of that engine. True power."

We are both floored by the car. I run my hand over the steering wheel. It also seems smaller than other steering wheels I've been used to. The slick design gives the feel of being in a racecar. We both remark on all the amenities we find in the car. I make a point of showing Tom the odometer at zero. As I shift the car into drive, my heart races with excitement, and we exit the sales lot. I'm nervous about driving it. With the chassis low to the ground, it feels comfortable to drive; it's responsive and easy to maneuver. The entire car reeks of coolness. It even forces you to sit in a relaxed position. The expansive front windshield gives a sweeping view of the road.

"The seats are comfortable," I say. The seatbacks adjust, which is a novelty to us, since both our cars have problems with the seats being able to move. We blare our favorite station, 98 WCAU-FM, on the stereo as we fly down the road. I can't imagine going back and getting in the T-bird again. I'm sick of car problems. I crave reliability, and since my drive is so long, I want some comfort in going to work. I feel the smooth gray felt-like ceiling of the car, and think about the cloth-like ceiling of the T-bird. It has started falling off, which I've remedied with staples. I think about arriving at my dancing gigs in a Camaro.

We get to the gas station and the attendant walks over to take my order. It feels tremendous to sit behind the wheel of this brand-new sexy hot red sports car.

"Fill, premium," I state. Tom is antsy to drive, so I switch seats with him after we fill the tank. We head to McDonald's to get coffee, rather than Wawa, so he can go through the drive-up and show off to his former co-workers. A couple of the crew members come to the window. Tom is chatting with them and tells them it's his new car. He bullshits them with a story that he landed a well-paying new job while ostentatiously embellishing on an existing fable of tapping into some trust fund money. We drive back to the dealership. I enjoy watching Tom drive. He runs his hand over the dash and up and down the steering wheel as he drives. He keeps turning and looking at me with an irresistible sexy smile.

We arrive back at the dealership and walk into the showroom. Several of the salespeople stop what they're doing and turn toward us. I feel uncomfortable. I sit back down with Tony the Salesman and Tom hands the coffees to the dorky-but-dutiful Chad the Sales Manager. We get right into a discussion about payments. There are mountains of paperwork to be completed. Tom is such a little rascal, feeling me up under the table.

Whenever they produce a payment amount, I sigh and Tom looks at me and says, "We'll do it…" I wish he would play along with what I'm doing — let them think any amount they suggest is unreasonably high.

After a half hour of dickering with me over the sales price, Tony is clearly frustrated after I decline his last colossal monthly payment that could rival a home mortgage payment. When Tony asks me what the most I can afford to pay each month is, my naiveté is evident when I stupidly answer, "I don't want to pay more than $350 a month."

After an hour of more game playing, Chad comes back with, "If I get you a payment under $350, can I earn your business today?"

I am exhausted from the process and feel like I lost at this game, but finally I'm the proud owner of a 1989 Chevrolet Camaro. And my payment is under $350: by six cents.

We wait anxiously for the car to be "prepped." Despite the torture of the money business, I am beyond excited about the prospect of a new car. All-in-all, I still feel great. I walk to the bathroom and splash cool water on my face. I look up in the mirror while my face is dripping wet and say to my reflection, "Three Hundred Forty Nine Dollars and Ninety Four cents a month."

It's very scary. I think about how much it will depreciate when we drive it off the lot, but I can't believe I'm the owner of a brand new 1989 Camaro. My gut is still in knots from the whole sales process. I think about the cost, and wonder if I should go out there and cancel the entire thing and walk away. I pace back and forth for a moment, thinking and worrying. Then it strikes me that I'm the only one creating pressure. I make peace with myself and resign my thoughts to feeling confident with my decision. *It's time to enjoy life: You're young enough to take more risks and old enough to do what you want.*

With the ugly sales process behind me and by forcing the payment and monetary piece of this transaction out of my thoughts, I become grounded in a wave of euphoria over owning something I've always wanted. I allow myself to enjoy this moment.

We leave the piece-of-shit T-bird at the dealership as a trade-in and Tom suggests we drive into Philadelphia, so I pull over and let him drive, wanting to experience the joy of the music, the car and the ride. I enjoy taking in the smell and feel of my new car. We drive fast with the windows down. The air is freezing, but refreshing. With "Never Can Say Goodbye" by the Communards blaring from the stereo, we drive down to the Gayborhood and Tom sees someone he knows walking. He slows down, so he can wave at him from the car. Tom loves it. Then we head down to South Street. Tom is the greatest dream to me, and the car is an accentuation of the greatest fantasy turned reality. We drive over to the University City section of town. There are a lot of hot young frat guys to innocently cruise. We drive up to groups of guys and get out and walk into a Wawa to get a pack of cigarettes and then return to the car slowly. I catch him making eyes with one cutie as we walk back to the car.

When we're back in the car, Tom smiles, lets out a chuckle and says, "It's just flirting."

"Oh, I know. I'm just wondering about your style for picking up guys outside of the gay bars or locker rooms. I've hooked up with some but I've always felt so limited and guarded flirting out in the straight world. What's the secret?"

"Well, Thomas, we don't need to worry about that any more. When I was on the hunt I would forget about pegging someone as gay or straight. The guy either looks at you or he doesn't. Then it's all about confidence. Everyone has their own style."

He puts his hand in mine and says, "I love you, honey."

The more he magnetizes stares from other men, the more his secretive, private, needy side appeals to me. It gives me room to exist in his life. I reason to myself that I am not only physically appealing to Tom, but possess the skill set necessary to satisfy his emotional needs beyond the basic physical needs. We stop at another corner where there's a frat house with a group of hotties sitting on the porch. As we're stationary at the stop sign, one of the guys makes eye contact with me. Tom is all over it. "That's yours — now own it. Go dump these empty cups in that trash can. I'll pull over up there."

"You kidding?" I ask.

"Nope — go ahead, now. Just have some fun with it."

Instead of jumping out of the car in my usual deliberate method, I casually lift myself out of the low-riding car and cast my eyes downward as I walk to the trash can. I look down, then up right in the direction of the dude that was looking at me. He's still looking. I continue the stare and add a small grin. I lift my chest and return to the Camaro. It feels extremely good. When I get to the car, Tom has moved to the passenger side. It feels good.

Tom sidetracks my thoughts with, "Let's make a guest appearance at Gatsby's." We drive back over the Ben Franklin Bridge into Cherry Hill.

We spend the night and early morning dancing, drinking and kissing at GB's. Tom and I are so much in love. It means so much to be with him and to be free to be me. Gatsby's is like a different world – a place where everyone is speaking your language and everyone is related. It's a place where you can be yourself. In my dreams, I never imagined I could enjoy the excitement of dating and romance where it's okay to pursue men I desire.

GB's is mobbed since it's "Dyke Night" — all beers are a quarter tonight as well as tomorrow, which is called "Quarter Night," so everyone's pretty hammered. As we dance to Donna Summer's "This Time I Know It's For Real," I send up a prayer of thanks to God for this incredible bliss.

When we walk out at 3:30 after closing, I'm soaked in perspiration from dancing right up to the last song. It's clear I'm too bombed to drive when we exit the club. Rain is coming down pretty hard as we leave, so Tom tells me to hang out under the tarp while he goes to fetch the car. I stand there by myself in a crowd of people chatting and saying goodnight. When Tom pulls up, I notice the car is even more shiny and bright with water droplets on it. As I approach the car. Tom jumps out and walks around to the passenger side. He opens the door and tosses me the keys to drive, saying, "Love your car!"

I am experiencing an exhilarating feeling that sends chills up and down my spine, having a sobering effect. This royal treatment is divine. I turn slightly and take a sweeping look at the crowd – all watching me. I get in the car and turn up the radio and take off with a little more boost than usual.

"You're buzzed," Tom says. He's wrong. I'm not buzzed. I am fucking drunk off my ass.

"I'm okay," I reply. Tom is focused on the road in front of him.

"Pull over and let me take it." Tom didn't drink too much. He'd get a little buzz going on, but unlike me, knew when to stop.

"Did I embarrass you?" I ask, sensing he may be harboring some negative thoughts about me.

"No," he says, taking over the driving. I probe a little more, still feeling something isn't right.

"You sure?"

"Can you go out one night and not get drunk?" I'm taken aback by his candor, but not the response. I appreciate him being fully expressed, but it still stings. I reach into a box of stuff I had in the T-bird and find a cassette that I push into the tape deck. Taylor Dayne's "Don't Rush Me" plays. Her music, like medicine, heals and soothes my feelings. For as elated as I had been, the stone cold high from the effect of alcohol had a way of dimming the illusion of euphoria enough to see reality.

We drive in silence for a while and I put the seat back slightly and close my eyes, conscious but hopeful that sleep will take me. I'm angry with his comment and feel like going off on him.

"You asleep?" he asks. I stay quiet and keep my eyes shut. I want to block him out. I let myself fall on his lap when the car turns. For a moment, I don't know what to expect. Would he push me away or embrace me? He begins rubbing my head.

"I love you. You're everything to me. You gave me $4,000 without even batting an eyelash. That's how deep your commitment is. How can I compete with that? Baby, you are the most compassionate man I've ever known. How do I show you how much I love you? By talking shit because I'm jealous. I'm jealous of the fact that you're so much more than I am, Tom."

I roll over to hide my growing smile. Tom begins tickling me.

"You little shit. You were listening the whole time."

I turn back around and look up at him.

"I love you," he says. He is glassy-eyed with tears.

CRUISING

Wednesday, November 2, 1988

I'm sitting at my desk, staring out the window in pain. Coupled with an agonizing hangover, I'm caught up in thoughts about car insurance. I was so concerned with being saddled with a high car payment that I didn't give any thought to the impact this car would have, given that Jersey has some of the highest car insurance rates in the country.

Tom got up early to drive me into work. He wanted to take the car today to drive around.

"What's wrong with you, dude?" Janet asks, sitting at my desk filing her nails.

"Bought a new car," I announce. Matt and Tammy come over and listen to me talk about the features of the Camaro. They're all excited for me.

Janet closes her eyes and shakes her head and teases, "Aw shit, dude, now you got your guido-mobile, what's next? Gold chains around your neck?" We start getting busy with customers, so our conversation ends.

Noon

Nadine calls, and she's beyond pissed that I didn't meet her Mother to surrender the military ID card like I promised.

"Why you are being such a bitch about this?" I ask. "I have the ID card and intend to keep using it until I'm ready to relinquish it. That'll be when it expires or when the divorce is finalized."

"You aren't listening to me! My C.O. told me to get the card back from you, and there's no more discussing it!"

I can't imagine the fucking Army would be on her back about getting the card back, even if she told them she was divorcing me. My parents agreed that I shouldn't have to give the card up until the divorce is final. She starts telling me to meet her Mother again and I snap, "No! It's you and me, babe. If you want the card back, you're going to have to do it face to face."

We agree on a time and place to meet today and then she says, "Tom, you better be there, because God help me — if you aren't there, I'm going to get the military police after your ass."

"Fuck you," I say, not one to respond well to threats.

"Real nice. You better be there."

"What time?" I ask.

"Seven."

I slam the phone down and storm into the bathroom, feeling bitter about several feelings: missing her as a friend, and angry with myself for cursing at her.

6:00 p.m.

Tom picks me up and we drive to Fort Dix to see Nadine. We drive to the PX and look around for her until 7:30. She's nowhere to be found. I'm ultra-pissed she didn't show up, as is Tom after I explain how demanding she was on the phone. We head home, but Tom makes a small diversion on the way and drives by the Society Hill apartment complex he likes in Washington Township. It appears to be quite nice and probably a bit more than we can afford. We've already looked at a couple of really crummy places.

"Your parents keep asking about the two of us living in the one bedroom. The story about you sleeping on the couch has got to be suspicious to them. You know, I have the other bed in the storage room. We can set it up in the spare bedroom and that will give the appearance that you sleep alone."

He doesn't have to bother putting out such an eloquent sales pitch for the place. I'm sold on the notion that as long as we're together, I'm happy. I love and believe in him, and whatever he wants to do is fine with me. Tom has a lot on the ball for someone his age; I trust his judgment.

"Sure — let's get it."

Tom squeezes my hand and says, "Oh, that's great. Cool. I'll put a deposit down tomorrow!"

Sunday, November 6, 1988

I'm booked solid with eight jobs lined up. Three are daylight gigs, which are a bit peculiar because I never know what to expect. Sometimes these end up being for couples or individuals, not parties. Mitch doesn't book gigs for individuals, so when I arrive at that kind of job, I feel a shade of nervousness because the person lied during the order phase. I prefer nighttime jobs because the cover of night makes it more comfortable and exciting.

We take Tom's car. The first job is in Bristol, Pennsylvania, for a chick celebrating her 25th birthday at a friend's house. The party is a small gathering of about seven or so ladies. The girls offer us lunch after I dance. The layout of cold cuts and cake is appealing, but I resist. Coming out into the glaring midday sunlight is weird.

On the jobs, someone always asks Tom if he's my bodyguard. Sometimes he says he is, and other times, he just says he's my driver. I suppose this a bit of an adventure for him, too.

The second job is in the small town of Roebling. The crowd is nice here, too. This time, in a big, bright, beautiful house positioned right in the middle of town, I dance for a rather large bride-to-be. She has a great smile and as I hug her during the show, I think about how much her fiancé has to love her because, despite my orientation, I feel she exhibits absolutely no sex appeal whatsoever. Weight aside, she doesn't smell nice, or wear any makeup. It's like she isn't even trying to be attractive. The rose tattoo on her neck further detracts from her appeal. Nature bestowed her with a sweet smile and rosy cheeks. I say a silent prayer for her.

After the job, I feel a terrible pain in my gut. "I feel sick," I tell Tom, when we take off in the car.

"What's the matter?"

"I don't know. I just have this horrible cramp in the pit of my gut."

I feel an overwhelming urge to use the bathroom, so I ask Tom to pull over at a gas station. I take my gym bag in with me. The bathroom is putrid. I lock the door and drop my pants and use all my leg muscles for support to hold myself up as I squat over the nasty, cracked and stained toilet seat. Flies rally to keep me company as my bowel erupts. I wish so much that I could sit down and relax from exhaustion as the pain subsides. After a moment's peace, the intense pain returns with a vengeance. The pain is sharp, and I almost lose my ability to hold myself up over the disgusting toilet. My insides empty out what seems like another gallon, finally completing a draining but relieving process. Only now do I realize there is no toilet paper in this fucking dump. I lift myself back up on my feet and shuffle over to the sink. I carefully lift my legs to remove my pants and white underwear. I turn on the water and soak my underwear completely, then use them to clean my ass and toss them on the floor. There's a small chunk of what was probably once a pink bar of soap on the sink, now covered in dirt and grease. I'm not going to even touch it. I zip open a pocket in my gym bag and locate one of the miniature bars of soap I collect from hotels. I use it to scrub my face, hands and butt, then locate a small towel in my gym bag to finish cleaning up. I find a fresh pair of black jockeys and carefully pull them on. I spot my once-white undies sitting on the floor where I dropped them. How revolting. I fling them into the toilet and wash my hands again.

Suddenly, as I get ready to leave, I look over at the filthy underwear lying in the nasty toilet and it strikes me as the funniest thing. Someone is going to come in here and think the last person's ass must have exploded!

I walk back to the car and Tom asks, "Are you okay?"

I nod and we drive down Route 130, arriving at the third job about 10 minutes early, so we sit in the car and talk.

"I'm nervous," I confide.

"Really?"

"It happens," I reply, knowing it happens every time. I'm just experiencing it more than usual this time because of my recent malaise.

"Are you sure you're okay?" Tom asks, reaching for my hand. "You look a bit pale."

"Squeeze," I say, hoping to jump start my energy from his passion and love.

Tom obliges and asks, "Can we cancel if you don't feel well?"

Knowing full well that's not an option, I simply state, "I'm fine, I'll be all right."

Reaching deep within, I find the energy to lift myself up to go into the apartment to perform for a bachelorette party. There are all kinds of people here: old, young, women, men, and even children. I meet Shirl, the sister of the girl getting married and the person who ordered me.

She says, "Christine's fiancé is here. I hope that won't be a problem. I mean, we told him to relax, and he promised he won't be hostile. At least as long as you don't touch her."

Oh, wonderful, I think. This girl, Shirl, is pretty but her hair is dyed blonde and chopped short to her head with some kind of frosting to it that looks almost white. It looks like a straw hat.

I'm not thrilled about dancing for a woman when the man she's going to marry is within five feet of me. I try and check my attitude and ask Shirl if I can speak with the guy. She calls out, "Randy," and a tall dumbass rises and walks over. He looks me up and down.

"You call this a dancer? He ain't nothing."

I remember that I'm a professional and extend my hand, offering a handshake. He accepts the gesture, shaking my hand with a cold, sweaty palm meeting mine. I grimace through a forced smile, saying, "I'm Tom. This is kind of awkward, man. I'd feel better — I'd actually be able to perform better — if you wouldn't mind stepping out during my show."

Randy shakes his head. "Nope. I'm going to stay right here and watch, and you best not touch her." Something in his eyes strikes me as odd. I don't pay him any mind. I dismiss him by shrugging my shoulders, take a deep breath, and turn to ask Shirl when she wants to start.

He turns and yells out, "Barry, toss me another brew, bud!" and walks back into the den.

Shirl puts my music on, and like a wave of cool water, it soothes me. It lifts my spirits and in my mind, I stand alone in the room with the future bride. I don't even bother learning her name. I strut up to her, reaching out my hands. *Come on, Sister, have fun,* I think. *Let's enjoy this together.* She takes hold of my hands and we slow dance for a moment. I put her back into her chair. I throw myself onto the floor in a slow dive and roll around from woman to woman, running my hands through my hair, down my chest, and then touch the muscles on my arms. I'm the center of attention now. I catch everyone's eye as I jump back up and progress into my routine. I continue walking around the room without smiling, focusing on the bride-to-be. Teeming with confidence, I remove my shirt and slowly continue until I am naked except for a g-string. Pleased with my performance thus far, I build up my energy level and burst into several new and unpracticed moves that I've been anxious to incorporate in my routine. The third song is a slow jam that I perform on the floor. I roll around, gently hugging myself, imagining being entangled in Tom's arms. I think of his hands softly moving up and down the sides of my body. I look up toward the bride-to-be. Everyone has quieted down. She parts her lips, revealing a bangin' smile. I wink at her and smile back. I let my head drop to the floor and as I lift my neck and chest, I allow my head to remain on the floor. I drag my head gently on the floor as my body lifts and falls. I imagine lying on a raft in the ocean, with my body bobbing up and down, naked, adrift on the sea. The hot rays of the sun are burning, so I roll over and put my hands under the raft into the cool water. I find my way to the beach and, now up on my hands and knees, I drag myself with every smooth groove of the song up to her lap. I delicately hold her hand and bring it to my cheek. I close my eyes and kiss her hand as the song draws to an end.

I am taken back to reality by an unexpected round of applause from the room. I shake my head and smile, looking at Tom, who is also clapping. I wave my hand at him and everyone else to stop. I was coherent the entire time, but in some way I was in my own world. I'm happy I did well and pleased everyone. I wanted her to be comfortable and at ease. I turn to look at the bride-to-be. She is being shuffled next to me for a picture. Soon everyone is jumping up next to me for pictures. I pose with several of them. One Kodak moment is of me laying belly down across the laps of six girls as they sit on a bench in the kitchen.

Much later — 1:30 a.m.

Driving home from a tenth, yes *tenth*, job of the day, we're both worn out. The last gig was for a card group of wealthy women. I performed in a white-and-tan den in front of a roaring fireplace. The room could have been the centerfold of a decorator's magazine.

It's late; I'm in a rotten mood because I have to get up in the morning to go to work. My fuse is short, and so is Tom's. It's amazing how much the frustration of scrambling to find the locations of job after job exhausts our level of patience. Tom is listening to his tape of Christian pop music and it's annoying me. I can't pinpoint what it is, but there's something about it that's irritating. Maybe because we've been listening to it all fucking night and he doesn't even bother asking me what I want to listen to.

"Can we listen to something else? We've been listening to this all day."

"I thought you liked it."

"I do, but I'm sick of it."

"Well, I like it," he says in a tone I perceive as very pompous. We keep fanning the fire of our immature disagreement and Tom jabs me with, "Just because you gave me money doesn't mean you own me."

"You're being a control freak with the music. Besides, I didn't give you anything. I lent you the money to get you out of being sent to jail, you jackass."

"Jackass?" he repeats.

I immediately regret calling him that. I wish I could hit a rewind button and take it back. We drive in silence and I think about his words, searching my soul, trying to determine if there's any merit to them. *Am I am holding the money over Tom's head as some way of controlling him? No way!*

I'm angry he feels that way. *Is there a part of me that paid the money to solidify the relationship? I never contemplated these motives. Was this a calculated invest- ment I would get a return on: both my money back, and his love and affection?*

I don't know which I despise more — the idea that he pegged me on some flaw in my character, or that idea that I'm really so pathetic I needed to pay someone to be with me. I'm *beautiful*, for God's sake! I gave him the money to help him, not help me. This was an unselfish act. I feel myself calming down in light of my shame.

Tom says, "You just wanted to get out of your parent's house."

My rage is reignited over a feeling of sudden inadequacy. I snap, "Go to hell!"

Tom whips back, "I'm already here."

We're quiet for a moment and I feel such anguish inside. I want his apology. I want to hit stop, reverse, rewind. I want him to be clueless to my motives, my vulnerabilities. In the snidest tone I can muster, I ask, "How long are you going to make me suffer, listening to that fucking music?"

With that said, Tom pops the cassette out, rolls down his window, and flings it out of the car. He turns to me and says, "Happy now, asshole?" and belts me right in the mouth with his hand.

I'm immediately engulfed with rage. I reach over and retaliate. My palm is clenched into a fist, so what I intend to be a mere slap ends up being a punch right to his head. I hit him so hard that his head slams into the window. I tighten my body, bracing for his response. When none comes, I'm filled with sadness, knowing our beautiful relationship is far from perfect. It will never be the same again, stained as it is with a memory of physical violence. I think, *When you love someone, how can you hurt them physically?* We acknowledge the destruction of our relationship through additional nasty verbal bantering until Tom hurls another punch in my di- rection. I dodge the punch, but the violence provokes a flashback to my childhood, to years of being slammed around by my Dad.

I begin hitting him repeatedly, not sensing any control over the beast within. I can't stop — I don't want to stop — I just want to keep beating him until he's dead. With one arm up in defense and the other trying to steer, Tom loses control of the car, and we veer off the road; the car runs up onto a huge pile of dirt on the shoulder. Since we're driving at a fast pace, the Lynx flips up on one side as we drive over the pile — and within a split second, the car flips over! The boom box I have on the floor between my legs flies toward me. I block my face, but I feel an excruciating pain as it slams into my head. I'm upside down, but fully aware of everything. I immediately look over at Tom to see if he's okay. He appears fine, so I tell myself to relax. I keep thinking I may black out, but stay silent and aware. I feel blood running down my face, and have the urge to dash out of the car.

Fuck it. Rather than go crazy, I close my eyes and try to relax. *Thomas, just relax,* I tell myself. *Don't think about anything.* I don't want to acknowledge the accident. I just remain frozen.

Tom says, "Damn, we fuckin' flipped the … fuckin' car." I'm immensely relieved he's unharmed. He immediately turns and pokes me when I don't respond. Tom jumps from the car and runs around to my side. He opens the door and says, "Tom? Tom! TOM! Are you okay?"

I don't move or open my eyes. I know I must look a sight, with the blood dripping down my face. Part of me is still and lifeless at my relief that we survived the accident; part of it is pure immature bullshit, to attract attention from him and make him feel bad. It was a stupid fight and I contributed a big part to it. I should know better.

Within a few minutes, there are sounds around me as people start to gather. The rescue crew arrives, and I can see the shadow of fast-flashing lights through closed eyes. I remain silent and don't move. It's my way of coping, and I don't know what's prompting me to continue to behave like this. Sounds, shadows and voices are now all around me. I can hear the rescue people talking about removing me from the car. People are now looking down at me; I can feel their stares. To avoid embarrassment, I keep still and quiet, as if knocked out cold. One woman feels for my pulse. They're discussing how to get me on a stretcher without moving me.

I open my eyes and say, "What the hell…"

I lift my head and the female paramedic gently holds my head back, saying, "Don't move anything. It's okay, Bud." I sense she's a lesbian.

They get me out of the car very carefully and place me on a large wooden plank with a neck brace. I reach up and touch my face and look at my hand, covered in blood. I panic, wondering how severe the cut is.

"Look…" I say, showing my bloody hand to Tom and the paramedic.

"How did you get that cut?" Tom asks.

"I think the boom box hit my head when we flipped over," I say.

Tom lifts his shirt and wipes my hand. He wears fear on his face as he holds my hand and says, "It's just a scratch. You'll be fine."

His hand is quivering. A cop summons Tom over to a group of cops and firemen. The whole scene is surreal. It all happened too fast and I'm still wishing for a rewind button to go back and undo this mess. The rescue workers are great; they don't take any chances and take my vital signs again. They remind me to remain still. Tom returns to hold my hand and looks down at me. His eyes fill with tears and as he blinks, they drop down his face in perfectly symmetrical trails. I smile and he softly rubs my head, mouthing the words, "I'm sorry." I hear one of our songs, "Baby I Love Your Way" by Will To Power, playing in my head.

Upon arrival, the admitting nurse, clenching a clipboard, says, "You're at Underwood Memorial Hospital in Woodbury. Do you have anyone you would like me to call?"

"Where's Tom?" I suddenly realize he's gone.

"Your friend is being looked at. Do you have medical insurance?"

I say, "Through work. I don't think I have the card on me."

"Who's the provider?" I reach up to my head to see if the bloody gash has disappeared. It hasn't. She persists, "Provider?"

"I..." I begin to respond, then decide this can fucking wait. "...can't remember right now."

I can't believe the difference between the curt nurse and the rescue crew. They wheel me into a curtained-off room and two medical people remove my clothes and put a sheet over me. Tom comes in and stands next to the bed.

"Are you okay?" we both say at the same time.

He smiles and says, "Fine, but the car is totaled."

"I'm not surprised." I want to see him smile. I miss his smile.

"What's that saying?" I ask, and then answer, "'What doesn't kill us makes us stronger?'"

Tom finally grins. "I'm sorry, Tom," he says again. He leans down and kisses my forehead, running his fingers through my hair. A skinny Puerto Rican male nurse comes in and cleans up my forehead.

"Does it need stitches?" I ask.

"No, it's just a minor abrasion. Looks like a scrape."

"Cool," I answer, feeling relieved. Tom and I stare at each other for a spell, without saying a word. We both regret what happened. We can forgive each other, but can we forgive ourselves? And can we ever forget? Tom's warmth and love sets my mind at ease and relieves my tension. The nurse leaves, and after a while, a doctor appears and notices us holding hands. We don't flinch, even as he approaches.

He asks Tom to leave the room. "I need to examine him. Would you mind waiting outside?" The doctor feels my forehead. He says, "Looks nice."

"Nice? I think it was better before the accident," I state.

"Yes. You'll be all right. This is fine. There won't be a scar. Do you feel pain anywhere else?"

"No." He asks a few other routine questions, and that's it. After he finishes with me, Tom rushes in and asks what he said. I tell Tom he said I would be fine, and there was no damage done. Tom honestly looks relieved that I will be okay. He asks why they didn't do any tests; he was concerned about how hard I hit my head on the boom box. I tell him I just want to get the fuck out of here — we've been in the hospital for hours now. We then realize we don't have a ride home.

"I'm going to get some money out of the MAC machine and get a cab. I'll be back. Wait here, okay?"

I sit down and recline in a green couch in the reception area.

The sweet smell of Tom's cologne precedes his entrance. In other words, I smell him coming. He turns the corner, comes up to the couch, and sits next to me. "Forgive me?" he asks.

Without hesitation, I reach for his hand and say, "I love you."

He looks at my forehead and says, "I'm so sorry about your head. I feel terrible." I take in a deep breath and smile. Tom looks lovingly into my eyes. He softly says, "Are you feeling up to allowing me do some making up tonight?"

I keep smiling and we squeeze each other's hands.

The taxi driver comes into the reception area and sees we're the only ones sitting here. Again, an obvious downward glance is made at our hand holding. We're hit with a blast of arctic air as we walk out of the hospital, so it's great to discover the cab is toasty warm when we get in. Sitting here, holding hands in the back seat of the cab, listening to some music from the 5th century B.C., it somehow feels soothing. There's something safe about the cab and the old driver.

When we arrive home around 4:30 a.m., I'm truly dead tired. I set the alarm.

"What are you doing?" Tom asks.

"I have to show up for work, or I'll be in deep shit. I could lose my job."

We hit the bed, still dressed, and end the weekend.

Monday, November 7, 1988

I wake up with excruciating pain in my head and body from sheer exhaustion. I force myself to listen to the fucking alarm clock and drag my weary ass out of bed. I glance at Tom, lying there looking so peaceful and handsome in his sleep. I think of and count my blessings; for as miserable as I feel, a wave of contentment sweeps over me and I find the strength to move forward. I love him so much. I trip over a pile of clothes on my way to the bathroom.

In the shower, with fresh lukewarm water pouring down on me, I try to think good thoughts. I've got a new car to drive to work!

It's still dark out and bitterly cold as I take a brisk walk to the car. As I walk, I consider turning around to go back inside, undress, and get back under the covers with Tom. Every day is a struggle to keep the job at the bank. I'll make $52 today after taxes, for eight long hours. I can make $55 in a half-hour of dancing on one of the lowest-paying jobs. But dancing won't last forever. The bank job just seems so demanding and frustrating. I despise wearing this stupid shirt and tie, too.

I turn on the car and enjoy the roaring sound of the engine. I push in the cassette we bought from the DJ at Gatsby's and turn up the sound. The first song, "The Only Way Is Up" by Yazz, is so cool.

I arrive at work and pull up next to Janet. She takes a double take. We jump out of our cars and Janet's eyes are wide open. "Oh, shit, this is so great! I forgot you mentioned the new car last week." She goes on, "My next question is 'Can you afford it on what we make?'"

Before I can respond, she answers her own question, "I guess with the dancing money, you got it made. What happened to your forehead? Bang it on the headboard?"

"We had an accident last night." I begin telling her what happened.

Matt pulls up, and soon all my coworkers are standing around my car looking at it. Everyone is very complimentary and happy for me. Having to explain the bandage on my forehead over and over is more painful than the injury.

Sue finally pulls up in her Mercedes. She congratulates me on the car and then says, "Okay, all, let's get the bank open."

Tom calls me around noon to ask me how I'm feeling. He's so special. When I say I'm fine he asks, "What did everyone say about the car?"

"They're all happy for me. Everyone loves it. This is certainly one of my happier Mondays."

Tuesday, November 8, 1988

Sue summons me into her office after I return from lunch. This can't be good. "You've used half of your ten sick days in the last three weeks," she tells me.

"Sue, I've had some car problems and accidents, but I can only say it's been a fluke that they've all occurred so close together."

"I know you're interested in moving up to a Head Teller position. I'd like to switch you and Tracy." Tracy is an Assistant Head Teller. Sue goes on, "She wants some experience on the platform, and I believe working in her position as the Evening Supervisor will help you develop your supervisory skill set."

I'm elated, and barely listen as she goes over the new schedule and tiny bump in pay. All I can manage is, "Thank you very much," smiling from ear to ear.

Driving home is actually a pleasure. It's been drudgery lately with the distance and the traffic, but driving this new car makes it not only bearable, but also desirable and enjoyable. My spirits are floating as I crank up the radio, thinking, *Could life get any better than this? One minute I'm cursing life, the next minute I'm embracing it. Here I am, driving the car of my dreams, going home to a handsome man in love with me, a fantasy I never dreamed of. I'm a male exotic dancer, which is a dream realized. I have a great body, which is the result of many prayers answered, and I'm now a supervisor in a bank, another dream realized. Life is certainly worth living.*

I arrive home and find my love cooking dinner. I rush up and throw my arms around him, sharing the news about the promotion. This gorgeous man listens to me dutifully and attentively, as if everything I have to say is brilliant.

"I have an interview tomorrow," he shares. "It's not definite, but I put in an application at the McDonald's in Deptford for a shift leader position."

"That's cool," I say, careful to avoid saying anything else. I don't want to set any expectations, raise his hopes or diminish his day's accomplishment. "Wow, how did you get down there to put an application in without a car?"

"I walked!"

"Oh, that's some good exercise, Honey. That's quite a distance from here."

I'm impressed with his display of gumption. I restrain myself from further talk about my mini-promotion, which is all I can think of.

He says, "The insurance company confirmed the Lynx is totaled. Since I only had collision on it, we won't get anything for it. Now I need a car."

Saturday, November 12, 1988

One of life's greatest pleasures is waking up late on Saturday on a day off. I roll over and pull Tom's pillow into my face and take in his aroma. I roll back over, holding the pillow against my chest. We decided to take a drive to the base gym last night, so my arms are aching this morning from the workout. Tom's working. He got a job at the Deptford McDonald's as a non-supervisory employee, and we're renting a car at a painful $15 a day for him to get back and forth to work.

I roll out of bed and walk into the kitchen for coffee. Back in the bedroom, I open the closet door and take inventory of Tom's huge wardrobe. He has tailored Italian suits, expensive shoes, belts, cufflinks and matching suspenders and ties. Tom is about two or three inches taller than me, so borrowing suits for work is out of the question. I do wear some of his ties and suspenders once in a while. I pull out the sweater he was wearing the night we met. It smells of the Obsession cologne he wears. I put it on, along with a pair of his dark blue jeans. They're a bit long, but don't look too bad. Wearing his clothes makes me feel close to him. I open his black jewelry box on the dresser and sit in front of the mirror, trying on his things. Tom has one of his ears pierced. Although I like the single earring on guys, I don't find it personally appealing enough to get one myself.

I put on his gold watch and thick gold bracelet that reads T-H-O-M-A-S. I was never one for wearing jewelry, but it feels very adult, masculine and stylish to wear his stuff. A grin forms on my face as I recall growing up, when my brother and I would raid Mom's jewelry box for gaudy costume jewelry when we'd play like we were pirates or kings.

The mood to cook hits me, and serves as a prelude to a memorable evening. I make a tray of homemade lasagna for us. When Tom gets home, I've got the table set with a bouquet of flowers and candles. It's quite a romantic scene. After eating, we get into bed and spend time talking and catching up on the day's events. Soon we're kissing passionately and I wrap my legs around him, bringing him close to make love. It isn't long until we sense that the urgency of release is near, and declare sweet sentiments of commitment to each other. Waves of sexual bliss flow through me as orgasm comes. After a quick shower together, sleep takes me in seconds.

Sunday, November 13, 1988

The scent of breakfast rouses me from sleep. As my eyes open, I notice that Tom placed a blanket over the blinds and curtains so daylight wouldn't find a way in to wake me. This romantic gesture — this kind, yet simple deed — further deepens my love for him. I make out the sound of bacon sizzling, which I can barely hear through the closed door. I walk into the bathroom to brush my teeth, then go into the kitchen. I find Tom wearing his sexy black silk robe, cooking. I am buck naked and step up to him, placing my arms around him. He turns to me, looking ruggedly handsome with the shadow of a two-day-old beard, and smiles as he looks down at my erection pressing into him.

"How do you want it?" he asks, pointing to a couple eggs.

I smile and reply, "On your knees!"

My distraction is enough to make him turn off the stove and play. We're on the kitchen floor and soon I'm grabbing his wrists, holding them like reins behind his back and using them to pull his body into mine. "I knew from the first time I saw you smile at me that I wanted you," he pants. His back is to me and as he turns to accept my kiss, my heart bursts with joy, knowing that forever he's all mine. I am slamming my balls so hard they are making an audible smack off his ass. It's not long before Tom reaches his breaking point. I love his long groan of explosion as he comes. Soon after I feel my own fireworks and we collapse into each other's arms for a few precious moments.

I put my hands under the water and we wash our hands together.

"You're such an incredible turn-on," I say, as we slowly move our hands together under the water. It feels soft and comforting, and the silky liquid soap brings a clean smell to the air. I lean forward and we share another lasting kiss. The feel of our hands and tongues together send chills up and down my spine.

We eat breakfast and spend the rainy morning being lazy, sitting home with each other. It's nice having time off together.

1 p.m.

We're lying in each other's arms on the floor watching television. Tom looks into my eyes. "Did you ever feel funny about kissing another guy?"

"The first time I was kind of nervous about it, and didn't think it could be as exciting as it was with women. Once I kissed the first guy, I got sprung with the feel of his moustache brushing against my lips. There was no comparison with kissing girls."

Tom smiles and giggles a little. "But you went in for more, after that first moustache brush, eh?"

"Sure did," I say. "I love being so close to you."

Tom breaks our embrace and rolls over on his belly, supporting his head on his hands. "I like the illicit nature of kissing guys. The fact that it's like 'forbidden fruit' makes it even more exciting," he says.

I feel the same way. "You're right. There's something so daring about it. I mean, it feels perfectly natural to me now, but there's still an element of doing something you shouldn't that adds to the attraction."

"Enough talk, time for action," he says, and we roll into another embrace and kiss. Lovemaking with Tom is new ground for me. I experience the burning desire of lust combined with all the passion and feelings of love. The event is completely fulfilling. As his strong, manly hands gently caress my body, his strength makes me feel a sense of complete contentment. Giving and showing him my strength, my muscles, my power, and watching him enjoy me towering over him is such a ferocious blast. I lust to combine my juices with his and can feel our spirits entwine as we hold each other in a tight grip. I enjoy his scents, his sounds and his feel. I look into his eyes and know he's longing for me as much as I am for him. We are soul-dancing together on the floor as the quiet storm rages outside, pattering on a metal grill. Something deep passes to each other in our bonding. Our lovemaking is fierce and wild, yet soft and tender. We bounce, and then we lay still. The differences in touch from the hard and aggressive to the soft and passive are erotic, and light me up with a natural high. His body is like fresh fruit that quenches both a hunger and a thirst as I enjoy it with my hands, with my teeth, with my tongue. It's finally his scent that arouses me to the point of orgasm. I enjoy achieving climax with him as together we reach the pinnacle of pleasure. We find each other's eyes and open our minds to a new height of relaxation and completion, then fall back down into each other's arms, weak from the intensity and physical exertion.

Tom calls his friend Chris O'Connell to confirm previously-made dinner plans for later this evening, and then we head to the base gym. On the drive, Tom tells me more about his friend Chris — a very openly gay guy with a big personality. Chris is provided with no-cost housing as a senior staff member at Bancroft, an organization that offers a wide range of services to people with autism, developmental disabilities, brain injuries and other neurological impairments. Tom met and became friends with Chris when he used to work at their Mullica Hill, New Jersey campus, assisting in providing educational and vocational interventions to individuals the organization serves.

Tom has mentioned Chris several times, and they've spent time chatting on the phone at home. He's also said that he lists Chris as a reference on job applications and on his resume. I'm anxious to meet the man Tom holds in such high esteem.

When we arrive at the gym, Tom reads a magazine while watching me complete a 25-minute high-intensity spinning class. I grab a quick shower, and when I return he suggests, "Let's bring your Mom some flowers." I certainly don't mind, and am a bit embarrassed I didn't think of it first. There's a flower shop right inside the PX mall, and Tom finds an arrangement of orange, white and blue flowers and asks, "What do you think of this one?"

"That's cool." He enjoys holding my credit cards, so I allow it.

"$17.95, then $1.08 tax, brings it to $19.03," the saleslady says. He pulls out my Visa and hands it to the cashier. She asks Tom to print his address and phone number on the sales slip. Without hesitation, Tom writes in my parent's address and phone number and signs my name. He doesn't even attempt to forge my name; he just signs it in his handwriting. The precision with which he handles the entire transaction makes me a bit tense, but I shrug it off as he smiles and hands me the bouquet.

Mom adores the bouquet, and we have a delightful time with my parents; so nice, in fact, that I think it's surreal.

8:45 p.m.

Arriving at the Bancroft campus, I notice it's very quiet and buried deep in the woods — the perfect setting for a horror movie.

We park and Tom holds my hand as we walk. Chris lives in a cute white cottage with a screen door and black shutters. He answers the door wearing a white turtleneck shirt with a paisley vest over it. He's mostly bald, chubby, about 5'7, and looks older than the thirty-something Tom says he is. Most striking is his sexy black beard. Chris invites us in and we sit together on his sofa. I begin soaking in the sights of my surroundings, relaxing to the sound of soft jazz playing. The living room's décor consists of carved wooden African figures on shelves with track lighting fixed upon them, glass tables, beveled mirrors, and a neon palm tree. A huge living tree dominates the room: it grows up one corner, its leafy vines covering much of the ceiling. His place has a scent that's a combination of incense and something delicious cooking.

Chris serves us a glass of wine and some salmon-cucumber appetizers garnished with small pieces of pimiento, while he and Tom catch up on the buzz going on at Bancroft. Eventually, Chris breaks the one-on-one interchange with Tom, saying to me, "When Tom and I worked together, we'd work until two or three in the morning and then head over to Bottoms Up or Studio."

Bottoms Up is a gay club in Mays Landing and Studio Six is in Atlantic City. They always seemed far to me, but I suppose from this area the drive's not too bad. I've had my share of adventures in both.

"Why did you leave Bancroft?" I ask Tom, wondering about the salary he was earning here.

Chris rises and walks over to sit next to me. He places his arm around me, looks into my eyes very closely and says, "You have very nice eyes. I can't make up my mind what I like more — your eyes or your smile."

"Thank you," I say. Somehow Tom is able to evade my question, and I get the feeling Chris is helping to change the subject. I make a mental note to pursue my line of questioning on Tom's Bancroft career later, when we're alone.

Chris looks at Tom and says, "Am I annoying you by complimenting your lover?"

Tom, looking quite confident, simply says, "No."

"Good, then you won't mind me saying I'd love to make a sandwich with the two of you," Chris says in his slow, deep voice. "I'll be the meat, you guys be the bread."

"Cold cuts? No thanks!" Tom jokes.

Chris responds, "No, Mary, hot roast beef!"

Dinner is outstanding, consisting of succulent marinated steaks and broiled shrimp served with a fresh salad. Chris completes the meal by serving some cherry pie. We shower him with compliments on the meal.

After eating, we sit and have a cigarette with some coffee while Chris dominates the conversation. I just smile, quietly absorbing and enjoying his exuberant personality.

"I Love Your Way/Freebird Medley" comes on the radio. "That's our song," Tom says, squeezing my hand and turning to glance into my eyes. We peck each other on the lips.

"I thought it was 'Waiting for a Star to Fall' by Boy Meets Girl," I add.

Chris kids, "I think I'm going to be sick."

"So, tell me about this man I'm in love with," I ask. Chris leans back in his chair and rubs his massively thick beard with one hand, thinking.

"He always got along so well with the residents," Chris responds, staring at Tom admiringly. He adds, "He's a great friend," grinning and looking at Tom as if to give the impression he's admitting something for the first time. "You seem like you're pretty cool, too, Tom," Chris says, again changing the subject to me. He rubs his hand on my leg and continues, "You have incredible legs. Building your leg muscles is what gives you that beautiful butt."

Tom and Chris chat for a few more hours. Even though I'm not an active participant in the conversation, I listen attentively, eager to learn more about the love of my life.

It's 2:30 a.m. when Chris gets up to go to the bathroom. I nudge Tom and say, "It's getting late. Are you ready to go?" He nods, smiling, and puts his arm around me. He pulls me close and I naturally rest my head on his shoulder. We express our thanks and say good night to Chris, and I sleep all the way home while Tom drives. I crawl into bed around 3:15, trying not to think about how few hours I have to sleep.

Monday, November 14, 1988, 5:30 a.m.

I curse the dawn as the alarm clock goes off, then settle back down into a calm feeling when I realize that waking up in the apartment, wrapped in Tom's arms, makes the morning much better. Finally I get up, stumble into the kitchen, and put the coffee on. When I'm all dressed and ready for work, I make a cup of coffee and hold it in both hands as I watch Tom sleep.

Tom awakens and sits up in bed, yawning and stretching. "Good morning, sunshine!" I say.

"You look hot in that grey suit," he answers, then asks, "Is that coffee?"

"Yeah, you want a cup?"

"I'll get it. I have an interview today at Crown, that rent-to-own place in Bellmawr. They have a sales manager position open."

"Oh, wow, that's marvelous. Good luck, Buster," I say, putting my cup down on the dresser.

Tom gives me a cynical look, reaches up to me, and pulls me down to him. Hugging me and tickling my belly, he says, "Buster?...Buster?...Buster!" making me laugh out loud. "What's up with calling me *Buster*? Do I look like a Buster to you?"

I'm smiling as he stops tickling and brings his cute face in close to mine, brushing his lips against my chin. "I wanted to be original," I say.

"What about Darling or Honey or *Lover*? What's the deal with Buster?"

We embrace, and he convinces me to undress and enjoy a long, satisfying session of lovemaking.

8:30 a.m.

As I walk into work and see Tracy sitting at my old desk, I realize I was to come in later to start the new Assistant Head Teller job on the evening shift today. Shit. I could've been sleeping in Tom's arms right now. For a moment I debate driving home, but by the time I get home, it'll be time to leave to be back here by 10:45. As I walk over to the kitchen to hang up my coat, trying to find the silver lining, I think, I can use some overtime, and dive into my new role and responsibilities.

Week of November 14, 1988

Every night Tom and I venture to auto dealerships looking for a car to replace the Lynx. My head is saying I'm a fool to toy with the notion of putting a car for him in my name. My heart is telling me I shouldn't blow the chance when I've got an opportunity to demonstrate my faith and confidence in building a life with someone I love. Since his credit is as wrecked as his car, his options are limited.

At a dealer on Route 47, I spot a used Yugo for $500. Tom absolutely refuses. Then I see a used black Toyota pick-up truck for only $5,000. I could see myself behind the wheel of the truck more than Tom. The price is reasonable, and the mileage is low. Seeing my interest in the truck, Tom directs me to a brand-new truck for $15,000 and humbly suggests we buy it.

I'm here physically as we progress through the sales process for acquiring the new truck; but mentally, I'm lost in thought. I hear Tom whisper promises to pay, coupled with his classic line, "We'll do it." Teeming with confidence, I take a deep breath and go through the motions, bringing us closer to the moment of truth where I will sign for the car. Thoughts and worry about taking on the debt-load cloud my confidence. I want to feel responsible enough to be in a real relationship where there's mutual trust and mutual contributions. Right now, I hate myself for feeling I'm the only one with anything to lose. I want him to trust me, and know I believe in him and us.

I have the pen in my hand, ready to sign the papers — and I can't bring myself to do it. It's so hard to get up from this car dealer's desk and walk out. I'm fearful we can't afford it. I love Tom and want to spend the rest of my life with him, but it's all too sudden, and more than I can take. What bothers me most is the virtual ease with which it can be done. One signature and I'm another $15,000 in debt.

Once we're in the car, Tom is pouting and says again, "We'll do it," and tells me how little I'll have to worry about it, especially since he's going back into management and will be bringing in a much bigger paycheck. "You really showed a lack of confidence in me and in our relationship by leaving the dealership without signing for the car. You're afraid to solidify our relationship. This thing we got going is real, Tom."

I can't help but snap, "I can't believe you're questioning my commitment! I've got a lot more invested in this than you." I'm angry and frustrated that he feels the way he does. He's entitled to his feelings, but certainly he has to realize how much he's asking. I try to don my "fuck it" attitude but can't find it. I'm not about to let myself step into the responsibility for two fucking car payments and the rent.

That stance lasts until Thursday, when I cave in to his nagging, my own guilt, and the pressure of the situation, and buy Tom a brand-new 1989 gray Ford Escort.

It has a manual transmission and no bells and whistles, but the total price still hits $11,500, since we don't have anything to put toward a down payment. The factor that finally weighed the most on my decision is this unexplainable feeling of love for the man. I believe in this relationship, and know that I've "invested" a lot more than cash. I can't limit doing whatever is necessary to make our lives better today if I hope to build a future with this man.

On Friday, I receive dozens of phone calls from various banks and finance companies calling to verify my employment and decision to put another car on my credit. Still struggling with trying to figure out what to do, I find myself being as negative as I can with them, hoping and praying they won't finance the car. I hold fast to the notion that I can use that as an excuse for not taking on the additional debt.

One loan officer tells me flat out, "I don't think we can carry this deal for you. Why do you need a second car?" and I reply, "I know. I can't afford it. I'm buying it for my partner."

In addition, I receive several calls during the week from the management at the new apartment Tom is arranging for us, also on my credit. They tell me the entire approval for the apartment is based on my credit. "You know," the words of the rental agent buzz in my head, "Mr. Shaw is a credit risk."

Plus, there are calls from various other creditors asking me about my requests for increases to my card limits. I assume Tom is making calls to increase my credit card limits, using my name to make the calls. He told me he could get my credit limits increased, which I didn't mind. The word *risk* weighs heavy on me.

I never mention the new apartment to my parents. They never see me anymore. Even on nights when I drive over to the base gym for workouts, I don't stop in to see them because I'm rushing back to be with Tom.

Saturday, November 19, 1988, 4:45 p.m.

"I got a cashier's check from our account at the First Commercial branch in Glassboro yesterday, and put a $527 security deposit down on our new apartment," Tom says as we drive to Deptford Mall in his new car. "Guess it's finally a reality. We're moving into Society Hill next weekend."

"You like your new car?" I ask him.

"Yes, Honey. It's great."

"You don't mind that it's stick shift?"

"No, not at all. It's so much more power, and saves gas, too."

It seems fast to be moving into the new place, but I'm excited thinking about decorating it in black lacquer furniture.

At Sears, Tom says, "We need a washer and dryer in the apartment. It'll make it easier than having to deal with carrying everything down to the laundry room."

"What about the washer and dryer we have in the apartment now?" I ask.

"I have those and the dishwasher from a rent-to-own place," Tom answers.

"How much are they?" I ask, not recalling having to write any checks out to a rent-to-own store. Tom did write out a lot of checks, but I was watching the entries in our register and didn't see anything for that. He doesn't answer me — we just keep walking.

"Is it a monthly rental or do you pay it annually?" I ask again, not hearing a response. He takes me by the hand and leads me down a deserted aisle.

Hearing no response, I persist in my line of questioning. "When do you expect to get a check from the insurance company for your stolen car?" Another burning question I've been wondering. Haven't heard a fucking thing about that since it happened. "What's taking so long with their investigation?"

Even as I pose the question, I have doubts as to his story. Anyone else would be more forthright about such a debacle with an insurance company. He turns and looks at me and kisses me: right in the middle of the appliance department of Sears. The moment in time is suspended as I bask in the feelings. The sense of freedom and openness is uplifting, and lights me up. His distraction is enough to make me change my thought patterns. Now enraptured with picking out appliances for our place, I feel grown up, playing house with a companion who fits into what I've always dreamed this should be like. Tom comes upon a washer/dryer set he likes and we locate a salesperson. Tom knows the type of loan I need to buy them, some kind of home improvement credit line above and beyond a standard Sears charge card line. The set costs just $799.99 for both the washer and dryer.

Brandon, our chipper sales associate asks, "Can you fill out this credit application for me?"

Tom takes the clipboard and begins filling it out. I observe him entering my information alone. While the fact that he's got all my personal information stored in his brain should create a sense of panic, I feel a sense of belonging and warmth overwhelm me. He's right beside me, and I trust him. The sales guy suggests we walk around the mall for about an hour while they approve my credit. After the credit is approved, Tom works out the arrangements for picking them up, and we leave.

In the car, I ask, "Are you having them delivered?", vaguely concerning myself with the details regarding the process of getting them from the store to our apartment.

"We can pick it up. I'll rent a small van or something." Tom is struggling with trying to get the key in the ignition.

Back at home, we sit down and watch TV together.

"We never rent movies," I say, frustrated by the channel surfing we're doing with the remote.

"You're right! How about we go into the bedroom and make one?" Tom jokes.

I shoot him a bright smile, saying, "I'm game! Let's go!"

In the bedroom, as I sit on the bed to untie my sneakers, Tom sits behind me and his hands come across my shoulders and to my chest as he brings me in for a hug. Then he lowers one hand and brushes it across the bulge behind my zipper. "Nice," he says, feeling my hard-on and lowering the zipper. As Tom puts both hands on the sides of my jeans and lowers them, along with my jockeys, my erection pops out. Tom begins cupping my balls and massaging them gently with one hand. With the other hand, he softly jacks me off. My head goes back and my eyes close.

Tom repositions himself in front of me and I allow a deep gasp to escape my throat as his head bobs up and back. The picture of us in this act feeds my desire. I have my pants bunched around my ankles, and Tom turns his white baseball cap around as he continues. Soon he finishes removing my shoes, socks and pants. Tom quickly sheds his clothes and repositions himself again, this time on my lap. Lost in lust, we breathe hard through our noses and catch each other's scents as we inhale. It's not long before we blast our loads until we're soft and useless in each other's arms.

Sunday, November 20, 1988

I'm up and active early this morning. By 10:00 a.m., my chores are done and I have lots of energy. "I'm going to the gym," I say.

"The base gym is an hour away," Tom says angrily.

I'm not sure how to read or react to the severity of his tone. We're silent for a moment.

"I have a friend who's the manager at a health club right in Laurel Springs," Tom finally says. "I think I still have a membership card." He produces the card and says, "My friend Mark gave me a free membership."

I want to ask him about his friendship with "Mark" from the gym, but I let it go.

We arrive at a mini-mall in the middle of what seems like nowhere. It's neat how the mall seems like a leftover from the '70s. "Nowhere" turns out to be what's called the Marketplace Mall in Laurel Springs. Inside, the décor is primarily wood paneling throughout. Tom leads me to the Holiday Spa and we walk inside.

"Can I help youse?" asks the gum-chewing blonde minding the reception area.

"Is Mark here today?" Tom asks.

"Can I tell him your name?" she asks.

"Tom Shaw." She disappears down a hallway and returns a moment later with Mark in tow. Mark is a few inches shorter than I, but has an interestingly sweet smell and the shadow of a goatee growing on his cute face. I immediately suspect his sexual orientation as his eyes widen as they behold Tom. They shake hands and Tom introduces us. "He's interested in working out closer to home. I have this membership you gave me. You know I never use it."

"Oh, sure, it's okay," Mark says, standing there with his large gym-worked arms and shoulders accentuated by a white Polo shirt.

Tom abruptly says, "I'm going to walk around the mall, I'll be back," leaving me in Mark's custody. I shoot Tom a disapproving glare, to which he grins, winks and turns to exit. When Tom leaves, Mark's smile fades and his eyes lose their sparkle. He is evasive as he rushes me though a short tour of the facility. He weighs me and records my weight on a card. He goes over the gym's hours, benefits and workout machines in a mechanical, non-personal manner. We walk back into his office and he writes out a pass for me to work out today and two other times for free, in hopes I take out a membership of my own.

"You know Tom long?" he asks.

I clear my throat and answer, "Uh, not really. Couple weeks now."

"He's cool. Got a cock like the head of a hammer," he says, filling out the forms with his left hand and holding his right palm down on his beefy leg. I widen my eyes and smile but say nothing. He asks a couple dozen questions and generates more than a one-word answer to the one about my aspirations.

"I want to build up my arms and chest. Keep my legs and ass solid."

He nods, saying, "You look pretty hot already, bud."

"Thanks, so do you."

He's happy with that remark. It lands me an offer, "You want me to close the door?"

"Ah, thanks, man, but Tom and I are together."

"Oh, you mean youse are lovers?"

"Uh, yeah."

"Oh, sorry, man. I didn't mean to mention we fucked." This guy is obviously a master of the art of tact.

I have the heavy weights to myself, so I jump at the chance to spend a half hour lifting. I spend another half hour on the brutal treadmill. After my workout, I shower with some minor temptations but resist the urge to play with the invitations. After I finish, I walk around the small shopping mall looking for Tom.

It's pretty abandoned. I'm curious as to where Tom is. There are more empty stores in this dump than open ones. I guess in its heyday, it must have been a busy place. I walk out to the parking lot, but there's no Tom. I wait another hour, sitting on a bench outside. I call our apartment from a pay phone, but only get the machine. I'm worried, as thoughts of Tom getting into another accident run through my mind.

Finally, Tom pulls up and gets out of the car. I don't budge for a moment. I watch him approach me and finally lift my ass up. I should be reeling with anger, but I'm not. I walk toward him, dragging my feet, knowing he owes me some love for his tardiness. I'm going to make the most of it.

"I'm in trouble, aren't I?" he asks. His power over me is relentless. I feel so relieved seeing him and knowing he's safe from harm. We get in the car and take off.

"I'm sorry I'm late," he says immediately.

"Where did you go?" I ask.

"How was your workout?" Tom reaches for my hand.

"It was good. I signed up for a membership, since I'll be losing the military ID card from Nadine any day now."

"That's good. Mark's a nice guy."

Tom drives to the Black Horse Pike Shopping Center in Audubon. It's an outdoor mall with all the stores connected by a covered sidewalk. There's a JC Penney and a Montgomery Ward department store on either side, with small five-and-dime type places in between.

"I used to work at the Penney's here," he says. We park and take a stroll around. We stop at Woolworth's and get a pretzel from their snack area, which has an outside window. The pretzel fuels my growing hunger. "I'm famished!" I declare.

"How about we eat at Bob's?" Tom says, looking up toward the Bob's Big Boy restaurant across the parking lot. We drive over and hit the all-you-can-eat buffet bar.

While I murder a second plate of ribs, Tom reminds me, "We're moving next Friday and Saturday. Did you remember to get off from work?"

"I can get Saturday off, but Friday is out." I make a mental note to mark it in my calendar.

"It's going to be apartment G9; G is for the Granada building. I'm so excited. It's a prominent place to live. Our new address will be G9, Society Hill, Washington

Township. Won't that look classy on address labels?" I smile, feeling joy from his happiness, though I still have some nervousness about bankrolling the move and higher rent. No matter how much Tom tries to quell my fears, logic has me apprehensive about the move.

Wednesday, November 23, 1988

I got calls from Nadine's Mom on Monday and Tuesday telling me to meet Nadine today after work to give her my ID card. I told her I might be there, I might not. Nadine's Mom, Lucille, is hard to read. She has to be in Nadine's court, but she has to realize that all I ever did was for Nadine's benefit. I made mistakes, but I loved her daughter; that has to count for something.

Nadine calls around noon to set up a meeting. Again, with the "come by yourself" shit. We agree to meet at the Burger King on Fort Dix. She says she'll be in a white pick-up, by herself. She's so cold. I have come to think of her as so much a part of my DNA, that to be rejected is like having a body part removed.

Tom meets me after work, and we drive down together in the Camaro. I adore the new car smell. During lunch today, I washed it, so it gleams bright red.

I feel excitement in anticipation of seeing her again. Just seeing her in person is enough to ignite a medley of huge feelings. We pull into the Burger King across from the Commissary where we used to work, where we fell in love. I take in a deep breath as I see the white pickup and pull up next to her. She isn't alone. Her latest fuck buddy, Dennis, is sitting next to her. The voice in my head says, *Bitch, I'm not alone either.* When our eyes meet, we look at each other for a second. Then she declares, "Well, I guess you spent some money on that!" I pause to let that sink in. Knowing how I forced us to scrimp and save for the future, she has me pegged as a tightwad.

"Let's go over to the food court in the PX," she suggests.

"Right behind you," I reply. My thoughts continue, directed at her. *Little do you know you'll always be loved by me.*

We walk in and find a table. I sit down, and Nadine sits facing us. Nadine makes no attempt to introduce Dennis, who is standing behind her. I introduce Nadine to Tom and they barely look at each other. No love lost. Both have known me intimately. Dennis has his arms crossed over his chest, trying unsuccessfully to look menacing. He's not bad looking: shorter than I and built all right, but he pales in comparison to my Tom. All I can think is that the bitch has great taste in men.

"So..." Nadine begins, "Here we are." Expecting this to deliver a crushing blow of emotion, I am surprised when I feel nothing in my heart for a moment — until, whoops, here it is. A wave of excitements sweeps over me at finally being close to her again. For a second, I fade back to days when we'd sit in this room, in this very booth, and talk, laugh, fight, cry, dream and make a million plans together. It seems like a long time ago. I'm here to do one thing: to give her the goddamned ID card. But I sense Nadine and I both want this moment. I remember all the special moments we shared in this very room, where we took all our breaks together and fell in love. This is where Nadine took me to her heart and told me that we were the only friends we had. We had friends, but her point was well absorbed by my needy heart. I had every girl I ever wanted, but Nadine offered something so unique. A thought crosses my mind: to take her by the hand and beg her to get out of here together.

But the time for begging is over. It didn't work. I trust the good Lord knows what He's doing. She doesn't love me anymore. It's over, and I can tell by the look in her eyes, the sound of her voice. It's another person in front of me. It's not my Nadine. She's not the angel I knew. It's a Nadine alien to me. The Nadine I loved is long gone. I left her here a year ago with a confused boy. I mutter my thought, "How sad is that?"

"Huh?" Nadine asks. She tells me what she's been up to, about how some of our former co-workers are doing, and all the while, I'm staring at Dennis, who is now behind her. Nadine's mother comes out of the commissary, where she's a cashier, for a cigarette break and to observe. Several of our former co-workers and my former friends are already in the room, and they're soon joined by others, all enjoying the free entertainment. Everyone knows what's going on; Nadine and her Mom took care of that. Dennis approaches her Mom immediately, and they sit together and look over at me. As Nadine blabs and everyone glares, I look to my side and see Thomas, sitting there looking confident and at ease.

I feel like I was sleeping, and have now awakened to find a dream come true. With a sensation equal to thunder and lightning, I am re-grounded in who and where I am, and realize I'm better off now than ever. I think about our life, and revel in the fact that he's handsome as hell, with his sexy short hair and red cheeks. He turns from Nadine and winks at me, empowering me and helping me find my bearings. This is my future now. Nadine is now asking me about my folks, about my brother, her voice slightly annoyed due to my distraction with Tom's face, to which I answer, "Yes, fine, fine..." *Everyone's fucking fine, Nadine,* I think.

The song "Everything Your Heart Desires" by Daryl Hall and John Oates comes over the loudspeakers. It was the first song that came out when Nadine and I were separated by her leaving for the Army. I identify with a whole new set of non-Nadine experiences from the sound of it; I find joy with the path I'm on. Nadine and Tom are now having a strong discussion, which I'm oblivious to. While I look at Tom, I think that any feelings I might have had about things not being right with him are now gone. I have a huge sense of pride in being part of something that's bigger than just being with Tom — I'm gay and it's fucking great! I'm delighted to be a part of Tom and all he stands for in my life. To me, Tom embodies the spirit of what being gay is all about, and I find myself bursting with a new sense of pride in who I am. It's easier being gay and accepting it than fighting it and playing games.

"Are you listening?" Nadine snaps, her mood changed by some volley of words with Tom.

"What?" I ask.

"Just give me the ID card and that's it. I don't know why you keep resisting me. I've agreed to give you whatever you asked for. Why won't you surrender the ID card?" I freeze momentarily, embarrassed by my lack of attention to the conversation due to my daydream. Nadine continues, "You can't hold onto that ID card like it's me. It can't keep you warm at night like I used to."

With that, Tom chuckles, saying, "He doesn't need you for that. By the way, I do that 'special thing' he likes much better than you ever could." He is referring to rimming, which I introduced as a need to Nadine during our time together. With Tom, it's even better because I want to do him as well.

At that, Nadine sits back in the booth, crossing her arms, squinting her eyes, and says in a loud tone, "Well, well, well. Are you boys faggots?"

I stand, physically and mentally, and pronounce, "I'll give you the fucking ID card when I get the divorce papers." Dennis steps forward as if he's got to protect her. I move to get right in his face and bark, "See this expensive gray suit I'm wearing? I don't want to get your blood on it." He backs down immediately.

Nadine responds, screaming, "NO! That's not good enough! I want it *now*! I'm fucking responsible for it, you fucking faggot!" Knowing almost everything about me, especially how sensitive I've been about the struggle with my homosexual tendencies and the feelings I've had, she's delivering a serious low blow.

Her insult, delivered loud enough for the world to hear, launches her Mother off her ass and she approaches, belting out, "What do you think we were meeting for today? You're wasting our time!"

Tom reaches over, knowing I came prepared to surrender the card, and grabs my hand in the middle of the crowded room.

"I want that fucking card!" Nadine says, slamming her hand down hard and loud on the table.

"Let's get out of here," Tom says, calmly and with maturity. I realize there's a place inside my soul nobody has touched before, and when I found Tom, I discovered more than I had been searching for. Tom showed me a world where I can enjoy total love, happiness, satisfaction and pleasure, all with one partner. He helped me realize I'm in demand, I'm beautiful, it's okay to be who we are — and most of all, that there's no need to be embarrassed. Just act like you're in control.

If ever I doubted it before, I know now where I belong. I belong with another man. I love the way he feels. I belong to a new family now. My family has always been inside of me, and now I can find members everywhere who can relate. Tom lights fires and desires in me that rage out of control. He's my future.

We start walking out. Nadine storms off to her Mother and Dennis. As we turn to walk out the door, I catch sight of Nadine for the last time in my life. I win the round and the match. My regrets over Nadine end today.

Thursday, November 24, 1988

We have dinner tonight with Mitch at the Melrose Diner in town.

"I understand you want to work with us," Mitch says to Tom. "What we have here is a need for someone to be an assistant to a female dancer. I don't like sending them out alone. You know, it's mostly nights with these jobs, and it could be dangerous for them going to some of these places. Not that I ever tell them that. I don't expect you to either. One of the guys is in deep at school and can't keep the job. Like I said, it's mostly nights. Would it conflict with your day job?"

Tom sits back and says, "Not a problem. What do I have to do?"

"You pick up the girl at her house in Philly, or you can meet downtown somewhere. It's up to you and Jessica. We'll call you with directions, schedules and times, and you pick her up and go to the job. You make sure she gets paid and doesn't get raped, robbed or beat up. Not a problem."

"Sounds cool," Tom says.

"We'll give you fifty bucks a gig to cover everything, including gas. If it's a long distance, I try to get you ten, fifteen bucks more. We ask the dancers to give you a cut of her tips, but that's on her. We haven't had any complaints."

"What do they usually get in tips?" Tom asks.

"Depends on the girl," Mitch answers. "You get a hundred bucks if we're only sending you out on one job for the night. That's rare, though. Usually they're booked pretty solid for three to six jobs a night. Plus a hundred for a reversal."

"What's that?"

He explains, "If you got a job in Plymouth Meeting at 10:00 p.m. and a job downtown at 12:30 a.m. and then got a job back in the Plymouth Meeting area around 2:00 a.m., then that's making a round trip. We make the dancer kick up an extra $50 to you, so you make $100 on the third job."

Mitch goes on, "It's a pain in the ass. What we try to do is book 'em in order. If the first Plymouth Meeting job calls us first and books, we try to keep them at the time they want. If the Philly job calls second, we book 'em at the time they want and we're still fine. You get me? If the second Plymouth Meeting gig calls in requesting 2:30 a.m., we'll try and get 'em to go at 11:00 p.m. so you're tight scheduled, but in order. If they can't, there's nothing we can do, 'cause you want the business, right? So we try and put another girl on both Plymouth Meetings, and if we still can't do it, we pay you the extra money. You get fifty bucks for all three jobs and another fifty for the third job. You end up with two hundred; you can do the math."

"Sounds good," Tom says, looking excited by the prospect of the money, yet bewildered by the explanation.

"Let me tell you about missing a job: Don't. We don't make money, you don't make money, and the girl doesn't make money. Most of our work is from referrals, so we count on repeat business. With that said, your job is to find the place. You have to map it out before you head out that night and be sure you know exactly where you're going. I don't want to hear about flat tires, broken-down cars, or being sick, and there are no subs for you. If you need a sub, this one can do it if he wants to, so long as he's not working," Mitch says, lifting his chin in my direction.

He continues, "If your car breaks down, then pay cab fare out of your cut; it's cheaper than missing the job. The events are one-time only occasions like bachelor parties or birthday parties, and the person ordering it can't have it done any other time. There aren't any rain checks. I don't refund any money, so if you miss a job, you bought it. Get it? The jobs for the females start at $155, just so you know." Tom nods. "If you get to a job and they cancel, they're still paying. If it's C.O.D., we've got their credit card on file securing it, so they either pay you in cash or it's going on their card with an additional fee for the bother."

Tom nods his agreement. He looks excited at the prospect of the amount of cash he'll earn. I'm happy to have it as well. I am, however, somewhat disappointed that he won't be joining me on my gigs anymore.

"When can I start?"

Mitch looks at me. "I'm going to set him up with Jessica." I've never met her, but I nod knowingly and smile. Heading to the car, Tom asks me what Jessica is like.

"I don't know her. There are only a few girls I've done joint jobs with, and they're pretty cool. Overall, they're much nicer than the dudes. I guess Mitch thought I knew her." Tom is clearly excited about the new job.

"Mitch didn't say when I start?"

"I started the same day as my interview. Don't be surprised if there's a message on our machine when we get home for a job tonight."

"Do you think he liked me?"

"Hell yes, Mitch liked you immediately. You're making $15 more than I made when I started, and I do both the dancing and driving! Even though Mitch makes sure all his females have assistants, only one male dancer has an assistant. This guy, Savage, is built like a brick shithouse and is always in demand. He gets someone to help him on all his gigs. He's very sexy — I salivate over him all the time. He's rabidly straight, though, and actually not very friendly to the gays. One time I was opening for him at the Shark Club, and he was walking around the dressing room in just white socks. It was too much to take standing up. I had to sit down immediately. He has an ass I would pray to. Of course, he knows he has it going on and never lets you forget."

I'm glad he got the work. The money sure will help with our growing expenses.

In the car driving home he blurts out, "$50 a job! Jessica has two jobs a night and works three nights a week — that's $300 for three days, and it's so easy!"

"T, I know, it's great, but it's not like they're handing you the money for nothing. Be careful."

50

AUTOPILOT

Friday, November 25, 1988

It's damp and rainy out today. Of course I can't get off work as Tom asked, but Sue has mercy on me and lets me leave at noon. When I get there, the apartment is littered with boxes. Tom went out during the day and rented a U-Haul truck; he's driven it around to the front of the sliding glass doors.

"The ground is so damp out there, I hope the truck doesn't get stuck," he says. There's crap everywhere, including cords and wires from the various electronics. Despite having the sliding doors open and the fact that the cool air is circulating, we're soon drenched in sweat from moving furniture into the truck. We're not in any way prepared for the move. We didn't put anything in boxes, so everything is a complete disaster to carry and unload. It takes three times as long as it probably should to load the truck.

"We need a dolly — it would make it easier on our backs," I suggest.

"I know it sucks and this is both mentally and physically draining, but Tom, I've been doing it all day," he says, obviously frustrated.

Immediately on the defensive, I shout, "Well, I haven't been sitting around jacking off! I've been at work!"

Then we fight like little boys over who's going to drive the moving truck over to the apartment. "Fine, fine, you fuckin' drive," I say, and turn away. Tom's way of giving up the argument is different; he throws the keys to the truck at me when I turn around. The keys hit me in the back and it stings. I feel rage brewing over. Not reacting physically isn't an option, since it will make me appear weak. I pick up the keys and hurl them back at him, but in a last split second I hold them in my hand so my gesture is threatening. I end up just looking stupid, because he doesn't even flinch. I storm out to the truck and get behind the wheel. Tom comes out and gets in the cab with me.

Soon after, we enter our new apartment, turn on the kitchen light, and notice all the room there is. This place has two bedrooms plus a den, with over 300 more square feet than we have now. A moment of peace reigns.

After unloading the truck, I'm ready for bed, but we head back.

Back at the old apartment, it's about 11:30 when we finish reloading the truck again. I say, "Why don't we call it a night and get something to eat? Are you hungry?"

Tom explodes, "We aren't stopping until we're all done! Besides, you have to work tomorrow. I'm not doing it all by myself!"

I volley back, "We're not even half finished."

"I don't care. We're moving all night!"

"Screw it," I say, and storm out the sliding glass doors, saying, "I'm going to get something to eat." As I make my way to the car, I remember I left my car keys in the apartment. I walk back to the front door and sit on the floor in front of it for a moment, trying to calm down. I think of how immature I acted, and find good thoughts. After a moment I regain patience and energy and get up and walk into the apartment. The sight of him furiously engaged and focused in taking his desk apart frustrates me. I walk up to him and softly suggest, again, "I'm tired. Come on, let's rest!"

"GET BACK TO WORK!" he roars, without diverting his attention from his task.

I feel enormous rage well up in the pit of my stomach, then stand right up over him and scream, "NO! I'm fucking sick and tired of this. Let's stop for tonight and get a fresh start in the morning. I'm not kidding. I'm fucking drained!"

With that, he darts upward and inadvertently hits his head on my chin. Startled, his response is to backhand me right across the face.

The slap ignites a flashback to years of childhood torments from a variety of abusers, and then a feeling of betrayal comes over me. I leap forward and force him to the floor using all my strength, pushing my chin into the side of his head with all my might.

"MOTHERFUCKER!" I mutter through gritted teeth. I'm locked on thoughts and emotions geared to cause the pain I feel.

As I pin his head down to the floor with my chin he cries, "Go home to your Mommy and Daddy!"

His words only make me want to hurt him more. He's right. I'm immature, and acting like a fucking baby. The more I hurt him, the more I consciously know these things can never be undone. I'm smashing the beautiful relationship we share. It will never be the same again; and that adds fuel to my fire, making me even more upset. I have no grip on reality — all I can do is watch the machine take over and destroy. I begin smashing him in the head and face with my fist. He puts up a strong defense and has no chance of launching an offense as I ram my fist into his face again. We find ourselves back on our feet, boxing each other. Tom strikes me and I come back with more anger, fueled by my disappointment and all the energy that I can gather up from my feelings of defeat.

Finally, we break the match and go to our corners, out of breath, licking our wounds. If I was exhausted prior to our fight, I'm literally debilitated now. I turn and walk to him, feeling miserable as I fall to my knees in front of him and then to the floor; my head finds its way into his lap. I realize Tom is right. We're in the middle of this fucked-up move, and there's only one way to go.

"Come on Chief," I say, lifting him up. In the bathroom I start helping him clean his bloody nose, and he pulls the cloth away to do it himself. I view my reflection in the mirror. We don't speak as we pack up another several boxes and carry them to the truck.

Tom goes to work on another project, so I drive the truck alone to the new place and unpack the boxes. As I walk back to the truck, a familiar-looking car slows down and sounds the horn. I can't make out the driver. He stops and gets out. It's that guy Dave that I met at the club a while back. He closes the door to his lemon-yellow '70s Nova, and comes forward, extending his hand for a shake.

"Tom! What brings you here?" he asks. He's sporting the same khaki pants he wore when we tricked. I visualize his hot, naked body in the shower we shared, and feel my dick stir.

"I'm moving in."

"Cool. My Mom lives in 'J' building. You movin' in by yourself?" he asks.

"No, I met someone."

"Is it a dude who lives over at the Crossings in Glassboro? My brother told me he saw you with Tom Shaw."

At first I'm a little taken back; then I recall the night Tom and I met and ran into Dave's brother Michael at the bookstore.

"Yes."

"Be careful, that guy's an asshole. We dated. As a matter of fact, I lived with him for a couple weeks. He stole a lot of my shit."

My heart drops as I think, *Tom slept with Dave?* Small world. Dave feels it necessary to describe Tom's apartment: "Blonde furniture — woodsy and a bookshelf, Amy Grant poster, nice stuff." He continues, "He works over at the McDonald's as a manager."

"He didn't steal any of your shit, Dave. Lay off him, okay, Bud?"

"Oh, sure, man. Sorry." Trying to change the subject, he offers, "This is a great complex. Nice apartments."

"Yeah," I ask, "How is it both you and your brother turned out gay?"

"Pretty cool, eh? Now you're going to ask me if we ever did anything, right?"

I smile and shake my head, "I don't want to know."

"Come on, now. I know he's hot and all, but we haven't done it." Dave grins. "Well, I guess you won't be calling us to fuck around again?"

"I won't."

"Good for you."

"See ya," I say, anxious to leave.

"Oh, hey, we liked having you. When I tell John I saw you he'll be mad I didn't invite you over. Sure you don't want to stop over some night?"

Dave is clearly a dimwit. Any energy used telling him off would be a waste.

"I told you," I begin, but he cuts me off, "I know, gotcha. Don't want to mess up what ya got."

I regret what we did. Especially now, knowing he was with Tom.

"Does Tom know you fucked us?" he asks.

"Look, I gotta go."

Dave smiles. "Well, I guess I'll see you around. You have our number in case you need any help with Tom. Enjoy Society Hill!"

I nod without smiling, and jump in the truck while he stands watching. I'm suddenly ashamed for my part in the fight Tom and I just had. I stop at 7-11 and pick up a rose and some candy for him.

When I return to the apartment, I find that Tom had a pizza delivered, and it sits on the bed. "I waited for you," he says, opening the box, offering me a slice.

I hand him the rose and candy, saying, "I'm sorry."

"No, I'm sorry, Tom. I haven't been very sensitive. There's no excuse." We kiss; and as our lips meet, my eyes close and I feel more grateful than ever for his soft, tender lips and warm mouth. We roll on the floor with me on top of him. I open my mouth and taste and gently bite his face, his cheeks and lick his ears. He trembles with excitement as I continue teasing his ear with my mouth, whispering soft words of passion and desire. Soon we're kissing again and I reach down and lift his shirt. I'm kissing his belly button, licking it, then his chest. I drop to his jeans and bite the inside of his legs through his jeans. I bite his cock through his jeans, and he purrs with delight. I stop at his belt and rest my head on his hips. His body is so soft, so smooth. I move back up to his face and he grabs my ass and gives it a good hard squeeze. We're both horny and anxious but it's good to enjoy this soft foreplay. We respect the limits of our exhausted bodies, and give in to hunger over sex by devouring the pizza while sitting on the bed. Looking around the bedroom, I notice it's a shambles.

I tell Tom about my encounter with Dave. "He told me he lived with you and you stole some of his shit."

"It's more like the other way around. Dave lived with me until he met John, and they both stayed with me a week until they got their own place. They took one of my Persian carpets, two beach towels and a toaster. They never gave me a dime the last week they were here."

"Dave didn't mention that John stayed here."

"Well, there you go. Soon as he met John, they stayed here a week and took off."

"I told him we were together and he proceeded to warn me about you, saying to be careful and all."

"Did he come on to you?"

"Yeah."

"And you told him to fuck off, right?"

"'Course."

"They're trash. They better leave you alone."

I finish eating and start pulling the covers off the bed in an attempt to begin transferring the bed to the truck.

"Don't bother starting that," Tom says, coming over and placing his hand on my head. "Why don't you go to sleep? You're exhausted."

I climb into bed without protest and collapse from exhaustion, saying only, "Why don't you join me?"

Soon Tom wakes me gently, saying, "I'm going to make another run with the truck." He sits next to me on the bed, running his fingers through my hair.

"Thanks for letting me sleep," I mutter. I feel his eyes on me, but don't open my eyes out of sheer lust for sleep.

"I'm sorry I hit you. I forgot you worked half the day and then came right home and jumped into this mess. It's not your problem. You're such a good man," he says, still petting my head.

I knew the day we were moving, and neither one of us did anything to prepare, so we're both to blame. I just thought we could move all weekend. I don't know why he's hell-bent on doing it all in one night.

No sooner does Tom leave than the phone rings. All I can imagine is that the fucking truck broke down and it's Tom calling, stuck on the side of the road.

"Hi, it's me, Dave. I just got home and was talking to John about running into you."

"I'm in bed, man."

"Bed? Want some company?" he says, not getting the point.

"What's up?" I ask, half-pissed about being woken up, half wondering why the fuck he's calling this number.

"You know, I think you got better lookin' since I last saw you."

"Well, thanks, man, but check it out, I gotta crash. Think I told you there's no sense in talking."

"We like you, and I when I told John I saw you, he said we should try and hook up with you again. Just say the word. You better be careful with Tom. There's something about him that just isn't right. He's a real phony, and not a decent friend. I called my brother. He said he *did* see you and Tom at the bookstore. Better be careful — my brother doesn't like Tom, either."

I hang up.

The phone rings again and I let out a huge yell: "FUCK!"

I thought Tom left, but he's still here. He walks in and shrugs his shoulders silently, mouthing the words "Who is it?" while blowing out cigarette smoke.

"Dave," I say aloud, rolling my eyes. "I hung up on him. He must be calling back."

Tom answers and asks Dave, "Why are you calling here?" His next remark is, "Okay, look, we're going to take care of this right here and now." Tom hangs up and turns to me and asks, "Do you know where they live?"

I tell him the story of my experience and remember that Dave had given me their address. I feel a bit embarrassed when I find the piece of paper Dave gave me still in my wallet. I never thought about it after I put it there. Tom reads it and says, "Lands End Apartments – I know exactly where this is."

Then he looks at me and orders, "Get up, get dressed. We're going to pay a visit to those two sluts right now!"

"Now?"

He nods, saying, "I'm going to get my point across right fucking now." I climb out of bed, curious, mystified and yet feeling complimented by Tom's chivalry. I just play along and don't put up a fuss or ask any questions. As Tom drives to Dave and John's new apartment in Lindenwold, he shares this: "So you know, Dave and I just jacked off watching a porn. Nothing more. I know where these two live now. I never touched that skank John. I'm furious they're coming on to you after they know you're with me."

I don't find John skanky; he's clean and has a terrific butt. But I keep my thoughts to myself. Finally, we arrive at the apartment complex where they live.

We reach their door, knock, and almost instantly Dave answers, saying, "Hey, guys!" Tom pushes his way by Dave, walking right in. Dave turns and shoots me a puzzled look.

Two twenty-something girls and a guy are watching TV and sharing a joint. John walks out of the kitchen in tight gray sweat-shorts with his shirt off, carrying a bowl of popcorn. He has more of a belly than I recall, but still I feel my dick stir at the sight of him. I find myself waiting, wanting for him to turn around so I can catch of glimpse of his terrific ass in these great shorts.

Tom says directly to John, "I came over to tell you that Dave's been coming on to Tom. We're lovers now and not interested in either of you. I'd appreciate it if you kept him on a short leash. I don't want to have to come over here and kick the shit out of the both of you."

Tom's presence is such that his projection and overall appearance is quite direct, as well as threatening. I feel flattered by Tom's gallantry. I hold my head up high.

John, now lying on the floor, looks over at me and says, "You look familiar. Do I know you?"

Tom goes over and kicks John's popcorn bowl across the room, making a huge mess. *"Whaaat?"* John says in an alarmed voice, raising his hands up in dismay.

"Give me a break, you fucking slut," Tom says. "Of course you remember him. He's the best fuck you ever had." Tom turns to Dave and screams in his face, "Don't fuck with him!"

Tom motions for me to go ahead of him. Dave, still standing by the door, holds it open for me, and avoids eye contact with Tom. In the car, Tom takes my hand and we drive back to the Crossings, where he tucks me back in bed.

"Aren't you coming to bed?" I ask.

"No, I'm going to do more moving," he says with a smile. "Get some rest, Champ."

I give him an extended blink with a smile and say, "You too, my little hero." It was out of character to see Tom in such an aggressive role, but it felt good.

Saturday, November 26, and Sunday, November 27, 1988

All weekend we spend cleaning up the new apartment and getting settled in. It's exhausting work, but well worth it by the time we're done. I put up a little fuss about the decoration of the apartment, having visions of dark brown leather couches and black lacquer furniture contrasted by neon lighting. I pout a bit about it, but Tom provides a sympathetic ear and encouraging words of reason to quell my discomfort. His words are the perfect fit: "I know you want to add your signature to the décor of our new home. All the furnishings belong to me, and though they're nice, you didn't help pick them out. I want the new place to be a display of our mutual likes and flair. Going with black lacquer furniture and leather couches will clash with what's already in place. I don't want you to take this the wrong way, but that style doesn't reflect how mature your tastes are."

What can I say to that? He wins.

Monday, November 28, 1988

Two weeks to the day after his interview, Tom is offered a manager's job at Crown Rentals in Bellmawr. They ask him to start work immediately, so tomorrow is his first day. I'm so happy for him. They're starting him at $8 per hour — more than the pitiful $6 per hour I receive from First Commercial.

I receive word from Sue that my request for a transfer has been approved. I'll be going to the new branch opening in Woodbury — way closer to home. Everything seems to be falling into place for us. Sue is sad, but understands that movement within our growing company is part of life, since she's moved several times in her own career. Plus, joining the grand opening team at a new branch gets you lots of exposure from Senior Management — great for career growth.

Wednesday, November 30, 1988

Tom calls me from work to regale me with news. His first day at the new job is going very well. His boss seems like a decent guy. I'm relieved — not just for the income, but for his happiness. People need to have a sense of purpose, and I believe a job fills a need to contribute and achieve a sense of accomplishment.

I get home from a ferocious day at work dealing with trying to find teller differences. My head is killing me. When I blink my eyes, I see teller machine tapes. I decide to take a bath in the freshly-cleaned tub to relax and try to unwind. I bring a bottle of Merlot into the bathroom with me. I have a huge wine goblet filled, with the intention of losing focus on everything. Sitting in the tub, I can't help but dwell on the fact that I've recently bought two new cars. I can't imagine how they are able to find a bank that is willing to approve my second car loan, knowing I'd just purchased another car. It does feel good knowing I own a 1989 Camaro, and it's only 1988. I fill my glass again. I like the fact that I have a great-looking boyfriend. Even the sound of the word, *boyfriend*, gives me a sense of happiness. Life is sweet.

Friday, December 2, 1988, 4 p.m.

"Can you come here and pick me up?" Tom asks.

"What? Why?"

"You remember the problem I have with my car key fitting into the ignition?"

"Yeah, what happened?" I ask, nervously sucking on the tip of my thumb in anticipation of more car problems.

"It stuck today when I was going to lunch, and I called the dealer. Can you believe two guys came out and picked it up? The one guy was able to jimmy the key into the ignition and took off with the other guy in tow. I told them I'd get a ride."

"When was that?"

"Around lunchtime, about one-ish," he says.

"Wow. I can't believe they came out," I say.

"Me either."

"Okay, handsome, tell me how to get there." Tom provides me with good directions to the Crown Rentals in Mt. Ephraim. It's right on the Black Horse Pike by the CVS Pharmacy.

On the way, I pass the one landmark he mentioned — the Mt. Ephraim police station on my left. It looks just like Tom described it, with sand-colored stucco on the front. Just as he mentioned, the CVS is just ahead on the right, with the Crown Rentals attached to it. Tom took me for a drive in this area once. There are half-a-dozen rental trucks parked on the side of the building, decorated with big blue crown logos. I walk in and immediately notice Thomas behind the counter, looking extremely delicious in his long-sleeved gray dress shirt tucked into sexy black dress pants that do an amazing job of outlining his sexy shape. His sleeves are unbuttoned and rolled up slightly, his shiny belt buckle catches the light, and he gleams in here like a ray of sunshine. For a moment the sight of him is suspended, as he slowly turns with a clipboard in his hand and smiles at a co-worker. His dashing looks give me a huge sense of pride. He turns and sees me, and his face lights up as our eyes meet. He comes from around the counter and introduces me to a couple of guys he works with. They're clearly straight. His boss is in his office, a fellow called Cornelius Dinkins. Tom checks with him about being able to leave, and Dinkins comes out to introduce himself to me. Everyone is very friendly.

Once outside I ask, "*Cornelius*?" giving Tom a strange grin.

"Yes, you like that one, huh?" Tom asks, laughing.

"Hey, I need gas and cigarettes," I say, pulling up to the convenience store in the same parking lot as Crown Rentals. I look at him. "You're obviously out to all of them?"

"Well, not really. I just told them my roommate is gay, and that you were coming to pick me up." With that we laugh, and I punch him on the shoulder. He exits the car to fetch cigs as I get gas. He looks back and asks, "Marlboro Red Box?"

"Yeah," I say, thinking I haven't bought a pack in a month. I've done a great job of cutting back. Tom shakes his head, scoffing at my selection. I say, "Go get your Marlboro Lights, you sissy."

As he walks away, an unexpected flood of misery flows through me. I feel a longing for Nadine, and a sense of regret over our last meeting. The whole situation feels empty and lonely. No matter how much I don't want to feel this way, the negative force envelopes my thoughts, and brings my spirits spiraling downward. After filling the tank, I pull the car around and park and, while Tom is in the convenience store vice-shopping, I dash out of the car to a nearby phone booth and drop coins in. I have her phone number burned on my memory. It rings. I wait. What will I say? I don't care. I'm thinking, "Don't do this." Suddenly and without reason, I feel so alone without her. It's so unnatural. To my surprise, she answers.

"Hi, you still at work?" she asks, without malice in her tone.

"No, no…I'm at a pay phone."

"What's up? I'm on my way out."

"Where are you going?" I ask, regretting the question as it leaves my lips.

"Going out to dinner with Dennis."

The words spill out of me. "I miss you, Nadine. I mean…I can't stop thinking about us. It doesn't feel right now. It's still like my whole world has changed without you in it. I keep thinking about just last year, and the time we were together every day. You were such a big part of my life; I think I'm going to cry again."

Silence.

I continue, "God, this is so hard. Five years, Nadine. It's hard. I miss you. I miss my friend."

I can't believe I just said that to her. It's true, this moment, but I don't want her to hear it. I regret saying it, regret showing emotion, hate myself for feeling less than tough. What the fuck is the matter with me?

She's still silent.

My senses start returning. I realize I'm on the phone with a stranger now. The love Nadine and I shared was a good thing, and it will always be there — locked in time. That was our time. But this is a new time. It's Tom's love that surrounds me now. What am I worried about? He's everything I ever wanted. No reason to be afraid. This is my destiny.

"Tom is very good looking," she finally says, gently and honestly.

"I'm sorry about everything. I want to thank you for the time we shared, Nadine. I'll never forget you." I can hear her breathe, I can envision her face.

She says softly, "I'm sorry about what I said and how it's been."

"Me too, me too. I'll be okay. I'm sorry I called."

"Listen, don't be. You got to be strong and go on now."

"Nadine?"

"Yes?"

"You were right. Love is fucking intense. I can't believe you went through all the trouble to get me and you won my heart. You did it. You're a special woman. Good luck with Dennis. He's a lucky dude."

Her voice cracks as she says, "Well, I have to get going, you know."

"I know. You take care. We'll talk soon." I hang up and sit on the curb. It strikes me that she didn't mention the ID card once. I kick a pebble with my shoe and stretch my legs out. I can feel reality coming back when Tom pulls up in the car. He gets out as I rise to my feet.

"What are you doing?" he asks.

"I'm okay," I say.

"Come on, let's go get something to eat, Champ," he says, with eyes so bright, and I see this moment is one to embrace. I get up and dust my pants off. When I get in the car, he reaches for my hand and brings it up to his soft lips. Everything is as it should be.

Sunday, December 4, 1988

"There's one right around the corner, in Washington Township," Tom says, referring to a roller-skating rink. We drive over and it's literally right around the corner, off Delsea Drive. On the way over, Tom boasts of being able to skate backwards, but unfortunately, he isn't able to deliver on that when we start. I never mastered skating backwards either. I loathe the fact that I couldn't conquer that feat, especially thinking back to my teen years with this girl Stephanie I used to date. There were these guys who could dash around the roller rink backwards or frontwards and do all sorts of stunts. I felt so unimpressive in their company, especially since Steph had dated a few of them.

A date roller-skating with Tom turns out to be a wonderful idea. We have a ton of fun racing around the rink like two boys. As in most roller-skating rinks, there's a DJ playing great music, along with strobe lights. When the lights dim and a slow song comes on, Tom is gutsy enough to hold my hand while we skate. A little girl skating by herself suddenly comes up behind us, separating our hands, and holds on to each of us. She continues to skate with us until the slow song is over. We have a great time and stay until closing at 10:00 p.m.

As we approach the Camaro, I notice something is wrong, and start jogging toward it.

"It's been broken into!" Tom yells. Apparently, one or more losers tried to steal it. The driver's side window has been broken and there's dirt and mud all over the seats. The plastic encasing the steering wheel column is busted and all over the floor. I'm devastated. Looking at the sheer mess, my heart sinks. We stand for a moment, motionless, frozen, trying to assess the situation and the damages. Tom scopes the parking lot, now filling with all the people from the closing rink.

"I'm going to call the police. Stay here with the car," I say, shaking from a feeling of sadness and sudden depression. I feel violated. I can't believe someone would do this. I can't believe someone could purposely destroy something so beautiful in an attempt to steal it. Anger keeps tears from filling my eyes. I get a grip on my rage, knowing there's no one and nothing to strike out against, and knowing it will be repaired by insurance.

"Are you okay?" Tom asks.

"I…" I can tell he wants to embrace me. A crowd forms and then dissolves quickly, as people hurry to get on with their own lives. The little boy in me is in need of the hug, but I find my staunch reserve and finish, "I have a Triple-A card. I'll have them tow it to the dealership."

Tom says, "Go call Triple-A and the cops, and I'll wait with the car."

"What police department do I call? What township or town are we in?"

"Washington Township," Tom says. As I turn, I catch a couple of comments from the people still gawking about how bad the car looks. I get to the pay phone and search my pocket for some coinage. I shouldn't have to use a pay phone for this call. I walk up to the cashier and ask if I could use their phone to call the police, explaining what happened in their parking lot. They're very sympathetic and helpful, allowing me to use the phone in the office.

After what seems like an hour, one cop arrives and writes up a five-minute report. He doesn't smile or offer any sentiments of remorse over my obvious loss. He couldn't give a shit. He asks to look at my key to the car, and upon inspecting it, says, "They couldn't steal it because of the anti-theft system. It's built into the chip in your ignition key," pointing out the chip in the key to us.

"You really don't need to worry about it being stolen," he continues, "other than if they load it up on a flatbed and haul it away. Besides, the whole steering column has been broken. They'll leave it alone tonight, if you want to get it towed in the morning. Besides, the dealership is closed. How are you going to tow it there?" His smug attitude irritates me.

"I'm worried they'll vandalize it if we leave it here," I say.

"It'll be fine. There's not much more that can be done to it," he says.

Despite his advice, I have Triple-A tow it to the dealership.

I've heard of car thieves and car theft, but it was something that happened to other people. Experiencing it personally allows me to suffer the rage and feeling of disappointment that victims of this crime endure. I can hear Mom now: *What kind of person has their car broken into? An irresponsible person.* My parents are of the belief that bad things happen to bad people. They always say if I cared more, or if I paid more attention, bad things wouldn't happen to me. They're very much against any form of risk-taking. Buying the flashy car was asking for trouble.

Somehow, risk-taking is woven into who I am.

The cop hands us his card, telling us we can pick up the report in a "few days," and takes off.

Tom can see that I'm visibly distraught. He comes up to me and places his arm around me. "Come on, lover, let's walk home." Part of me welcomes the fresh air and exercise the walk will provide. We get to spend time together talking, and this is bliss. A few raindrops fall as we start walking, but they soon stop. Tom walks beside me, holding my hand. His hand is soft and warm. It feels good to hold. Holding

Tom's hand is a great way to send an "up yours" card to the world.

I ask, "How long will it take us to reach home? How many miles is it?"

"About an hour or so. Listen, I know you're feeling down right now, but think about us. We got a great thing going. Do you know how much I love you? Doesn't matter about the car. It'll get fixed. We'll be okay."

He looks over at me. I shoot him a smile. He continues, "Tom, you're proof to me that there are still wholesome people left in the world. People who can love without expectations. It's hard to find that in any lifestyle."

I like what he's saying, but I *do* have expectations. I'm getting something from Tom that I want: his love and affection, his looks, his charm, his sex appeal. Everything is a trade-off. Everyone expects something.

I remain quiet and let him continue. "Night after night, I keep thinking you won't be there when I wake up in the morning. But to my daily surprise and delight, you're always there, by my side. I made up my mind that there's only one man in the world for me, and that's you. I haven't seen better days than the time I've been with you, my love. I want to live my life with and for only you, Tom."

I bask in his words as if they are golden rays of sunlight — warming, relaxing and distracting my troubled soul. Again, he knows just what to say when I need it most. I ponder my life with him. It is truly better than any experience I've had with anyone. Being with Tom has taught me one thing: God has a plan for us, and it's definitely worth living to see how it unfolds — to see the reality that around any corner, you can find something amazing. Just when you think you're at the lowest possible point in life, something comes along that's enough to make you stand up and go on. God has given us free will in life, but also I believe He has provided a path full of surprises, twists and turns.

On the final road home, a cop car pulls up next to us. "Where you guys headed?" the cute cop asks. I tell him what happened and that we only have about another 15 minutes of walking left to Society Hill. Tom, anxious for a chance to get in the attractive cop's SUV, asks, "Society Hill isn't too far for you, is it?"

"Hop in," the officer says, offering a great smile accented by a sexy moustache.

"Sure!" I follow Tom, ascending the step up into the back of the SUV. We peer at each other, and I wonder if Tom is thinking what I am: that this could be a scene from the start of a gay porno. If only. It has to be past midnight now, and the road is very, very dark. The cop redeems my faith in public servants. He's a hottie, in his late 20s. Tom makes small talk with him in the two-minute drive to our apartment complex. We thank the officer and walk into our apartment, a bit sweaty but a lot tired.

Tom and I jump in the shower together and immediately start having sex. Tom is more playful than usual, and I can't help but wonder if this sudden showing of freak in him is due to the recent meeting with the handsome cop. Tom's eyes are closed as we share an intimate moment, entwining our bodies into a satisfying love-making groove. What makes our sessions enchanting is the give-and-take aspect. Tom is an intensely generous lover, and we both enjoy the excitement of foreplay. We're both attentive and sensitive to each other's likes and needs. We take time when sharing ourselves physically. It's amazing how every time we make love, we make sure we both reach the best orgasm possible. Everyone gets off on something different, and getting caught up in his sexual fantasies — as well as being brave enough to open up and share my own personal and intimate fantasies — allows for an incredibly fulfilling experience every time. Tom and I are comfortable role-playing, and always catch the flow of what the other is looking for in the fantasy.

In today's fantasy role play, Tom invents a scenario where he's my submissive high school soccer player student, and I assume the role of his aggressive gym coach. It's rare that we begin a session deciding what role we'll act out. We just start making love, and the words come out as we assume the positions desired. During the whole event, we're constantly saying how much we love each other. The lovemaking is always extreme, and I've reached heights where the pinnacle moments have been so heartfelt that I've ended with tears of sheer joy running down my face in response to an explosion of pleasure, passion and true affection.

Monday, December 5 to Friday, December 9, 1988

The week sucks. We begin the routine of having Tom cart me in to work in the morning and pick me up at night. Despite the struggle to survive on the new tight schedule, Tom is very supportive about the whole thing, and it's good to have someone strong in my corner. I often think about the fact that he lost both of his parents at a very young age, and wonder if it enables him to harbor more pain within.

During the week, I receive my car payment book in the mail, and final confirmation of my transfer to the new Woodbury branch next week. The new office is slated to open December 15. Tom begins complaining often about Crown Rentals. He doesn't care for the working conditions and the type of work they have to do.

It's Friday afternoon. I'm sitting in the drive-up where I've been working for the past few weeks in my new capacity of night supervisor. Janet walks up and tells me Tom is holding for me and asks, "Why don't you guys come on out to the Concord with us tonight? It's been a long time since you've darkened their door."

"Sure, Janet, I'll ask him." I pick up the phone, "Hey, Sunshine!" I exclaim, pleased to hear from my heartthrob.

"Check this out," he says. "I get into work and Cornelius is out sick. It's just Adam and me."

"How did you guys get in? Does Adam have keys to the store?"

"Oh, Cornelius was there when we got in, but went home sick. At one point, I'm sitting at his desk for a second, looking for a report. I notice this memo to Carver in DP, and it's an outline of a plan I laid out to Cornelius about the direct withdrawal feature."

"The one you and I were talking about a couple weeks ago?"

"Yes. Remember the checks you mentioned that gyms put through people's accounts in payment of membership dues?"

"Yep."

"I called Carver and asked him if Cornelius mentioned that it was my idea, since I didn't see that I was mentioned anywhere in the memo. Carver said Cornelius told him it was his idea. Never mentioned me."

"Shit. Are you going to mention it to Cornelius?"

"No. It just gets me. You give everything you got, and this is what you get."

I'm disappointed but not surprised. I say, "That really sucks. What an asshole. Hey, welcome to corporate America. It's a cutthroat business out there. You should confront Cornelius with it, though. He needs to know you know."

"Hell with it. Just going to get the fuck out of here, that's all. I'm sick of this shit."

"Tom, you need to find another job first, I would say."

"Yeah, I've been looking around."

"Listen, Janet wants to know if we wanna go to the Concord tonight with everyone. It's been a while since I went there."

"Sounds cool."

Spending time with Tom and my co-workers at the local watering hole is a festive diversion. We have a couple of drinks while taking in the show — there's a local "long-hair" rock band performing. I get to introduce Tom to Linda and a few of the other employees, to put faces with a number of the names I talk about. The feeling of being in love, of knowing he's all mine and I'm all his in the ultra-straight environment of a rocker bar, is delightful. It feels egotistical to know they all know I'm having sex with this hot guy.

The fun stops when we get home. There are a dozen new bills waiting in the mailbox. I sit on the couch and begin opening each one, while Tom makes popcorn. I feel annoyed, discovering Tom has been charging a great deal of things on my credit cards. "Tom, what's up with all these charges?" I ask, handing him some of the bills. He takes the statements and scans them quickly. Then I ask, "What ever happened with the insurance money you were supposed to get for your car?"

He passes the pile of bills back to me with, "We'll do it," and that's that. End of discussion. *Was it a discussion?*

It's quite out of character for me, but I put them back in their envelopes and throw them on the table and out of my mind. Was his car really stolen? Was there a car at all? I'll probably never know. *Why is he withholding something from me? Why am I allowing this to go on? Get the credit cards out of his wallet and stop this*, I think. I try to find some rational thoughts to counter my desire to leave the cards with him. Finding none, I change my thoughts completely.

Saturday, December 10, 1988

I wake, squinting, with the sun-rays peering through the blinds. Tom is awake, his lips trace a slight smile as he lights another cigarette, obviously comfortable or self-satisfied, or both. The urge to spark up and join him comes and goes. I take a puff on his cigarette and hand it back to him, thinking on how I need to kick this habit.

"Your parents are coming today for a visit," he reminds me. I had almost forgotten we'd invited them to dinner today. He leans in and kisses me. His soft lips brush mine, adding fuel to my already-raging morning erection. In a way, I perceive Mom and Dad as somewhat supportive of me in my decision to move in with Tom. I know it's that they think I'm dodging memories of Nadine, and I just need to get out and see some of the world beyond Wrightstown. I'm clear on the fact there would be no support if they had any notion I was romantically involved with Tom.

After feasting on his succulent rump and a sufficient time fucking, we spend the rest of the day cleaning up, preparing for their visit. Tom cooks. He's excited about playing host, taking care of everything from preparing a beautiful buffet spread to calling to give them directions.

Mom, Dad and Danny arrive and come into the apartment arguing with each other about the directions. "Did you have trouble finding it?" Tom asks.

"Dad missed the turn and we went straight after the little bridge," Danny says.

Football finds its way onto our TV at Dad's request. Mom takes the grand tour of our home more seriously than Dad and Danny do. True to form, she opens a drawer here and there to inspect and be nosy. I don't mind. She's been the only member of our family to show any real interest in me after I passed childhood. She's been an emotional counterweight through a lot of the bumps and bruises I've endured. I wish we could be closer.

Although the discussion over the attempted theft of the Camaro monopolizes the first hour of the visit, the remaining two hours are pretty fun. We have a little help yourself bar area in the kitchen set up for cocktails. The buffet idea is great, and they remark on how nice the apartment is, how tasty the food is, and how clean everything is. Mom and Tom go out for a cigarette, returning with laughs and smiles. It's a great visit.

After they leave, we get ready and go out in search of some more fun. Tom usually doesn't like partying in Philadelphia, but we venture into the city to a gay club called Key West for a couple of beers and then head home with a nice buzz. Tom and I lie naked in bed, covered in sweat as we make love. I roll him over and exasperatedly fall on his back and breathe hard in his ear. He wipes the sweat from his face in the pillow, and the sweet scent of our musk fills the air. We whisper passionate secrets to each other, complimenting each other's attributes and bonding ourselves physically and emotionally.

Over the weekend, we find out the Camaro will take more than a few weeks to repair so I break down and rent a car.

Monday, December 12, 1988: 6:00 p.m.

I'm attending a dinner meeting at Charlie Brown's in Woodbury for the bank, in order to meet the other branch staff and discuss the opening of the new branch. This is a great steak joint, so I sit and feast on a juicy ribeye, and suck down two Bloody Marys with extra horseradish, listening to various speeches. Among those present are my new branch manager, Letitia, and her boss Steve, the Regional Manager. The new branch will be a regional office of the bank. First Commercial spares no expense in establishing new offices. The steak dinner is fabulous, and it's a nice way to get to know some of the staff in an informal atmosphere prior to working together. After dinner, we map out projects and discuss who's doing what prior to opening. Steve is going over the same ground rules for de novo offices that I experienced with the opening of the Mt. Holly branch, and repeats all the corporate bullshit about how important this new office is for the company.

Even though there are only 15 branches, none of us really knows each other, since the bank is growing so fast. I meet this married 22-year-old woman called Stephanie who will be a Personal Banker, and she keeps flirting with me. I'm going over as a leader of Personal Bankers group — the same position as Janet's.

A waiter comes out and interrupts Steve's speech. "Is there a Tom Marino here?" My heart jumps as I stand. "Phone call," he says. "Follow me." I follow him, excusing myself from the meeting.

"Hello?"

"Hey, Sport!" It's Tom.

"What's shakin'?" I ask.

"What time is your shin-dig over?"

I check my watch; it's just 7:55, and we're supposed to go to 8:30. "8:30. Why?"

"I'm in love with you. What do you expect? I miss you. Can I convince you to blow off the rest of that happy horseshit and come home? We can go out."

"I can be home in 15 minutes," I say, glad to ditch the boring meeting. I go fetch my coat and motion to one of the people in the meeting to come to me. I whisper that I need to get home for an emergency and to please tell them I'm sorry, I have to dash.

10:00 p.m.

Gatsby's is packed when we arrive. I love walking in holding Tom's hand. Nick is working the door, taking cover charges. He acts chipper when he sees us. Next to him sits an almost empty glass of soda, with a straw in it for effect; Nick makes it well known to everyone that he's a recovering alcoholic. In an effort to convey friendship, I wink at Nick when our eyes meet. Just the sight of Nick makes Tom upset. He says, "I hate the fact that you slept with him." We walk to the main bar and I order a Manhattan.

"I'm going to buy a drink for your friend Nick. Add a little rum in his Coke!"

"Don't do that, you know he's…" I begin.

"I know," he says, signaling a tall drag-queen barback over. She's apparently another acquaintance of Tom's; they exchange greetings, and Tom whispers an order to the Tina Turner lookalike, pointing out Nick. I watch the dizzy drag-queen stroll though the busy bar with the drinks on a tray. She stops just short of Nick and looks over at Tom. Then hands Nick the new drink, taking his empty glass. All those AA meetings, all that hard work to stop drinking…down the drain. Tom finds it amusing.

"You're wicked!" I say, and jump up and walk over to get the drink. I approach Nick and take a sip from the drink. It's harmless.

Nick attempts small talk: "How are things?"

"Good, Chief, and with you?"

"Good, thanks." I regret how I left things with him.

"Later," I say and offer a handshake.

I return to Tom, who maintains eye contact with the dance floor. Finally, he says, "He's too easy."

The combination of the very smoky atmosphere and the Manhattans soon bring a feeling of euphoria. I feel high, relaxed, numb and off the planet. Walking around the bar wearing a gray tank top, I feel loved and like I belong here. I notice dudes looking at me, at my body, in my eyes. Some whistle, some make comments, and it feels good. Some dude walking around collecting money for an AIDS cause sticks a small rainbow flag on my chest when I hand him a buck.

I have a terrible habit of getting drunk off my ass whenever we go out. With my buzz going strong, I continue to down more liquor. Tom goes off to chat with some effeminate queen he knows, while another friend of his, Wayne, comes up and starts chatting and flirting away. Suddenly realizing how boring he is, and not caring that he's in the middle of a sentence, I announce, "I have to take a piss." I get up and prance through the crowd toward the bathroom. As I maneuver through the crowd, I bask in the warmth of even more eye contact, winks, and glances. I soak up the attention my crotch receives as it competes for stares with my face. I flash a smile here and there and finally find the door to the potty room. I catch my reflection in the mirror, and it's hard to describe the admiration I feel, wishing I could capture this look forever: bottle my fresh, dashing looks and sell it to everyone.

Being buzzed lowers my already nonexistent inhibitions as I piss in the middle stall, side by side with other fellas, knowing I can run with the big boys. A cutie stands pissing in the stall to my left. His Prince Charming face is striking, intensified by his healthy, thick, sexy hair that hangs down right below his ears. I'm attracted to the point of my mouth watering for a taste of him. I force myself to keep my stare focused straight ahead, baring as much butch as possible. Though blurred peripheral vision, I catch his head turning to sneak a peek at my dick. In less than a second, he returns his view forward and I sneak a peek at him. We look at each other and smile. Then we shake our cocks as we finish our business.

As we wash our hands, he asks, "Want to go in the stall?"

"Yes, very much." I can't lie, but continue, "But I'm hooked up."

"So?" he asks, pulling a joint from his shirt pocket and lighting it. He takes a drag and offers it to me. I move the joint to my lips and then grab his waist and push him into the stall. Just as we close the door to the stall, I hear what sounds like a busload of queens walk in. As we drop our drawers, I get hold of myself and pull my pants back up. This cute dude with his prime bubble butt exposed, begging for a fucking, turns, stunned, and starts bitching. I stick my tongue in his mouth and we suck face for a second or two, then I shove the joint back in his mouth and exit the stall, still zipping up. Opportunity and temptation is everywhere in this playground, but I have to admit — I have everything I want in Tom.

I find Tom sitting at the bar, and seeing no available seats as I approach, he jumps up and offers his. "I'm okay, I want to stand," I say.

Tom is engaged in a conversation with the bartender about something or other. I find a pair of eyes looking at me from across the bar. It's a rugged-looking, thirty-something fellow wearing a flannel shirt. His five o'clock shadow is extremely attractive, and it accentuates his already-striking thick, black, masculine goatee. He smiles when he catches my eye, revealing a beautiful smile with gleaming white teeth. His shirt is open enough for me to spy a well-built hairy chest. Mr. Flannel and I steal random peeks at each other, flirting and smiling. It isn't long before Tom catches onto the action and promptly asks, "Are you enjoying yourself?"

"It's, uh, fun." I apologize, embarrassed and ashamed of myself.

"It's not fun for them if they can't take you home." I assume he's right. I just can't help it — it's so damn enjoyable.

Wednesday, December 14, 1988
Kings Grant, Marlton, 7 p.m.

Sue is having a mid-week gathering at her condo for Matt and me — we're both leaving for the new Woodbury office — and for Tammy, who has decided to resign to be a stay-at-home Mom. She's pregnant, and married to a young, successful, rich Haddonfield attorney. Tom has to work until 9:30 tonight, so I hit the party solo and it isn't long until I'm buzzed. Sue's boyfriend Tommy is a bartender, so he's able to mix up Bloody Marys with a blend of horseradish that's perfectly tailored to my liking. Janet's also lit, and is attacking the cheese fondue. I'm really going to miss this gang.

When I get home it's just after ten, and Tom is curled up on the sofa watching TV. He's so cute. After taking a shower and brushing my teeth, I change into my shorts and cuddle up with him on the sofa. We chat a little about the day, then take turns massaging each other gently and kissing before finding our way to bed.

Saturday, December 17, 1988, 6:40 a.m.

The new branch is opening on a cold, rainy and dismal morning. We've been commanded to arrive at this ungodly hour, and upon entering the branch, I find workers still doing finishing touches.

I turn from fixing my tie in the restroom mirror and feel a swagger in my stride as I walk into the break room. I bought a new suit for the grand opening, and I find it difficult to be modest when my ego is so swollen with pride over how I look. The three-button gray suit is flattering, and I had the sense to pair it with a new red shirt and a slant black-and-white striped tie. The way the suit form-fits to my body, coupled with the way my hair is behaving, has me feeling confident and in control.

Then I'm asked to move not only my car, but the cars of some of the bank's executives, to a vacant lot across the street to make room for customer parking. Matt is also drafted into valet service. In an environment where playing favorites and ass-kissing are protocol, we comply without question.

After moving the cars, I'm soaked! I make my way to the bathroom to take inventory of my state. My freshly-pressed pants are damp up to the knees from jumping through puddles. My hair is completely wet. I walk out and Matt almost mows me down racing into the bathroom after me, looking as bad as I do.

A tall, very slender guy with receding blonde hair is in the kitchen making coffee. I noticed him before at the dinner meeting, and he's obviously gay, based on his extreme effeminate nature. Now I take a closer look, and decide to introduce myself. As I approach him, he turns quickly and smiles in a whimsical way, his introduction and demeanor overly exaggerated. "Hi, I'm Robert, but you can call me Bobby," he squeals quickly, extending his hand. I shake his limp hand, taking note of the way he carries himself. His open palm rests on his hip as he pours water into the coffee machine. His quick movements clash with his stature. He has to be six-three, and if he weighs 150 pounds, I'd be shocked. His waist is so tiny.

"I'm Tom," I say. He opens the closet, pulls his coat out and shoves two coffee packets into one of the pockets, saying, "My fee. Fucking assholes. Who the hell am I, the maid? First I gotta hang up everyone's coat, now I gotta schlep the coffee out."

I like him immediately. "Tell me about it," I say, grabbing another coffeepot to fill with water. "I had to park their goddamn cars."

"Oh... I thought you walked here," he says, making fun of my soaked state. We share a laugh. "You look familiar. Where do you hang out?" he asks.

"Gatsby's," I say, revealing both the truth and my sexuality in one word. Somehow it doesn't feel as scary telling Bobby.

He smiles widely, saying, "Girlfriend! I can tell this is going to be a lot of fun. I used to work at the Harbor Plaza office. That's where I trained, and Grace is from there, too. She's going to be the Assistant Head Teller here. I think you said you came from the Mt. Holly office at the dinner, right?" he asks.

"Yes, I've been with the bank for almost three years now." We walk back into the lobby with trays of coffee, cream, sugar, cups, stirs and napkins. Our new manager, Letitia, immediately walks up to us and snaps, "You guys need to help Ben move the MAC machine into place." The fucking ATM machine was just delivered today, on our grand opening — and now we have to help set it up. This shit should have all been done already. We walk into the ATM vestibule right outside the lobby to help heave the mammoth machine into place. Inside the small vestibule is me, Bobby, Vince — a teller from another branch — two MAC service techs and Benjamin, our Assistant Manager. Bobby launches a few complaints about the weight of the ATM: "Jeez, this weighs a ton," followed by another heave and, "Why wasn't this done before? Why do we have to do this? Look at Vince and Tom, they're getting all sweaty." Bobby is expressing what I'm thinking.

Ben says, "Yo, Bob, man, why don't you get the hell outta here, man." With that, Bobby swoops his arms up, then brushes his hands off and cries effeminately, "Fine!" We're all leaning together over the machine as in a football huddle, and Ben shakes his head while he watches Bobby exit. He says, "That guy's a fucking fag. What a pansy!" Years of built-up rage from hearing Dad call me that word fills me, and I begin to sweat even more profusely. I've come to enjoy banking as a place where I don't have to be subject to such shit. A response is required. I think about the years of torment in high school, and how I vowed I wouldn't stand for it in my work life. This is the real world, and I find refuge from most bigotry in the professional workplace setting.

In a split second I think of how I would want Bobby to respond if the comments were made about me in my absence. I think about how I want Ben to pay for his feelings, his comments, his views.

I think about what I want to say and do, then I think about what a retaliatory response could do to my career. *Will they think I'm gay if I respond to defend him? Do I want them to know or suspect I'm gay? Do I want them to know my sexuality? Do I want to risk my career? Do I want Ben to hate me? Do I want Ben to feel comfortable talking in front of me, so I can later share his rude comments with Bobby? Will these other dudes back me up if I go to Human Resources with this?*

I have the words; I have words I'd like to say, words I need to say, words that *must* be said. My split second of thinking drags out as the other guys burst out laughing and make noises of agreement like, "Oh yeah, check out how he walks…"

I don't think I've ever been more proud of being gay than right now. As I look at Bobby walk in his way across the lobby, like a drag queen out of dress, I smile and I withhold my comment. I close my eyes and look to Mary for advice: *Mary, dear Mary, guide me now. Give me strength to do the right thing.*

While the desire to tell them all to fuck off is burning on my tongue, somehow I feel a sense of calming. I get the notion that I will get my turn. I try to focus on the task at hand, but the thought of gays being bashed verbally and physically for years starts burning in me again.

"Tom's side is moving — the rest of you guys are fags," Ben says. "Tom, where do you work out, Bud?"

Me, visibly better built than any of them. Me, the champion. Here it is; here is my moment, delivered with a red bow on it from above. I say, "As a fag myself, I prefer working out at the gym on McGuire Air Force Base — there's a lot of hot military guys there." With that comment, I drop my side, and the whole machine rips out of their combined grip. I turn and walk out, saying, "Fuck you guys," pushing Ben out of the way. The struggle inside of me, raging like civil war, finally ends. I don't need to beat myself up anymore.

I walk up to Bobby, who is busy arranging flowers in a vase, and say, "Ben is such a jackass."

Bobby just smiles, keeping his eyes on the flowers, and says, "Don't worry about him, Doll."

By the time we open at 10:00, we're all ready to drop from exhaustion. I'm covered in sweat. We are all standing at our desks for some photos and as Letitia walks by me, she says, "Look at your shirt — it's all wrinkled. Didn't you iron it before you came to work?"

"I was moving cars in the rain, making coffee, moving the ATM, and sitting in the vault getting everything set up."

She lets out a very deep breath of exasperation and shakes her head. "You make it sound so dramatic."

I can tell it's going to be tons of fun working for this bitch. I miss Sue.

2:30 p.m.

When I get home, I find my love sitting on the sofa watching TV. I throw my keys on the table and loosen my tie as I position myself next to him, reaching for his hand. "Hey honey," I say, gently brushing his forehead with my hand.

He mutes the volume on the TV and lets me know that his employer, Crown Rentals, is going out of business. Before I can react, he puts his arm around my shoulder and says, "No worries. I worked on a couple collection jobs with this guy Dean who works in Crown's Philadelphia store. He knows the manager of R2O's Woodbury office, and he hooked me up with an interview today. I'm not sure when Crown is closing, but I got an offer to start at R2O in two weeks. Same pay."

"Wow! That's so excellent that you're right on top of things. Congratulations!"

He says, "I heard R2O is owned by a gay couple. Check this out…" Tom produces an R2O rental application from a folder on the table and hands it to me.

"Look at the section asking for the co-renter's relationship to the primary renter." The choices are spouse, fiancée, and roommate. "They put the roommate option in there for gay people. It's a gay-owned company!" I enjoy Tom's hope, apparent enthusiasm, and delight in reaching for any validation and recognition of gay relationships.

I lean in and kiss his soft cheek.

He lights a cigarette and slides back on the sofa with the cig in his mouth. His eyes close. He takes a long draw on the cigarette and opens his eyes. Our eyes meet.

"And how was your first day in the Woodbury branch? How was the grand opening?"

"Pretty groovy. I like it," I answer. "I met this guy called Bobby. He's a tall, thin queen, but he's funny as shit and I think we'll be able to start a friendship."

"Do I have anything to worry about?" Tom asks.

I like his jealousy, but he has nothing to worry about. I reassure him, "Not our type."

I share my interactions with Ben and Letitia. He listens intently, and as I finish he shakes his head, saying, "There's like a continuous stream of anti-gay remarks. All this bullshit only breeds hatred." He doesn't comment on how I responded. Rather than ask him, I slightly withdraw my confidence and consider whether I should have just decked Ben right then and there. Was my response too weak?

We stop by the liquor store and pick up a couple bottles of wine. When we get home, Tom makes us a little snack of cheese and crackers while I open the wine. We take it all to our candlelit bedroom.

The anticipation of making love with Tom is indescribable joy. Before you know it, we're down to our tight white jockey shorts, wrestling around in the sheets, kissing each other, tasting and biting. My mouth waters with sexual lust as I feel a strong desire to bond with him. Our tongues connect; soon we're facing each other, and words are unnecessary. I feel him wanting me. The heat of twenty candles further ignites our passions, and I lick him from his forehead to his toes, and all the way back the other side. I return to his toes and run my tongue around them, sucking them, and savor watching him squirm with chills from the same exquisite and intense pleasure as when I stab his neck with my darting tongue and bite his ears. He returns the favor by demonstrating an acute comprehension of the things that stimulate me.

Sunday, December 18, 1988

Mitch has me booked up with five jobs today. Oddly, there weren't any booked yesterday or Friday night. It's not like I don't need the money now, what with the new cars and the apartment. How quickly the money from dancing has become sustaining, instead of "extra".

Tom accompanies me on the first job, for a group of teenagers at a straight dance club at the bottom of a large hotel in central New Jersey. Inside, it's a massive dark room with a high ceiling and dozens of tables mobbed with 18-24 year olds. The DJ is blasting out a tune so loud that people right next to each other are shouting their conversations. It's pure pandemonium, way uncomfortable. We walk through the tight crowds, me lugging the boom box along. The customer requested me to dress in street clothes, so I'm inconspicuous. Mitch couldn't give me an idea as to where my group would be. I'm sure he had no idea this place would be so discombobulated. We weave our way up to the nearest bar and attract the attention of a bartender.

"I'm here to strip for someone." She shrugs her shoulders, shakes her head and looks puzzled. "Male exotic dancer!" I shout. She must think I'm insane, because she shrugs her shoulders and rolls her eyes.

"I don't think she can hear you," Tom blasts in my ear. I grab one of the note papers on the bar meant for phone number exchanges, and write out a list of songs I want from the DJ.

Eventually we spot a table with a bunch of balloons around it. I make my way over to the group and one of the girls, already trashed, says, "I'm Casey, you must be the stripper dude!"

"Where am I supposed to perform?" I ask, smiling, yet irritated by my surroundings, trying not to sound like I feel.

"Follow me...I'll take you to the DJ booth!" she belts out. We walk up to the DJ, who is encased in what looks like an impenetrable glass booth. This stupid bitch slaps her hand on the glass to get his attention and walks away, back to her group. He opens the door, removes his earphones and curtly snaps, "What?"

"I'm going to strip for the girls over there. Can I give you the songs I want?"

"There's already been a stripper here tonight. I can't play everyone's shit." From one entertainer to another, his well-thought-out and professional answer calls for some diplomacy and a tactful response.

"Hey Chief, come on now, I need your help. Here's my list, my agency got this cleared by management."

He takes the list, looks it over, and says, "I gotta get back to this, man." What a ferocious asshole.

Knowing there was a guy stripping here earlier makes me feel better. He paved the way for me to do it next. With no introduction from the DJ, I think people would think I'm some nutcase taking my clothes off in public, dancing around a tall, narrow table in a crowded nightclub.

I proceed to the table and wait for my songs to begin. The girls are all over the place, talking to each other, some drunk, some not. I think Casey must have told them I was going to strip because they start chanting, "Take it off, take it off, take it off..." This is a COD order; and based on the uneasy feeling I have, I approach Casey and insist on payment up front. She hastily hands over $155 exactly, $30 of which I get to kick up to Mitch. No tip included.

I catch sight of Tom, who's standing in front of a burgundy-colored curtain covering a wall. He shoots me a thumbs-up and one of his cute trademark winks. Somehow his love envelopes me and soothes my nerves. After what seems like forever, Taylor's "Prove Your Love" comes on. I begin dancing for the group, in one of the most cramped areas I've ever performed in. Not many people other than my group pay much attention to me. In fact, it's pretty much as if I'm nonexistent. The conversations going on around me, combined with the terrible lighting, make my performance feel like a sideshow attraction at a circus. It's difficult to escape to my special place where I can deliver the performance I know is my best. After "Prove Your Love," it's "Come Into My Life" by Joyce Sims — a decent song that helps me get more into what I'm doing. My mindset is focused on Tom, and I work thoughts of us in bed together into my mid-song routine. There's no enjoyment in this gig for many reasons, and I can't catch the familiar high that typically comes with dancing. As the second song concludes, I'm feeling good that it's more than half way done. Just when I think I'm going to make it to the home stretch painlessly, I feel myself panic as the DJ plays a song that I didn't request.

"Wild Wild West" by the Escape Club is a cool song, but it's not a tune I'm able to perform to. Maybe I can pretend I'm wearing a cowboy hat and chaps to get me into this.

Doesn't work. I smile and meander into a dance routine that I create as I go along. It's incredible how red my face must be. Here I am, in a g-string, trying to dance to "Wild Wild West" and feel myself totally blowing it. I know I look ridiculous, because I feel ridiculous! I pray for the song to end while I dance, gritting my teeth and showing a forced smile. As I muddle through nonsensical moves, trying to get in sync with the beat, I realize it's useless. My erotic dancing, the way I was taught and what I know, is all about sensuality. This performance is so fake, so fucked up.

I glance over at Tom during my pathetic routine, and know he sees through my duplicity. I feel robbed of the euphoric state of amnesia that comes with most gigs; this is painfully sobering. After the song finishes, we bolt for the door, with me still pulling on my clothes as we walk. Tom roars, "Wild, Wild West!" through wild laughter as we walk outside, and I'm laughing right with him as we get in the car.

I pull my shirt and pants off as I sit in the passenger seat, preparing to change into my next costume. As our laughter subsides, he smiles brightly and moves in for a kiss. I close my eyes and suck in a quick breath of air in anxious anticipation of how good his lips and mouth are going to taste. As we kiss, his hand finds its way inside my bikini briefs and through my g-string. I want him to always desire and need me like this. I want him to see me in his every dream. He slowly retracts his hand and we finish our kiss. It's a good moment.

We leave Della's in Ridley Township, and by the time we reach the last gig, I've changed from the cop outfit into the tuxedo. The name of this dump is The Centurion Club. I've never been here before.

Tom finds a parking spot in the rear of the dance club. He looks over at me, smiling, and asks, "Ready?" I smile back, nod and jump out of the car. I get a bottle of champagne out of the trunk, and Tom hands me the rose for this last job.

"Goddamn, you look really hot in that tux."

"You've seen me in this before."

"Yes, but you look really good, even after four jobs."

"Thanks," I say, aching for his kiss.

"I'm here for the Fraser party," I tell the girl checking IDs and taking cover charges at the front door. She says, "Oh yeah," with a big smile, eyeing me up and down. She motions to a male waiter walking in from the kitchen.

He approaches, and she interrupts her gum chewing to say, "Vic, can you please get that chick from the group that has the stripper coming? Thanks, Hun." She turns her stout figure back to me and smiles again, chewing gum like a cow.

When a young lady arrives, I ask, "Are you Cindy?" I ask, looking at my notes.

"Yeah, you look great!" she says, and continues, "This is for my sister Brenda, it's her birthday. The big 3-0 party tonight!" Tom and I follow her to the DJ, to whom I give my selections. The DJ here is awesome to work with. He asks me if I want a shot before going on.

"Well, fuck yeah," I say. He motions to the barmaid and in a few seconds, I'm hooked up with a Jack Daniels shot.

After my shot, he smiles and says, "Now you ready?"

"Yep," I say, nodding and smiling back, and he clears the dance floor.

I walk to the middle of the floor, waiting for them to bring the birthday girl to me. There's a huge mixed crowd encircling me, howling for the show. The DJ asks for the birthday girl and what appears, escorted by her friends, is a strikingly lovely young woman. They produce a chair for her to sit in and I begin my show. I'm rocking to the beat, then slow my moves and coast gently, envisioning Tom making love with me. I'm in my own world now; floating above our bed, watching us make love, feeling every kiss, enjoying every hug. I savor the flavor of his taste, and his smell. I slowly run my hands over my soft skin, feeling every muscle, and gaze at the playful crowd. After a third and final song they cheer and chant for a fourth song as I walk around the room, wearing only my red g-string. As I fade into reality, I realize I'm standing in a packed room with my naked butt exposed. It triggers a thrill, knowing that some of the men in the room can see it, but I'm distracted from that thought as I hear some of the men, even, chanting, "Take it all off!"

Despite how much fun I'm having and my own secret desire to keep going, I remember it's a big no-no to strip totally naked. Mitch's words ring in my head: "No matter how much you want to, don't overstay your welcome. Three songs are just enough." When the DJ plays the next song, Jellybean's "Who Found Who," featuring Elisa Fiorillo, one of my favorites, I decide to do it anyway. I've always fantasized about getting totally buck naked during one of these gigs. I look up at the DJ, who waves at me. The entire place is so into it now, clapping and chanting. The birthday girl is laughing and smiling and easy to dance for. I'm gutsy enough to take the g-string down to my knees while covering my penis with my hand. I gyrate and rock, while the ladies scream. I walk around and let the g-string drop to my ankles. I want to let my cock flop out, but I quickly bend and bring the g-string back up, never revealing it.

When I collect the payment at the end, I'm certain the last song is what lands me a $50 tip, plus a cool $39 more out of my g-string from the crowd. Two bills are tens — a huge compliment.

Later — home in bed

With a dozen candles lighting and warming our room, we embrace and kiss. I study his beautiful and flawless face and body. His features are so perfect and well-defined that it's almost surreal.

Tom says, "I have an insatiable appetite for you." I taste his face, and when his mouth relaxes and opens from my touch, his beautiful smile and white teeth beckon my tongue for exploration. I go in for another kiss, then we take turns lowering ourselves to spend time below. On one of his moves back up to my face from below, he stops at my stomach to kiss it and rub his face in it, saying, "Jeez, Tom it's so tight and sexy, I love it." It's extraordinary to be admired by the one you love. Better still, it's exquisite hearing his compliments and praise for my body, especially after all those hours in the gym.

Moving to deeper intensity, we find ourselves locked in another tight embrace, and our fusion causes a mutual explosion. He goes first, then I remove the condom and allow my own release on his stomach, with my sole focus on adoration.

Christmas 1988

I call Mom and ask if it would be cool if Tom joins us for the holidays. Christmas at my parent's house is a tradition, and since Tom's parents are gone and his relationship with his sister is non-existent, he's excited to be a part of Christmastime at my parents'. I can't imagine spending the holiday without him. Mom agrees, either clueless or in denial about who Tom really is in my life.

During the week, Tom gets our apartment decked out for Christmas. He's been raving about how much he loves the beauty of this season. At one point, while he's decorating our Christmas tree, I notice he pauses while placing one ornament and says, "I miss my Mom." I approach cautiously so as not to make him more upset, but eager to soothe any pain. I hold him from behind and wrap my arms around his waist while complimenting his work on the tree. We stand in silence for a moment as he places the ornament, then reaches for my arms and pulls them closer to him. I whisper sentiments of love and assurance that I'm his family now.

I have some time during the week to shop with and for Tom. Shopping during the holidays is always fun, but this year it seems more magical than ever. Stores are decked out more than usual, street decorations are brighter and more beautiful, and people just seem jollier. I get a lot of pleasure out of selecting his gifts. The crowds don't bother me at all this year; the fact that everywhere is so bustling and busy actually accentuates the season's joy.

Tuesday, December 20, 1988

After work, since Tom has to work late today, I drive downtown and browse through the Gallery Mall in Philly, along with those on Chestnut Street, and catch the light show at Wanamaker's. When I get home, Tom tells me he took care of his gift-buying for me, but I can't imagine when he found the time to shop.

We spend a few evenings the rest of the week going out to the local malls together in search of gifts for my parents and brother.

Saturday, December 24, 1988

I have to work today, but a sweet surprise softens the blow: I find a stuffed inter-office envelope on my desk from Janet and the gang in Mt. Holly. I open the envelope and find a bunch of shit like Band-Aids, rubber bands, paperclips, pens, and aspirin packets they've pulled out of the first aid box. There are pencils, a small packet of tissues, a box of condoms in assorted colors, coupons for Taco Bell and a pack of my brand of Marlboro Reds. I have to laugh when I find a note inside signed by everyone, inscribed "WE MISS YOU!! CARE PACKAGE FOR YOUR NEW DESK!!"

Later

Tom and I arrive at my parents' place at about 5:30. Danny introduces Tom to his girlfriend Debbie Flynn, a pretty, busty blonde he met in high school. I like her, but the entire family is still getting over his decision to split with his last girl, Sue Waters, a lovely girl, both beautiful and sweet. She was in his life when Nadine cheated on me with Nick. I remember her being a friend to me then, and having another young woman's perspective on the situation gave me some comfort and insight during that extremely painful time.

Being home at Christmastime is by far one of the most pleasurable experiences and memories I have of family life. Mom and Dad are always happy and behave with kindness toward each other and us, and the air is filled with the aroma of fresh-baked cookies and treats. The house is decorated within an inch of its life; and living in New Jersey, it's always pretty cold this time of year, so the fireplace is usually roaring every night. I take account of all the little things Mom has done with such pride and love to make the holiest of holidays most enjoyable for the family. Things like the little white snowflake decorations hanging in each window in the living room. The snowflakes have little plastic fruits like pears and apples hanging inside of them. We've always had an artificial Christmas tree, and although that sounds awful, it's just one of the Marino traditions we've come to love and enjoy. Mom likes all the branches to be perfect. She loves decorating the tree with dozens of various ornaments that she's collected over the years, including some really cheesy handmade ones Danny and I made in kindergarten and Cub Scouts. Some of the ornaments are so old they're falling apart. Sharing it all with Tom is the best feeling in the world and having him with me is very comforting.

We sit on the couch in the living room while Dad joins Mom in the kitchen to pour us some Cold Duck at the cute little mini-bar they always put together this time of year. I look at Tom and smile; he flashes one back, saying, "I'm glad we're together."

We hold hands for a mere second, then release. I say, "We've spent every night together since we've met…"

"Almost," Tom says. "All except one night when you were here."

Dad returns with our drinks and says, "Did you tell Tom about Mom's pork and potato pie?"

"I haven't, actually," I answer.

Dad chimes in, "It's out of this world! With the brown gravy…mmm…delicious."

Around 7:00, we leave for Mass. Danny and Debbie ride with my parents and we follow in Tom's car to the Main Chapel on McGuire Air Force Base, about 10 minutes away. I say to Tom, "Hope it doesn't bother you, going to a Catholic Mass."

"No, I'm looking forward to it," he answers, squeezing my hand. I try to imagine what he did last year for Christmas, since he hasn't been on speaking terms with his sister for a couple years now. I try not to think about him having to spend the holiday alone. We ride in silence and I sit with my thoughts. I think about my last Christmas, and how I spent it with Nadine. This time, though, I'm immersed in thoughts about Tom. As I stare at him while he drives, I think that all I had to do back then was get in my car and drive one hour south, and I could have found him.

As we get out of the car, it begins to snow. The sky is crimson. I feel a warm and remarkable sense of pride and happiness well up inside me as we walk toward the church. Under the cover of night, I open my palm and rub his fine rear end. Visions of his smooth, well-proportioned body come to mind. As we get closer to my family, Tom risks a quick feel of my crotch. Knowing we can't keep our hands off each other only solidifies the fortress of our relationship.

"I've been coming to this church my whole life," I tell Tom, yearning to hold his hand. The base is deserted except for the crowded parking lot of the church. With Tom at my side, we enter the church where I launched a million prayers over plans, dreams, and needs I brought here with me as far back as I can recall.

After Mass, we all return to my parent's house and Tom and I help Mom prepare some of the trays with goodies on them.

Tom joins Mom for a cigarette as they take our dog Schultz out. I look out the large bay window in the dining room and observe them chatting and smiling, illuminated by the spotlight on the backyard. I walk over to the couch and engage in conversation with Danny and Debbie.

Mom creates such a beautiful little picnic for us in the living room. We have her delicious pork and potato pie, along with our traditional fondue consisting of cooked pieces of steak and chicken. With the fireplace roaring in the cozy living room crowded by the big Christmas tree, Tom and I take turns stealing glances at each other. When no one is looking, he brushes his hand over my cock and gently gives it a squeeze. We enjoy sides of olives, cocktail onions, various types of sliced pickles, ice-cold cocktail shrimp, deviled eggs, cheese squares, a cheese ball and lots of other treats while watching *It's a Wonderful Life*. I catch a peek at Tom and can tell he's happy. We get a little buzz, as Dad keeps filling our glasses with Cold Duck. After midnight, Danny returns from driving Debbie home and we're all ready for bed.

"You want to sleep in my bed and I'll take the couch?" I ask Tom.

"No, this is cool," he answers.

Mom and I make up the couch and I bid Tom, "Good night," looking at him.

He looks up at me and winks, saying, "Night, Tom."

I snuggle into my fresh, cool sheets in my now-former bedroom and listen to the wind pushing on the small windowpanes until I let go of this wonderful day, missing the warmth of his body against mine.

Christmas Morning

Dad and Danny wake me by enticing our schnauzer Schultz to jump all over me in bed. It's a fun way to get up, and I'm delighted with it because it reminds me childhood. I roll out of bed and walk upstairs with them, holding Schultz. Once upstairs, Dad tries to wake Tom with Schultz, but Schultz is hesitant about jumping on a stranger. Schultz finally jumps up on Tom, and I enjoy watching Tom take pleasure in the wholesome attention and affection.

I sit on the couch with him and ask, "What did you wear to sleep?" I lift the blanket and find he's wearing the cute Christmas shorts he previously bought us. We both had the same idea; I have mine on, too.

"Coffee, boys?" Mom asks.

"Oh, yes please," we beg.

For a moment I escape to a dream where one day, Tom and I wake up in bed together in this house with my parent's blessing. I return to reality, grateful I'm able to share my life and family with him now.

Mom comes out of the kitchen with two mugs of coffee in hand. She's wearing a holiday apron covered in fruit with a white background, which she's donned every holiday since I can remember. We position ourselves around the tree, sitting Indian style, while Mom passes around presents and Dad snaps pictures.

Tom gives my parents his gift. He takes great pleasure in what he selected: a handsome set of oak TV trays. It's the perfect gesture, because during one of our previous visits, Tom picked up on the fact that my Mom complained about not having any decent TV trays. I remembered how impressed I was when Tom bought them at the mall —impressed with his memory, and his true interest in the spirit of giving for my parents. They open the gift and are absolutely delighted. Mom and Dad are so pleased with the gift that they both get up and each open one of the four trays.

"Oh, man, how nice!" Dad says.

"You remembered how lousy our TV trays are," Mom says, getting up to pull out the old green-tinted metal trays that sit lopsided when opened. Mom and Dad both get up to give Tom a hug and kiss.

"Thank you, Tom, They're wonderful," Mom says.

I sit beaming, also wanting to get up and give him a smooch and hug, but I just wink his way. He gets the point.

I bought Tom a fiber-optic flower decoration in a clear plastic casing. It's so pretty, and I'm delighted when he says he loves it. In the past couple of weeks, Tom mentioned wanting a professional DJ sound system with a mixing board, so I bought him one. His face lights up as he opens the gift. He takes a moment to glance up at me while looking over the components of the set, then gives me a look that I translate as a mental kiss.

We enjoy the next couple of hours opening and exchanging gifts.

When we finish, Tom turns and looks at me. He says, "Now it's my turn to give you my gifts." I want to hold his hand. He leaves to go out to the trunk of the car. Mom, Danny and I rise to look outside and observe him carry a pile of wrapped boxes into the house.

"What's all that?" Danny asks, holding the door for Tom as he enters.

"These are for your brother," Tom says, gazing at me. I instantly feel my face become red, not about us being two guys, but out of pure innocence in the fact that Tom's love for me is now apparent in front of my family. For obvious reasons, I have sheltered them from this colossal reality in my life.

The first package contains an ultra-expensive Guess jean jacket and pants set that he bought back when he was up in Manhattan. I run to the bathroom and try it on and the jeans are sculpted to my hips as if they were tailor-made. The second package contains a beautiful illuminated neon clock. On one of our jaunts to the mall, Tom and I were browsing in Macy's separately, and when he found me I was gazing at this clock on the wall. Can't believe he bought it for me. Knowing we can both enjoy these gifts makes me feel better about the expense, with a notion as to how Tom must have paid for them.

A third gift from Tom is a handsome sterling silver bracelet consisting of cylinder links. Another gift is a box of nice shirts, followed by a gift set of Obsession cologne, and *another* gift is a new pair of Puma sneakers.

In anticipation of any questions from my parents, Tom interjects, "I inherited a great deal of money from my parents." As I open each gift, Tom explains and justifies why he selected it, "Tom, those will replace the nasty beat up sneaks you're currently walking around in," he says, soliciting some laughs from my family. He has a sparkling way of cementing the foundation on which he builds his lies. I don't care about the lies, and I engage in seasoning them up a bit with my own responses. Actually, I hate having to fucking lie and fabricate excuses for why he's giving me gifts. I want to tell them I'm fucking gay. Part of me wishes Tom hadn't spent the money on my credit cards to buy my gifts, and is angry at him. But I choose to think, "Fuck reality," and to pretend this is real, and allow myself to bask in this attention and in this love. It may be a big façade, but it feels and fits rather snugly right now.

Tom looks at Mom and Dad says, "Your son," then looks at Danny and says, "your brother," and continues looking at my folks, "has been so good to me. I have to say, this is the least I could do."

With that being said, my family smiles and goes about their post-Christmas present-opening routine: Danny takes off in his car to visit some friends, Mom and Dad work on dinner, and we sit back to watch TV. Later, we get up and help with dinner and setting the table. I look at the dozens of Christmas cards from tons of friends my family has made over the years.

After a couple of hours, I ask Tom to join me as I take Schultz for a walk. Once outside, I look at him and say, "I love you."

"I thought you'd be mad about all the presents and the money I spent," he says. I appreciate his concern.

"The hell with my pride," I say, thinking aloud of a time when I once allowed it to make me foolishly shun an expensive gift Nadine once bought for me. I continue, "I love you. Tonight I want to be in your arms and thank you properly. They're very thoughtful gifts."

"I'm glad. Do you really like the bracelet?"

"I do," I confirm, looking at it around my wrist.

As we turn the corner away from my parent's house, he asks, "Is it safe to hold your hand now?"

I take his hand and smile. Tom asks, "You know something?"

"What?" I ask, looking over at him, his cheeks rosy.

"I love you," he says, his words expelled with steamy breath in the cold winter air. I take in a deep breath and a wide smile covers my face. Walking hand-in-hand, even in silence, is satisfying and rewarding.

When we get back, it's time to eat. We enjoy Mom's delicious pork and potato pie — which she only prepares once a year, at Christmas — followed by ice cream and homemade cookies. After coffee and some appreciative remarks to them for a great time, we load the car with our gifts, bags of cookies and leftovers and depart. I'm eager to be alone with Tom.

No sooner do we take off, waving at them from the car, than Tom says, "During dinner you said, 'Pass me the salt, *Honey*.'"

I fire off two questions, "Did they realize I called you that? What was their reaction?"

"Of course. They just looked at you, then me, then each other. They have to know."

"Shit. Oh well, no regrets."

"Right. No regrets. Glad you did it. It probably confirms their suspicions. This way they don't have to admit they know and can enjoy the façade that shelters them from reality."

Once we're home and settled, I go into the bedroom and retrieve the special gift I saved to give Tom in private. "Merry Christmas," I say, offering him the tiny gift-wrapped box.

He looks up at me and smiles, looking a bit taken aback by the surprise late gift. He opens the tiny gift and finds a black onyx ring. He says, "My God, it's great!"

"I didn't want to give you this before," I say.

"You are full of surprises," he says, looking up at me, still smiling. He tries the ring on and then leans forward to embrace and kiss me. "You have brilliant taste! I adore it," Tom notes, turning the ring on his finger. "Where did you get it?"

"Littman's."

"I love it, Darling," he says again, lying down on his back, resting his head on my lap while holding his hand up, away from his face, checking out his new ring.

I say, "And thank you again for all my wonderful gifts. You shouldn't have bought all that, Tom."

It's certainly magic being with Tom. I'm holding his hand and lift it gently to my lips. I examine it. It's soft and sensual, yet big and masculine. It makes me happy to look at his hand and hold it against my cheek. I run my lips over it and smell it. I rub his arms and put my arms around his body. He straightens out and I roll on top of him. We're watching *It's a Wonderful Life* again, this time on a video that Tom got in his stocking from my parents. We both love the movie, so we don't mind watching it again. Tom hits the mute button and brushes the hair out of my face and we share a long Christmas kiss. It's warm and sexy. I look into his eyes, trying to see into his soul, and I don't see any trouble there. His eyes are relaxed, calm. He looks at me with such love. He squeezes his arms around me tightly. "Oh, I love you so-o-o-o much, Thomas Marino," he says in an exhilarated tone. How refreshing; how complete I feel! Tom rolls over and hits the button to turn the stereo on as we make love.

By allowing ourselves to be totally open and fully expressed with each other, we can achieve a maximum level of pleasure. Our living room is dimly lit by candle-light. Tom's head is on my lap and my hands are on his head, caressing it gently. I take notice of my own beautiful beefy arms, the shape of my muscles and rounded shoulders accentuated by my gray tank top. Part of my pleasure is watching an-other male enjoy my skin, my flesh, my own body. Just as we reach the summit of pleasure, the radio station plays "Someone to Watch Over Me" — and no song could better fit this moment. I notice a single droplet of water on Tom's cheek that was not produced from the sweat of our passion. The droplet has a trail, leading to his eye. He wept, for I believe the moment touched him deeper than any has before.

We wake at 2:40 in the morning, naked in each other's arms, on the floor in front of the television in the living room. We're mutually parched and find our way to the kitchen, where we each pour bottled water down our throats, then find our bed and assume comfortable positions to get back to sleep. It's so wonderful sleeping in the arms of a strong, beautiful man. I feel so warm and loved.

"I love you," I whisper to my guy.

Tom, in a sleepy state, mutters back, "And I love you." The snow has turned to rain, and I listen to it hit the windowpane as I allow sleep take me.

Week of December 26, 1988

I start the week with a call to Janet. "Thought you forgot about me, buddy," she says.

"Nope. By the way, I received your care package."

"You did? Great! Did you like it?"

"Yes, of course. Thanks for the condoms."

"I hope you're using them with your butt buddy Shaw. How is your butt buddy anyway?" she asks.

"I don't think I'm ready to broadcast it to the world just yet, but I'm certain of one thing: I'm much happier with a guy."

She asks, "You still like pooter, though, don't you?"

"Sure, I love to munch on those snatches."

She giggles at my raw volley back at her. "I love ya," she says. "No one talks dirty to me here. By the way, how is Letitia? You gotta love working for her."

Letitia was Janet's manager at the Kings Highway branch in Cherry Hill. I knew they were friends. I'm not at all impressed with Letitia, and can't see the two of them as friends. Letitia is a refined ass-kissing, plastic and phony prude, whereas Janet is a down-to-earth, realistic and truly caring individual who would do anything for you. Her honesty and candor is refreshing.

"She seems cool," I lie, and then continue, "Well, Sugar Tits, I gotta run, I'm meeting Studly for lunch."

"Double bean burritos?" she asks.

"Shit, I miss that place. We don't have a Taco Bell here."

"Okay. Is Letitia busy?"

"Hang on." I go over and tell Letitia that Janet is holding for her. Letitia rolls her eyes and tosses her pen out of her hand and onto her desk, making it clear that this distraction is getting in the way of some major banking business. "Do you want me to tell her you'll call her back?" I ask her.

Letitia looks up at me, shrugs her shoulders and then smiles wide, revealing a beautiful smile, saying, "Why would you do that?" She picks up the phone and says, "Hey, lady, what's up?"

Tom picks me up, and over a quick lunch at Wendy's shares the headline of the day: "Nelson, the other sales manager, and I were at a renter's house today repossessing some furniture since she hadn't made any payments, and the lady hauled off and belted Nelson right in the kisser!"

"You're kidding!"

"No, really, it was hysterical. This old bitch slapped him square in the mouth." We take a quick drive over to his job at R2O Rentals to meet some of his co-workers.

I only get to meet Cathy, an assistant manager who works in the office, and another sales manager, Lonnie. We engage in some small chit-chat shop talk about the rent-to-own business, and Cathy recounts the slapping story until it's time for Tom to drive me back to work.

Driving back to the branch, Tom tells me Lonnie did some time in jail, and he's trying to find out why. "How did he get hired?" I ask. "Isn't there a section on the application that asks if you've ever been convicted?"

"Yes. I don't know. Nelson was telling me."

Moments pass and I say, "I can't believe my fucking car is still in the shop. I call the dealer on a daily basis for a status check, but keep getting told 'this part's on order, that part's on order' every day. The only thing keeping me sane is the fact that the repair isn't costing me a cent."

"Miss your baby, Baby?" he asks, smiling.

"Yep, I do." He stops the car outside the front door of my branch.

"Enjoy the rest of your day, Stud," he says, and we lean in for a nice, long, hot kiss. I pull away as I feel my dick start to inflate.

I sit at my desk and type some business development letters to local prospects. I discover myself becoming Letitia's workhorse, doing all her grunt work, including overseeing the entire branch's operations and most of her own work while she takes daily two and three hour "wet" lunches with the head teller, Karen, with whom she's developed a new friendship. Our charming Assistant Manager, Ben, a man's man, shows he's an expert at the fine art of ass-kissing as he and our Regional Manager, Steve, go out for lunches, "customer visits," and golfing in the afternoons.

Soon after Letitia and Ben discover my knack for preparing business proposals, their detailed handwritten drafts become simple two-line directives like "Formulate an invite to Sam from Rotary to our shin-dig on Friday night — include a plug on our services." I'm often left to fend for myself, with the responsibility of ensuring that the branch gets settled, training the new folks, coordinating the walk-in traffic, supervising everyone and managing and handling all the loans.

Despite the hard work, I crave and am intrigued by the retail banking business and gladly take it all on, absorbing as much as I can. I soon perfect my skills at lending to a point where I can bring deals to her with my recommendation, and she simply signs off on them without any review, trusting my judgment. Ben is useless. I learn to master his functions and responsibilities and volunteer to do all the remaining parts of his job. He gladly passes it all on to me and I take it all on. Ben's colossal monthly task of preparing the branch audit is completed, performed correctly, neatly prepared, and he is made to look like a superstar. Letitia makes changes and little criticisms here and there and I absorb them and try to learn from what she says. I find every bit of it challenging and fascinating.

Letitia and Ben decide to act busy at ten of five when I'm packing up to leave so they can play the martyr act. They get pissy when I push to leave at my scheduled quitting time, despite the fact that I got my work done and theirs. That's about the time when I'm solicited to help her with her homework from a class she's taking at the American Institute of Banking, or "requested" to type the minutes from a service organization for which she serves as Secretary.

Friday, December 30, 1988, 2:30 p.m.
Bobby comes to my desk, asking, "Karen still out?"

"Yeah," I answer.

The branch is busy, with customers from other offices that have discovered our new branch in their neighborhood. Letitia, Ben, Karen and Steve went out around noon for a pre-New Years' Eve drinking binge they call lunch.

Bobby says, "Fucking unreal. Vault and branch have to get settled, and what are we supposed to do?" Karen's back-up Head Teller is out on a vacation day today. Bobby continues, "Tellers need to do their turn-overs and the part-timers need cash. What the fuck am I supposed to do? I don't have combos to the vault."

"I don't either. We can go into dual control to get the combos, settle it, and then we can do the cash turn-overs and get cash for the part timers." Feeling the influence of Janet's coaching, I think and then verbalize, "Who gives a fuck, Bob? As I see it, this is their fucking problem. Don't get involved."

Bobby rolls his eyes, smiles and says, "I'm going to have a smoke. Come with me." I look at our lobby, now getting crowded with restless customers.

I meet Bobby in the kitchen and spark up. While exhaling smoke, I ask, "What about the work? Did you start having everyone settle for the courier?"

"I can't," he says, "The part-timers don't have enough cash."

"Let them open with what they have and Karen should be back soon. Didn't she leave a schedule for staggered settlement times?"

"Tom, she didn't even arrange our lunch schedule. None of us have had our breaks. We're so programmed to play follow the leader around here that no one had time to coordinate anything. Plus, they don't have any twenties."

"You're fucking kidding me," I say, and walk out of the break room and over behind the tellers to look out into the branch. I made sure the platform crew had their lunches. They're all busy waiting on customers. I decide to go into dual control with Bobby to get the combinations to the cash vault. I walk up to the teller line and take control of coordinating the settlement and change-over of business days. I direct Bobby to help me complete the cash collection, and get the tellers settled and the work ready for the courier.

Bobby and I sit in the vault and access the vault cash to settle the vault and branch. Once everything settles, we turn the work over to the courier, who arrives at 3:15.

"We made it," Bobby says, looking at me and smiling. Bobby and I return to the cash locker in the vault, sit on the floor and fill the tellers' cash disbursement vouchers. Tellers are strapped for cash, and the line of customers is getting longer as time goes by. People seem to be getting off from work early today, even though New Years' Eve is tomorrow evening.

We just about finish with what we're doing when, from the vault, we hear Letitia's cackle laugh. It's evident she's fucked up again. Both Letitia and Karen come to the vault door and enter. They look down at us, and without warning Letitia screams, "WHAT THE HELL ARE YOU DOING?"

Stunned by her behavior, I freeze and say nothing. Bobby quickly pipes in, "We got the work sent out in time, then settled the vault and now we're getting the cash ready for the tellers. The tellers needed money." Letitia blows her top again, this time yelling louder and throwing her hands up in the air like a hysterical lunatic, "THE TELLERS NEED MONEY? I GOT NEWS FOR YOU; YOU ARE NOTHING BUT A TELLER! YOU TWO JOKERS HAVE NO RIGHT TO BE IN HERE! WHAT A MESS!"

I nervously shift myself up to my feet, cross my arms over my chest and look down at the bricks of cash disbursements we've prepared. They are neater than I've ever seen them prepared, the paperwork is all perfect, and the tickets are all properly executed and tidily bundled.

"KAREN!" Letitia bellows again, "KAREN, LOOK AT THIS MESS!" Karen immediately kneels to pick up the money.

"GET OUT! LEAVE US!" Letitia shouts again. I can smell the alcohol on her breath. Bobby turns and walks out of the vault, heading back to his station.

"I'm not going to be blamed for any missing money. I refuse to leave until Karen audits this in my presence," I say firmly.

Letitia looks at me daringly, then downward at Karen and snaps, "KAREN, VERIFY THE VAULT!", still yelling. Inside, I'm scared, afraid and embarrassed, but mostly crushed that despite the fact that I believe I acted responsibly and correctly, she's displeased with my actions. I yearn to speak up, but stay quiet, and avoid eye contact with her.

Letitia bends down and picks up some money and snaps at me through squinted eyes, "What were you two thinking?" My short-lived disdain and questioning of my own actions is quickly replaced by a growing lack of respect for her.

"You, sir," she begins, in a patronizing tone, "are not authorized to handle any Head Teller work! I have your file. It clearly says…" She stops, looks around as if there is someone behind her. She resumes her tirade, "You know I talk to Kathy and I talk to Sue…You aren't ready to be a goddamn Head Teller… Everyone knows that."

My mind is swimming with questions: *What are they saying about me? What the fuck is in my file?* Rather than saying anything, I remain perfectly quiet, observing her struggle to count down the hoard of cash. At one point she opens a pack of money and new bills fly all over the floor. She throws the money down and says, "To hell with this. Karen, make sure nothing is missing!" and walks out.

Alone with Karen in the vault, Karen avoids eye contact with me, despite the fact that I stare at her every moment. The bitch returns when Karen completes verifying everything. "Is it all there?"

"Yeah, everything's fine."

I return to my desk, holding my head high as my platform crewmates instantly look down, after catching a glimpse of me coming from the vault where all the screaming came from. I'm shaking inside, but scan the lot of them with the most nonchalant look I can furnish.

5:20 p.m.

"I'm outta here," Bobby says, approaching my desk. "I'll see you at Gatsby's tomorrow night for New Year's Eve?"

"Oh, uh-huh. I'm anxious to introduce you to Tom."

He looks around, and then smiles as he sits in front of me, leaning close, and says in a hushed voice, "Glad no one is here right now. Listen, Matt told me you're a stripper."

"Boy, for a prick who tells me to keep it quiet, he's doing a swell job of broadcasting my side job."

"Well?"

"Sure, yes, I do strip."

"I want to hear all about it — call me tonight when you get done."

"Go home, Goofball," I say. He rises and shakes his head, then motions a gesture to call him. Just then, Letitia walks back from her visit to the bathroom and snaps, "Don't you have work to do, Tom?"

'6

TURBULENCE

Saturday, December 31, 1988

When I get home, Tom's ready to go out. I finally get a chance to tell him about yesterday's drama while I'm shaving for the party at Gatsby's. He leans against the frame of the bathroom door, with his arms crossed over his chest as he listens to me unload. When I'm finally silent, he offers, "You know what I think of that job. The shitty pay and all the petty bullshit. Man, I'd have told someone off a long time ago."

I respond, "You can bet that I'm not putting up with it for nothing. I'm hell-bent on making it, so everyone better get out of the way or I'll plow right through them."

"Oh, really?" Tom asks, a smile widening on his handsome face.

"What?" I ask.

"You're into that plowing stuff."

I join him in a laugh, approaching with my face half-covered in shaving cream. I say, "Yeah? How about I plow you right now, Chief?"

Tom dashes off, saying, "Oh, shit, don't get that stuff all over me!"

Once I'm ready and before we leave, Tom asks me to come into the kitchen. He surprises me by taking a bottle of champagne out of the refrigerator. I watch as he opens it, smiling my way. We both exhibit the same child-like look of horror and amazement when the cork blasts into a wall, leaving a dent in the plaster. He pours two glasses, and as we hold our glasses up, he makes a precious toast: "Tom, love of my life, you have made 1988 my best year. You're my partner and my best friend."

It's incredibly chic that he begins our evening with such a tremendous and romantic gesture. After we toast, I put my drink down and reach for him. I put my arms around him and go in for a nice long warm kiss. With my eyes closed and my mouth open to his, I feel shivers go up and down my spine.

We notice that GB's is packed to its fullest capacity as we arrive. I'm wearing a bright-red long-sleeve shirt, tucked into a pair of black dress slacks. As for Tom, getting back to basics never looked better, as his studly self is adorned in a pair of relaxed-fit khakis and a light-blue button-down. A thick brown belt around his well-proportioned waist compliments his sexy core.

I follow Tom to the door, and once inside, he positions me in front of him at the crowded main bar. We acknowledge a few familiar faces, and order a couple of beers.

John and Doug appear. John places his arm around me and kisses me on the cheek, while Doug shakes my hand. I can't help beaming with pride as I introduce them to Tom as my other half. John looks me up and down and has to say, "Those pants accentuate that cute, round bubble butt of yours." Doug adds, "Nice package, too." John goes on about my butt, telling Tom, "This guy has the perfect ass."

Tom's smile fades, but he seems cool. I nod and say loudly, "Squats, lots of squats at the gym," trying to compete with the loud music.

After a moment they move on, and a couple of Tom's friends gather around us chatting and chirping, until they slowly disperse in search of what they came for. Pat, whom we saw at the adult bookstore the night we met — the guy who used to work with Nadine at K-Mart — walks by and stops to quip, "Hey, I see you two are still together. Anything longer than a week is a record for both of you queens."

"Where are you working now?" I ask Pat.

"I'm managing the Wendy's in Bellmawr on the Black Horse Pike. Didn't your husband tell you? It sucks, *gurl*. Anxious to dance, I nudge Tom to escape.

"Excuse us, Pat," he says.

"Sure. I'll see you queens around." We move to the dance floor as "Heaven Must Be Missing An Angel" by Tavares comes on. It's an upbeat dance tune, and while everyone else is grooving, we're slow-dancing. Tom brings me in close, and as I rest my head on his shoulder, he softly says in my ear, "He's a mess."

"You knew he worked at Wendy's?" I ask.

"Yeah, I saw him there one day when I was working at Crown. I went over for lunch. His Wendy's is right near Crown Rentals on the Pike." The DJ blends a second Tavares hit, "Don't Take Away the Music," as I release the thoughts and snuggle my nose and face into his shoulder. I feel hot under the lights of the dance floor, but it's a good sensation. My eyes find his and my soul starts singing. As the song concludes, I realize I've been so lost in kissing him I can't remember starting the kiss. It strikes me that this love is intense to the point of being an addiction.

As we walk off the dance floor, I announce, "I see Bobby!" Bobby walks up with a huge smile on his face and puts his arms around my waist. He's a billboard for being gay: he's wearing a really festive outfit, and looks like he's wearing make-up, too. "Roberta!" I address him.

"Tommy!" he says, greeting me with a hug. I introduce him to Tom, and as they shake hands, Bobby pulls Tom in for a hug.

"You look familiar," Bobby says.

"You do, too," Tom says.

"Yeah, we probably fucked," Bobby says, acting silly, grabbing my hand and laughing. "Just kidding, Tommy, just kidding. He's very handsome. Tom, he did tell me how good-looking you are. Hey, I'm getting confused. You guys must...that must be weird, I mean, calling your own name out during sex."

He takes me by the hand and forces others out of the way so we can sit together. He wants to hear all about the erotic dancing. Tom departs to get us some drinks.

"You want to hear about all those gory details?"

"More like *glamorous*, you mean! Hey, I love entertaining — you know I'm dying to do drag in public. Tell me everything." I take him through it and he insists he wants to see me dance. "I'm pissed I didn't see you perform here! Fuck, that sucks! Promise you'll take me on one of your gigs!" He hugs me and says, "Oh, uh, be right back," and darts away, distracted by seeing some dude across the room.

"Yeah, later, Bobby Pin!" I shout after him. Dizzy queen. He's flighty, yet so very warm. You can tell guys like Bobby had to have been persecuted in high school. Here, he's free to be who he is, just like me.

Tom returns and takes a seat next to me, handing me a Manhattan. "'We probably fucked?'" Tom asks, repeating Bobby's words and rolling his eyes. We laugh on that one for a moment. As our laughter subsides, we look at each other with knowing and lustful smiles. A momentary silence, far from awkward, is filled with electricity flowing between us. Tom makes a facial gesture of a kiss and my smile widens. He has a way of lighting me up in every way.

"He's a goof," I say.

"Be careful with him. I sense he likes you a bit too much," Tom says.

I return a look that conveys disgust with the notion of Bobby's perceived affections toward me.

"Pleasure Principle" by Janet Jackson comes on, and I hastily push and shove my way to the dance floor. Tom isn't too far behind me. I tear it up on the dance floor, allowing the smooth sound of Janet's voice to penetrate my soul. The beat is very me and I enjoy dancing to it. Jeff dances his way up to us. "Happy New Year, guys!" he says, giving us a mutual hug and kiss. "Pleasure Principle" mixes into another song, and another song, and we keep dancing. Soon I'm drenched in sweat; we're in the center of the dance floor, in the limelight, owning the place. It feels so fucking good. All eyes are on us. What an amazing feeling.

Tom drags me upstairs to the piano bar, and we find a place to sit right near a bunch of older guys singing along to show tunes. It's cool how they know all the words of every song.

Tom puts his arm around me, and leans in to say in my ear, "It's an hour to midnight. Are you excited? Another New Year…" I turn to face him, hoping he will again entreat me with one of his warm, tender kisses. I hold back, praying he'll do it on his own, without a clue from me. Is he thinking what I'm thinking?

He doesn't kiss me. He turns to look at the drink in front of him. I follow suit. I say another prayer, thanking God and Mary for this man. I ask them to seal the bond between us — to make him know that no matter how desirable and attractive he is, I will love him no matter what.

We hear someone on a microphone downstairs and head down, knowing it's getting closer to the New Year. The drag queen Feressa, The Electric Woman, performs an amusing comedy routine. I'm buzzed, and Tom slips away to the bathroom.

Out of nowhere, a guy named Jon comes up and tells me, "Call me at work Monday, bro. Need to talk to you." Jon is a Personal Banker at First Commercial, like me, but he works in our Glassboro office. He's a 6'5" muscular cutie with a full, thick sexy moustache, a dimpled chin and an amazing butt. I know Jon has a drug habit, and I have suspicions he's also a pusher. Jon walks away and leaves me sitting there, confused about his sudden seriousness.

I bolt forward, catch up to him, and ask, "What's up, Chief?"

Jon looks me, his gorgeous blue eyes competing with his sexy black moustache for my attention. He says, "Don't be mad. I think he's just drunk." I shake my head, confused. He continues, "Tom has been calling me at the branch. He called right after you introduced us at Halloween to compliment me on the devil costume. Tonight he asked if he could suck me off."

I feel the floor drop out from under me, dizzy with disgust, anger and hurt.

Why would Tom wreck our burgeoning relationship? My split-second reaction is to deck Jon — but he didn't do anything. I should find Tom and deck him. Then I think I should ask Jon to elaborate; but doing that, or showing any evidence of being negatively affected by this news, will diminish my character. In any case, I suddenly realize that Tom — for some insane reason — simply verbalized what we both probably want, which is to do to Jon.

I suck it up and assume a new role, a new position in this production that is my life. "Actually, we both find you fucking hot," I tell him. "Would you like to play sometime?" Even as the words come out, I realize that Jon, whose news caused me to feel some disdain toward him, is truly much more of a man than I imagined.

"I'm not saying I'm not flattered," he said carefully, "and I might even be interested in you if you guys weren't together, but I thought you'd like to know what happened. I thought you guys were exclusive."

"Wow, thanks, but no sweat, man," is all I can say. He says nothing. I find myself on autopilot again. I contemplate the situation, and without even taking time to verify with Tom whether he did in fact come on to Jon, I continue to astound myself with my words and actions. Operating on pure emotion, I ask, "So, do you want to take a walk?" This is code for "Do you want to go fool around?" Suddenly I find my ego tossed off of the throne I created for it. Nothing is more sobering.

Jon nods and says, "Sure, outside?"

"Right behind you," I say, without hesitation, thinking I'm going to cover all my bases.

I follow him outside and he says, "Your car or mine?"

"Better use yours," I say.

"Right." We get in his car and begin kissing. Despite the excitement of tasting his hot moustache, my erection is partly pumped full due to sheer anger and a passion for revenge. As we go, we find we're too tall to fuck in his small car. He breaks out some poppers. Limited in our fuckfest by the size of his car, we do as much as possible to achieve orgasm. We shove the seats down and he sits way back. I hoist his legs up and it feels good to play as the pleasure allows me to forget my anger, disappointment and sadness over Tom's play for Jon. I allowed Nadine to have one over me with her affair with Nick. I allowed her to hurt my heart. That won't happen again. Before I feel hurt again, I'll win. I'll be first and I'll be on top, as always.

We finish and I exit the car with Jon. He lights a cigarette and I take it from him. He lights another for himself. "I better get back in there," I say.

"I'll call you Monday," he begins. "I'd like to have you over my place next week – it was hot in the car, so imagine how great it can be in a bed. Do you go to the baths in Philly?"

"I would…" I begin; but catching myself saying something stupid and dishonest, I spit and continue, in a callous tone, "Look, we had some fun, but now you need to stay away from both of us."

He nods and says, "I'm outta here," obviously a bit burned. I think my remark is cold, coming as it does right after a sexual encounter, but it beats the pain of having to clean up empty promises later. I burned the bridge to future encounters with Jon, but there are plenty of others out there. *Plenty of others,* I think, thinking less of commitment and loyalty. This relationship shit eats into my precious time to fuck around and sample what's out there.

After a stop in the bathroom, I go to the bar and it's about 10 minutes until the New Year. I order and throw back a few shots of Jack Daniels. Tom catches up to me with a glass of champagne in each hand just as the countdown to the 1989 New Year begins. At midnight, he plants a kiss on me and hands me a glass of champagne. With every ounce of phony acting I can muster, I return the kiss and smile. Inwardly, I'm sulking, feeling the pain of Tom's devious scheming. The thoughts induce a sense of a diluted self-image. I experience an impression of being suddenly unsophisticated, as my self-confidence plummets.

One of our songs, "How Can I Fall?" by the group Breathe plays. He begins mouthing the words to the song to me, putting his hand out in an offer to dance. I pull myself together and remember who I am and how much I really love him. I grab his hand and lead him to the dance floor. We dance and he holds me tight. I try to hold on to the fantasy that Jon is a liar, and that Tom would never seek sexual pleasures from anyone but me.

The remainder of the night sucks, considering the cloud of gloom hanging over my head, and my mood is evident in my behaviors and actions. A group of friends invite us to Denny's after the club closes, but I decline for both of us.

In the car, Tom says, "What's the matter? Why didn't you want to go?" I thought about Nadine's deception and the fact that if I'd never confronted her, I could have continued living the life we'd created for a bit longer. I want to hold on to the Tom I knew before we walked into Gatsby's tonight, but the question comes out: "Did you ask Jon D'Andrea if you could suck his dick? Have you been calling him?" Knowing Jon has nothing to gain by lying, I focus intently on Tom's response. His reaction and subsequent answers will dictate our future.

"It's not like that," he begins. Immediately, I feel my heart sink.

"What is it like?" I ask in a snide tone.

"I called him to see if he wanted to hang out sometime with us and he asked me if I would blow him. I told him 'no'."

Not only do I not believe Tom, I hate his attempt at a lie. Professional liars like me would have responded to those questions with a question. We drive in silence the rest of the way home. Tom reaches down to hold my hand, and it feels uncomfortable, almost nauseous, but I don't pull my hand away. I want to believe he loves me, but his actions are so discomforting. I want to ask, *Why would you call him? Why didn't you tell me you called him? If he came on to you, why didn't you tell me he came on to you? Do you want to have sex with him? Do you find him attractive? What do you like about him?* But I realize I know the answers to all those questions. In truth I want to be able to not give a fuck, not a single solitary fuck. Alas, I do care. I feel really hurt. I ask finally, "Do you want to have threesomes?"

Tom shakes his head, saying, "No, I don't want to share you." Noting a car pulled over by a cop on the side of the highway, I find a piece of gum and pop it in my mouth as we pass. Like gum will deflect a DUI. "I think it would be hot to watch another dude fuck you," I tell him.

"Okay. All right, fine. I came on to him. I was wrong and I'm sorry. It's clear you know. I'm sure he told you. You don't have to be a prick about it," he says.

"Me? You think I'm a prick?" I snap so loudly that Tom flinches. I continue, "Don't worry, I'm fuckin' over it. Trust me. I was just asking if you wanted to do threesomes. Do you want an open relationship so you can play around with whoever you want?"

"Tom, no. I don't want that and I don't want to fight. I made a mistake. I didn't mess around with him. Again, I'm really sorry."

I end the discussion with, "Thanks for owning up but Jesus, Tom, it had to be with one of my co-workers?"

1989

We never mention the Jon incident again, but it's an ember in a growing fire of doubt that I now carry about my feelings for Tom.

Working in the Woodbury branch isn't the best assignment I could have hoped for. I keep telling myself that I'm closer to home and I need to endure it. I have run-ins with Letitia on a daily basis but turn my thoughts to the fact that I've become a considerable asset to her in my new role as the senior personal banker. The majority of the folks in here are new to the bank, including Ben, the assistant manager. It's cool to be the one with answers for once, instead of the individual always asking for help.

On the home front, Tom has developed a new habit of going out at night "for a drive" to clear his thoughts.

"I like to go for a drive, to help me relax," he'll say. I accompanied him on a couple drives. He goes all over creation until late in the night. I consider it a waste of time and gas, not to mention the wear and tear on the car. I thought I would enjoy it because riding in the car as a passenger has a somnolent effect on me, but for some reason, it didn't work. He wouldn't get home until after 2:00 a.m., and I'd be exhausted the entire next day.

To accentuate the tension and anxiety on our relationship, I began receiving the credit card bills Tom ran up for Christmas. Also, I notice my JC Penney card is loaded with lots of small purchases of candy, cigarettes and little toys. Tom is addicted to sugar and is forever buying treats to satisfy his sweet tooth. He has a habit of buying little trinkets like a key-chain or lighter or something every time he goes into a store. These things add up, and I'm starting to carry a balance on cards I used to pay off each month. His deposits to the account are a fraction of what he earns, and somehow I expected his contributions would help absorb the $3,321.70 I shelled out to bail him out of the bank debacle. Instead we seem to be moving backward instead of forward. Something's gotta give.

Saturday, January 14, 1989, 3:00 p.m.
Downey's Irish Pub, South Street, Philadelphia

"Appetizers, fellas?" Mitch asks. The three of us are meeting for lunch at Mitch's request. I select clams on the half-shell from their raw bar; Tom selects Chincoteague Salt Oysters, and Mitch has the Seared Wasabi Tuna. We chase it with some Guinness in tall frosted glasses.

"We're glad you moved to Blackwood," Mitch notes. "Blackwood is much closer to a lot of the jobs than when you were up near Fort Dix or Wrightstown or wherever. You've had some work up north, but most of them are down here in the Philly area and down the shore." Mitch laughs, unexpectedly, and then says, "Are you having fun?"

"Yeah, but some of the jobs are wild, Mitch. Like the one on the farm down in Cumberland county. Jeesh!"

Mitch sits back and closes his eyes, trying to think of the one I'm referring to. His mouth is wide open, revealing some horrifying dental work. Finally he says,

"Oh, yeah, the farmer's wife deal?"

"What's up with the farm job?" Tom asks, looking at both of us.

Mitch says, "It was the middle of summer, and I sent him way down south Jersey someplace. It was broad daylight, wasn't it?"

"Yeah," I agree, adding, "in the middle of a humid weekday afternoon. I think I was on vacation from work that week."

"Oh yeah," Mitch says, directing his comments to Tom. "The guy takes Tommy upstairs, where his wife is lying in bed naked. The guy asks Tommy to bang her. Weren't they pushing 60 or something?"

"Something like that; it was scary. Real American Gothic and shit."

"What did you do?" Tom asks.

Mitch says, "He ended up doing his gig for them, and got the hell out of there. How is it going for you?" he asks Tom.

For a moment, Tom is quiet and still, probably trying to process the sudden subject change; then he answers, "Doing great, thanks."

"Great. I understand Jessica is happy, too. Working well for everyone." We both nod, and smile. Our food arrives, and we listen to Mitch talk about his recent vacation to Mexico while we eat.

The purpose of our meeting is for Mitch to tell me that he's increasing my work load and that he's going to have Tom assist another dancer as well, since business has picked up. He's nice enough to ask us first if we can handle it, given our day jobs. The meal is great and Mitch pats me on the shoulder as we part, winking at me and saying, "Thanks, guy." Lunch is his way of recognition. He certainly makes a wad of cash on me, and Tom's part in driving Jessica around certainly has to help pad his revenue stream.

Monday, January 16, 1989

"Hey Chief, what's up?" I say, answering a call from Tom soon after arriving at work.

"This place got robbed last night," Tom says, his tone somber.

"What? My God! What happened?"

"When I got in, everyone was here. Cathy said George, the General Manager, wanted to speak to me and the other rental managers." The rental managers at R2O Rentals don't actually manage anything. They're glorified moving men, just like at Crown Rent-to-Own.

"What did George say?"

"I sat down and he told me the store was missing $700. I asked him where the money was missing from, and he acted like I took it. Later, after talking to Nelson and a couple of the other managers, I found out he's been grilling everyone. It seems the money was in a bank bag on the counter for a few hours. Then Cathy went to lunch, and at about five on Friday, she went to make the deposit and the money was missing."

"Were you in the office? You don't usually go in the office, do you?"

"Yes, we all do. I was in there a few times, even when Cathy was at lunch." He was silent for a long moment. "After he finished interrogating everyone, George said he was going to fire everyone if the money isn't recovered."

"Do you know who might have taken it?"

"No, hey, it shouldn't have been left out on the counter. A customer could have taken it. You know all the skanky people who come in. I told Cathy that maybe we could get a loan from First Commercial to cover the deposit."

"You what?" I ask, confused.

"Cathy said that George told her he didn't report the loss to the cops or to the Main Office, but the deposit has to be made or he'll have to report it. We thought we could apply for a loan and all of us could pay it back, to save our jobs."

That makes absolutely no sense to me whatsoever. I share my feelings of how ridiculous that sounds with Tom, and point out, "He can't fire you without proof. You're right, it could have been a customer — or even him, right?"

"He wasn't in that day."

"Well, nonetheless, he can't fire anyone without proof."

"You don't understand! We need our jobs! Cathy has kids, Vern has kids, we all have bills and obligations."

I go ballistic. "You gotta be shittin' me! If you didn't take it, then why do you care? You don't have anything to lose. If he fires you, we'll sue them for unlawful termination, or false accusation, or some shit."

His tone calms down as he states, "We'll talk more about it at home, I guess. I gotta go. Can you please bring home a loan application?"

Not long after hanging up with Tom, Stephanie tells me Cathy from R2O Rentals is on hold for me.

"Hello, Tom Marino speaking," I say.

"Hi Tom, it's Cathy, from R2O. I work with Tom. We've met, do you remember?" I can't understand why she's acting so formal; we talk every so often when I call for Tom on the phone. She knows all about me.

"Hey, Cathy, what's up?" I ask, knowing what's coming.

"Well…I assume Tom told you about our predicament. He was mentioning that we could possibly get a loan from your bank?"

"I suppose, but I'm not certain I go along with what you guys are trying to do. Why don't you just notify the cops and let them investigate?"

"Let's face it, Tom, you know no one's gonna cough up the money. We figured that. We just want to save all our jobs."

"What's the chance the money was taken by a customer? If I were you guys, I wouldn't like to know I was working with a thief." Cathy reiterates what Tom shared; that George is going to fire everyone if the money isn't located. "What about George?" I ask.

"Who? George, our manager? George take the money? No way! Besides, he wasn't in that day."

"Cathy, I have to tell you, I just got off the phone with Tom and there's no fucking way I would pay back something if I didn't take it. Is George going in on the loan repayments like everyone else?" I ask, not letting go of George's accountability and responsibility for the missing money.

"No. Everyone was out that day. Only Tom and I were in the office all day." I wait a moment before responding, allowing my brain to absorb and process that.

"I see. Who's going to apply for the loan?"

"I am. Tom told me he has bad credit. We're going to pay it back together."

"Wait. Just you and Tom were in the office. So, none of the other rental managers like Nelson and Vern are in on this? None of them were in the office that day?"

"Yes, just Tom and me. Can you fax the loan application over to me now?"

When Tom collects me for lunch, he has the completed fax copy of the application. I ask, "Who do you think took it?"

"Like I said, I don't know," he answers, his face carrying a blank expression. Tom tells me he and Cathy carefully conveyed this grand scheme to George. After having it presented as an option, George was receptive to it.

"I can't believe George is going to allow you guys to proceed with getting a loan," I say.

"He can't tell the main office about the loss."

When I get back to the office, I ask Matt to work on Cathy's personal loan application.

8:30 p.m., at home

Tom doesn't want to discuss the matter anymore, so when he takes a phone call from one of his co-workers, I try to keep my eyes on the TV, while tuning my ears into their conversation. I analyze his responses, and the conversation legitimizes what I already know.

When he hangs up I ask, "Who was that?"

"Nelson. He said George gave him a rash of shit about it. He thinks George believes he took the money because he's black."

I sit back, dumbfounded for a moment, and then say, "Isn't George black too?"

"Yep," Tom answers.

"Oh, c'mon, that's stupid. George must have another reason to suspect him."

"I don't know. Anyway, Nelson wasn't even in the store the day it went missing. Are you hungry?" he asks, abruptly changing the subject.

"Yeah."

"Let's go get some ice cream." I don't feel much like ice cream, but go along. We head to Friendly's. On the way, while stopped at a red light in the center of Blackwood, Tom starts laughing, looking over at a Mobil gas station.

"What's so funny?" I ask.

Tom calls my attention to an abandoned gas pump at the station, with orange cones around it. "See that island over there, with the orange cones?"

"The one with the busted tank?"

"Yes. Nelson made that huge dent in the tank with the R2O Rentals van. He was backing in to get gas and crashed into it. He was like, 'Fuck! I thought it was going to explode!' It was funny, the way he put it. Said he almost pissed his pants."

Monday, January 23, 1989

I'm lost in thought during an early morning workout on the elliptical machine. I'm scheduled to go into work late today, so I hit the gym before dawn. Tom had a really booked weekend driving Jessica around to jobs. Last night they had to stay in a hotel, since the last job was late and all the way up in Edison. With Tom gone, I wasn't able to sleep well. My mind was glued to thoughts that consume me now. I feel a self-created wedge begin to form between us that keeps me from allowing the relationship to grow and move forward. With Nadine, I ruled over a rigid existence of self-denial and sacrifice focused on increasing our assets and income. The cost of my aggression was the relationship.

Now I find myself enjoying a sexually-fulfilling, loving relationship following

Tom's lead in managing a life that I perceive as over-indulging in the pleasures that money can bring. I know I'll need to ignore my instincts to return to a more conservative lifestyle if we're going to build a proper future. I grant myself permission for not doing so, citing the following reasons: One, I don't want to rock the boat and cause anything that would make Tom quit me; and Two, for the first time in my life, I'm enjoying the ride of careless and reckless abandonment.

Later — at work

I'm irritated and distracted by all the negative thoughts flooding my mind: Tom hasn't made any deposits into our joint checking account all month. As a matter of fact, I haven't seen one paycheck from Tom since mid-December. He's cash-rich and enjoying having his wallet constantly full.

I reach into my briefcase and remove the large yellow eviction notice for not paying December's rent. I was mortified when I found it taped to our front door when I came home from work Saturday. It was the first eviction notice I've ever received. We owe $585 for rent, a $58.50 late fee, and a $25 attorney fee. I purchase a money order for the total due of $668.50, and bring it home to surprise Tom. Lucky for me, my paycheck is in.

I expect Tom to be home, but upon arrival, I discover he's still not there.

7:00 p.m.

To avoid worrying about Tom's whereabouts, I hit my weight bench for a full hour, then go for a jog around the track in our complex, trying to pacify my aching heart.

10:00 p.m.

Where is he? Were they in an accident? They were due back today — early today. Where is he? Fuck. I call Mitch, anxious to find out where Tom is. I don't expect him to answer his phone at this hour, but he does.

"Mitch, it's me, Tom Marino. Do you know where Tom is? He's not home yet," I say, sounding desperate.

There's a short pause, then Mitch responds, "What? Oh, hello, Tom. No, they finished up late last night. Their last job was at 2:00 a.m."

"Have you heard from Jessica?"

"No."

"I called her and just get her voice mail. Where can they be?" I demand.

"Tom, I really don't know. Don't worry about it, and leave her alone. He'll surface," he proclaims, confidently.

"Sure thing." I hang up slowly.

I struggle to sleep, so I transfer more energy into cleaning the apartment while sucking back a whole bottle of Merlot.

12:30 a.m.

After I finally crawl into bed, anxiety and indigestion accentuate my restlessness for hours. I conjure up notions of Tom having been in an accident and lying unconscious in the hospital somewhere, with the staff having no idea whom to call on his behalf. Finally, I watch the neon red figures on the digital alarm clock reading 2:00 become fuzzy, and sleep wins.

Tuesday, January 24, 1989

After what seems like only a few minutes, the fucking bastard of an alarm clock blasts a sound so loud it penetrates my slumber, and I incorporate it into my dream until I'm conscious again. I immediately roll over, reaching out for Tom's body. Finding his side of the bed cold and empty, my heart sinks, and I roll out of bed filled with sadness. I miss my husband. Where is he?

I'm beside myself with grief and despair, but pull my thoughts and emotions together to get ready for work. This morning ritual helps distract my worry. I cover my face in the stream of water from the shower and scrub it hard with the soap, thinking again about him. Why did I allow my entire world to be focused on this man?

Looking in the mirror, I take pride in the aspect of my own beauty, as my reflection shows me looking striking in a light gray suit over a red shirt and tie. As I toss a black scarf around my neck, I'm reminded of my power to turn heads, and allow the moment to lift my spirits. I tell myself, Everything will turn out fine. I always like to think that a year from now these problems and worries won't matter.

I leave a note for him before I leave, and I hate myself for allowing it to dominate my every thought to the point of obsession. Once I reach work, I call home all morning, racking up four messages on our answering machine. I call Cathy at R2O to ask her if Tom has called into work.

"Haven't heard from him. Why?" she asks.

"Oh, he just..." I stop and compose myself, and in an instant finish my sentence in such a way as not to arouse suspicion: "he just didn't tell me what his schedule was today."

"He's due in at 4:00."

"Was he in yesterday?" I couldn't help but ask.

"He was off yesterday. Why? Didn't you see him?"

"No, actually, he was with his family," I lie spontaneously, "and I wasn't sure what was going on. We haven't had time to catch up with each other."

Sounding confused, Cathy offers, "I'll have him call you when he gets in."

I don't usually drive the rental car to work, since we don't want to take any chances with it based on our luck with cars, and I never drive home for lunch; I've been having lunch with Tom every day. Today is different. I drive home to see if he came home and went to bed, but he's not home. I update my note and race back to work. I scurry around the office and ask everyone to put Tom's call through to me when he finally calls, even if I'm with a customer. They sometimes just take a message, and I want to speak with him to ease this terrible feeling of worry in my gut.

We have non-stop customers right up until 5:00, making this the longest day I've ever had. When I finally leave work, I race home to see if he's there. When I don't find him, I don't know what to do. I search my mind for any places Tom can be, and can't think of how to contact any of his friends. I can't sit home another night and wait. I can't lie in the bed alone again.

In desperation to do something I decide to drive over to see Pat at the Wendy's in Bellmawr, wondering if for some odd reason Pat knows where he is. My stomach is tied up in knots as I pull through the drive-up window and ask the cashier for Pat. He comes to the window. "Hey, Miss Thang, what are you doing up here?"

"Hey... have you seen Tom?"

"No, why? Was he coming here to meet you?"

"He's been missing for a whole day and I'm worried sick about him."

Pat is distracted by something in the parking lot off in the distance and yells out over my car, "CEDRIC! CEDRIC!" I turn and see some kid in a Wendy's uniform leaning on a broom, chatting with a girl in a car. He turns casually toward Pat's loud voice and raises his eyebrows.

"GET YOUR ASS IN HERE!" Pat yells. He looks back at me and says, "Well, Girl, I gotta get back in. You can see I have my hands full trying to tame the animals. Nothing but kids workin' here." He hands me my order, and waves off my offer of payment. I engulf the food on the way to the gym for a workout.

I tear up my body in a blistering two-and-a-half-hour workout, including a punishing three-mile run on the treadmill. I push myself to exceed my usual nine-minute mile to punch out three miles in just less than 24 minutes flat. It's a struggle to exceed the results of my usual regimen, but I force it – taking the time to do it right, and then some.

After the gym, I'm still driven to avoid going home to an empty house. I stop at Gatsby's for a drink. Tonight is ladies' night, but I still manage to down more Bloody Marys than I should. It isn't long before I'm eye-to-eye with a cute twentysome-thing dude who's offering a subtle opportunity to stray and play while we dance to a tune by Paul Lekakis beckoning, "Boom Boom Boom Let's Go Back To My Room." Despite my eagerness to engage in the sexual distraction, my thoughts naturally float to the warmth of Tom's smile. After a realistic, deep dive into my feelings, I come to the conclusion that I have faith that he loves me, and I find the strength to leave. More than anything, my wish is to hold him again.

11:55 p.m.
Back at home, finding Tom still gone, I decide to hit the sack and wipe today off the books. I pop a sleeping pill on my tongue and chase it with a shot of Nyquil. I set the alarm and lie down, flat on my back without a pillow, and close my eyes. Within a few moments, I'll feel the effect of the drugs. It's always amazes me how they can unplug the stress and need to care and allow me to plunge into another day, fresh, rested and ready to face it all again. I say aloud into the darkness, "I'll probably wake up next to him tomorrow. Tomorrow will be better. He'll be home tomorrow."

Wednesday, January 25, 1989, 3:44 a.m.
The sound of the door closing brings me out of a deep sleep, and I open my eyes and listen. I hear footsteps coming to the bedroom. I lean over and check the time on the digital clock. There are butterflies in my stomach as I experience a feeling associated with a near-miss on a fender bender. Instantly, every part of me is alive and awake, churning with mixed emotions of anger and excitement. The footsteps stop, and I hear him taking a piss.

"TOM, IS THAT YOU?" I yell, louder than I expected, shocking even myself.

"Shhhh...Yes, it's me," he replies, still unseen.

"Where were you? What happened? Tom, did you go to work today?" I get out of bed, maneuvering slowly up to the bathroom door, feeling a profound sense of gratification. The sight of Tom drenches my arid heart to the point that tears well up in my eyes. He finishes his business, washes his hands, and turns to grab the towel. Standing there, drying his hands, he focuses on what he's doing and I feel alone. I'm lost in a maze of confusion, guilty for experiencing this flood of emotion.

It's obvious that something isn't right. A hostile barrage of thoughts brew inside me, making me feel ashamed for having been so stupid as to rise to a level in this relationship that Tom clearly hasn't reached. I don't feel like we're on even ground. As a matter of fact, I feel unbalanced and ridiculous for some odd reason. I collect my thoughts and try to gain some composure. As we move into the bedroom, I feel more tears well up. They cannot be contained, and roll down my face as my inner physical discomfort battles with my mind. I yearn for him to show some physical affection, in his usual fashion, and for every moment, every second that he doesn't, I literally feel my heart break. It hurts so badly, like my chest is going to explode. I want to grab him, shake him, scream, do something, but I stay calm, breathe and remain frozen in place.

He sits to untie his sneakers, again watching his hands. Finally, after a half minute that seems like hours, he looks up and says, "I did the jobs with Jessica, and then decided to go for a ride. I stayed at the hotel for another night."

Like gasoline poured on a flame, the explanation causes me to go berserk, shouting out with uncontrollable rage, "WHAT THE FUCK! WHERE WERE YOU?"

"I just told you. Stop shouting," he answers.

"Why didn't you call me? I was going crazy — worried to death about you!"

"I needed some space. Some time away."

"TIME AWAY?" I scream, "WHAT THE FUCK DO YOU MEAN YOU NEED TIME AWAY? WE JUST FUCKING MET!" I hate the way I sound, like a raving, insane, jealous housewife. The distaste of my actions only ignites the anger I feel even more. My thoughts and words come out in sync, as if the thirty-second filter in my brain that serves as a buffer between what I think and what I say has crashed: "You got some cash and decide to have you a good old time. I know there's a fucking gay club out there – what's it called? The West Side Club?"

Tom comes right back at me with, "You saying I fooled around?"

"I'M SAYING I'M FUCKIN' MAD YOU DIDN'T CALL, YOU FUCKIN' JACKASS!" I regret the words as soon as they come out.

He gets up and punches me square in the jaw, shouting, "I NEEDED SOME SPACE! LEAVE IT ALONE!"

As if possessed, I lunge toward Tom, blinded by uncontrollable anger and sadness at his behavior, provoked by his use of violence and outraged by my own lack of maturity. I grab him by his hair and began slamming my fist into his head, consciously avoiding his face. He lashes out in defense into my chest, and then reaches for my head, trying to pull me from him. His efforts are strong, but useless against my crushing blows and hell-bent intention to deliver punishment.

We slug it out for a good five minutes before we surrender to exhaustion, mutually spent, breathing heavy and licking our wounds. He's bleeding from his mouth. I haven't knocked out any teeth, but his lip is cut up pretty bad. I focus and realize I've just hurt the one most precious to me. I get up, feeling hurt and confused, and walk into the bathroom to take inventory of my injuries. With the exception of severely strained palms, and a few areas of pain from punches, I'm fine. The fight has left me drenched in sweat, feeling discomfort in every way possible. I'm reeling with disappointment in myself, in Tom, in this lifestyle. I take another long swig of Nyquil and lean back against the bathroom wall as Tom approaches the sink.

"What do you mean by needing your space?" I ask.

"I'm in this relationship because I owe you money. There's no other reason for it," he answers while looking in the mirror, nursing his lip with a piece of cotton. Like alcohol on an open wound, his words burn.

"Was this whole thing a game? You know I love you," I confess, my strength and appetite for fighting depleted. Totally out of character, uncontrollable tears come again, streaming down my face. Sobbing like a little boy, I am embarrassed to behave like this in front of him. Feeling my confidence sapped, it's easy to feel like a loser. As the tears continue and the feelings mount, I feel bad about everything. I'm sad things aren't working out; sad he disappeared for a day and night; sad he propositioned Jon, even more disappointed in myself for fooling around with Jon. I deserve to lose him; I question my actions and my worth. I'm sad he doesn't want to spend every waking moment with me. I get back into bed and bury my face into the pillow, trying to compose myself.

Tom comes into the bedroom and sits on the bed. I turn to face him and his face appears drenched in tears, his nose running, his eyes red.

He answers, "No, it's not a game. I really appreciate what you did for me, with the money and all."

Is he breaking up with me? I can't believe I'm hearing this. As I mentally prepare for his next move, I tell myself that I don't care about the fucking money. What hurts the most is the loss of what I thought was a mutual feeling of respect and love. As we sit in silence, staring at each other, I tell myself, *You're strong. You can sustain your self-reliance through another series of challenges.*

He says nothing. I ask, "Have you ever been in a relationship? I mean, do you know what it means? It goes beyond sex, Tom. Do you love me?"

"Yes," he replies, quickly and strongly. I can't understand what he's doing.

He lights a cigarette and walks into the living room. I hear him turn on the TV. I roll over and close my eyes, praying for direction and clarity until sleep takes me.

5:55 a.m.

I feel Tom wake me, saying, "I want to talk." I hear his voice and continue feigning unconsciousness. He climbs into bed and holds me, taking my head into his arms. "Can you forgive me for not calling?" he asks. "Are you awake? Can't believe I'm wrecking this. I hate that I hurt you."

Despite the fact that he vacillates in his message, these few words somehow cause a hundred sensations that allure me into believing everything is as it should be. I allow my resistance and doubt to drain away. As he snuggles close and squeezes me tightly to his body, I yearn to reach out and put my arms around him and pull in closer.

Rather, I turn my head and then the rest of my body away from him and return to dreaming. As he continues to hold me, I find that I don't care. The stress of the fight, coupled with all the Nyquil, has enhanced my need to escape this day. It's also reduced my need to focus on his words. Tomorrow is all I want right now.

7:00 a.m.

I wake to find myself locked in Tom's arms. I get out of bed and walk into the bathroom. Staring in the mirror, I see that my eyes are bloodshot and I have a bruise on my arm. Unexpectedly, Tom appears behind me in the mirror.

"You weren't in bed," he says. The sight of him irritates me all over again. He continues, "I tried to apologize last night, but you were asleep."

"That makes no sense," I answer, partly sure of my words.

"Tom, please. I don't know what happened to me. I wasn't with anyone this past weekend. I was and am for you. I guess we've both been under a lot of stress."

I swallow two aspirin tablets with a cupped handful of water. The water makes me instantly nauseous, and I lean against the sink, looking at my face.

"Take three."

"Three?"

"Yes, that's what I always do. Two won't do you any good."

I take the third aspirin.

"Fuck work today. Let's spend the day together," Tom suggests.

"Can't. Neither can you. I'm certain you have to be at work," I say. I somewhat regret declining his invitation to play hooky, feeling like a tremendous killjoy. I reason with myself that I'm already pushing my luck with this job.

Noon

Tom is on hold now, his third call this morning. "Cathy's loan was declined," I tell him when I pick up.

"Yes, she told me. It's probably because of our fight," Tom replies.

"You know I don't make the decisions. Besides, the decision was made on Monday, and you would have known that if you'd been around."

"Can we get together for lunch?" he asks.

"No," I answer, inwardly doing so for attention. My response doesn't buy me any, as he ends the call with a cold good-bye.

Thursday, January 26, 1989: 9:45 p.m.

We're driving to dinner as I re-read the letter that arrived indicating that my divorce settlement with Nadine is finalized and she will pay me $189 a month for six months for the credit card debt. Along with the letter was the first money order. We can certainly use the money. Tom's spending habits are out of control. Anything he wants is now within reach, and he spends money like water. The letter also called for me to surrender the military ID card prior to Nadine having to comply with the issuance of the money. She asked me in her letter to set up a date and time to arrange for me to give her the card, so I establish a time to meet Nadine's Mom at the Fort Dix PX on Saturday.

Naturally anxious to move past the negative feelings swirling around in my head, I told Tom I loved him when he got home from work. He replied that he was sorry and that he also loved me very much. We had a long talk, and it wasn't until 9:00 that we realized we hadn't eaten dinner. I'm starving, but have a strange craving for raviolis.

At this late hour, Tom surprises me by taking us to the Savoy in Philly. It's a must on the agenda after every night spent clubbing in the gayborhood, a regular stomping ground for the alternative crowd. We sit across from each other at a booth and take in the terrain of this greasy-spoon that we know so well. The place is a time capsule of the '50s, with prices to match. A red poster hanging on the wall reads, "Please share booths during busy periods." The cover of the red menu has an artist's rendering of a '50s family enjoying dinner, with the caption under the picture reading, "Healthfully Air Conditioned."

Saturday, January 28, 1989

I blame myself more than Tom for the fight, wishing I had acted differently. I should have acted like I didn't care. I've always been the one who didn't care, who didn't need anyone. I hate that I'm so deeply affected and attached to him; But I really love him, I reason, relishing the feelings that initiated my investment in him. I resolve to try to put what happened behind us, and move forward.

When I approach Nadine's Mom at the front desk of the Commissary, she's actually civil to me. She takes the card and places it in the pocket of the cashier's smock she dons. She hands me an envelope. "What's this?" I ask.

"It's your second money order for $189."

"Wow, I didn't expect this until next month." She nods. For lack of anything else to say during an uneasy silence, I say, "Take care of yourself."

She nods again and to my amazement, says, "I don't know if this means anything to you, but I know that you loved Nadine. I know you loved her more than anyone ever has, and I feel sorry for you." I don't know how to take that comment. Then this usually uncaring woman leans over and offers me a hug. I accept the gesture coolly, and smile as we part. I wave as I walk away.

I jump in the car and find Tom sucking on a cig. "How'd it go?"

"Cool," I answer, handing him the envelope, still sealed.

"What's this?" he asks.

"Next month's payment from Nadine."

"Already?" he asks, tearing open the envelope.

As we drive, I reach for his hand and say, "I think about the fact that I can never go back and reverse the cruel words I've said to you. I can't reverse the past. I contemplate things I would do differently. As much as I long to press rewind and record over the hideous parts of our relationship, I can't. I can try and improve, going forward by doing better. I can be sorry, even be forgiven, but I can never go back and make what transpired between us go away. I feel guilty every day for the callous words I said, and the physical fighting. The guilt lingers like the memory of your bleeding lip, heavy on my heart. Your misdeeds haunt me, too, but in spite of everything I still feel in love with you in every way."

"Quarrelling can be good for a relationship," Tom says after a moment of thought. "It improves communication, eliminating repressed feelings, and it's healthy."

I shake my head. "I never want to fight; it should only be something you have to do, and that should be in defense of our relationship from outsiders. With so many people out there trying to destroy and put down this way of life, you'd imagine our energy could be better spent elsewhere instead of fighting each other. The major reason for my current bout with depression is the fact that you said the sole reason you have me around is because I gave you money. The other issue is all the spending you're doing."

With that, Tom offers no response. It stings, but I don't want to beg him to tell me something he doesn't feel or want to say.

Wednesday, February 1, 1989: 3:45 p.m.

When I get home from work, I find another huge orange eviction notice taped to our front door. Rent for January was never paid, and now rent for February is due. I think about our checking account, which hasn't seen a dime of Tom's earnings since early December. I drive to the Glassboro branch and buy a money order for $321.75, exactly half of the January rent. I bring it to the apartment management office with a note indicating the rest will follow. *It's anyone's guess as to when,* I think. I'm not about to break into any of my savings to cover Tom's lack of participation in his financial responsibilities to our household.

6:30 p.m.

"Hi, Honey," Tom says, sounding chipper and energetic when he comes in the door from work.

"Hello, stranger," I say, disappointed he didn't get the same eviction notice reception I did. Tom tosses his keys down and joins me on the couch, where I sit folding a pile of clothes.

He looks over and asks, "What's for dinner?"

I detest his calm, untroubled attitude. I get up and walk in the den. I find the big eviction notice on my desk and walk into the kitchen and place it on a dinner plate. I place a fork on top of the note on the plate. I walk back to the living room and place the plate on his lap. I hate myself for consciously egging on another quarrel.

"Come on, why the attitude? Can't you get off my back?" he pleads, then does something decent and reaches into his wallet. He reluctantly removes his paycheck and hands it to me. I examine the check and smile. Regardless that the amount is a fraction of what we owe, he gets points for handing it all over. His contribution is recognized and it inspires me to kick up the difference to help us make ends meet.

I offer a smile and ask, "How was your day?"

Despite my inward feelings of doubt about his loyalty and support for this relationship, something inside me wants to find a way to bolster confidence in him and in us as a family. Again, I find myself taking a pulse check on my own feelings and I'm still very certain it's true love I have for the man and not just the sex, the fact that it's cool to have a gorgeous boyfriend, or that I need him to feel good about myself.

Saturday, February 11, 1989

The weekend before Valentine's Day, Tom surprises me by arranging a room at a hotel in Ocean City, New Jersey. The hotel is on the beach, and our room has a view of the ocean. "Before you think about the cost of this, follow me," he offers with infectious enthusiasm.

In the bathroom there is a whirlpool tub with a bottle of champagne waiting. It takes us seconds to get naked and into the tub. I look at him soaking across from me with my eyes half-closed, and purr, "I can't tell you how romantic this is."

He wraps his big strong legs around mine and says, "We needed an intervention from the stress."

I nod, smile and offer, "Stunning distraction, lover."

It turns out to be a flawless weekend.

After an incredible meal at the perfect bistro, we bundle up for a late night walk on the beach together holding hands. Back in our room, while Robbie Nevil sings "C'est La Vie" on the radio, we make love, then hold each other until the sun rises, watching it together on the horizon over the ocean. Bliss continues as we crawl back into bed, totally spent and relaxed, and sleep though the rest of the morning in total peace.

Tuesday, February 21, 1989

We wake to a snowy day, finding that about two inches have fallen through the night. When I put the coffee on, Tom stops me. He insists on driving us to work to reduce the risk of an accident, and says we'll stop at the coffee shop on the way in to sit and have breakfast together. When we pull up at the bank, we see Ben shoveling snow out front.

"See you later, " Tom says, grabbing my hand. We lean in to kiss and embrace, and I notice Ben observing us.

"Okay. See you later, then. Be careful," I say. I get out of the car and start walking up to the door. Ben stops me before I enter by shoving the shovel into my chest.

"Glad you're here, bud! Gotta pull rank on you; finish this up, pal," he says. Before I can react, Tom must've caught that action in his rear view mirror, because he slams on the brakes and his Escort slides as its tires skid on the slippery blacktop. Ben and I look over and watch as Tom flies out of the car and starts walking up. He looks pissed, but so tall and powerful in his gray dress coat. Tom grabs the shovel out of my hand and throws it on the walkway.

He looks at me and says, "Go inside – this isn't your fucking job." Not used to hearing him cuss, I am worried for a moment as to how upset he is.

I start, "Tom..."

He puts his hands on each of my shoulders, looks me directly in the eyes and says, "Go in, I got this. It's cold out here." The breath from his words is evident in the cold morning air.

Ben starts, "Hey, pal, this isn't your affair. What do ya..." I lose the sound of their conversation as I obey Tom's request and walk into the branch. I watch them confront each other from the large glass window in front of the branch. Ben bends to pick up the shovel and starts walking into the branch, shaking his head and waving his hand in the air. Tom stands firm, crossing his arms over his chest, giving the appearance of a father sending a scolded child to his room. Ben comes in and throws the shovel down, giving me a dirty look. By now, everyone has gathered in the lobby to watch the show.

As I walk into the back to hang up my coat, our Regional Manager Steve comes out of his office and barks at Ben, "Ben, pick that up. What's the matter with you, are you crazy?" I hurry my pace to hide in the kitchen, where I burst out laughing. Bobby is in the back, and he finds it just as amusing when I tell him why I'm laughing.

"I can't believe I missed it!" he complains. I walk back to my desk, wondering if I'm going to be fired. Ben and Steve are outside shoveling and talking together. Steve looks into the branch and right at me with an icy-cold stare. Up until today, I may as well have been invisible to him, so the thought of a possible confrontation with him sends chills up my spine. As Letitia arrives, Ben stops her and I can see him point to me and talk. I am certain they are discussing what happened with Tom. I'm a good soldier and wouldn't have minded shoveling, especially if Ben had just asked me instead of acting so damn cocky. I feel a bit uneasy about Tom interfering with my job, yet deeply moved by his chivalry. I may not get fired, but I know I'll never get promoted. I can almost hear what Ben is saying about me — just like the kids in high school. A little voice inside tells me to step up to the plate and be proud of who I am, and be proud of the man who defended me. I'm not alone in this. I have someone who cares about me.

They come in, and with the exception of a few dirty looks, we carry on with the business at hand. The branch is inordinately busy as people dash in to get money to go food shopping because of the snow. It's cool watching the snow fall all day. I sit facing the window, so the beautiful view provided by Mother Nature is a constant distraction.

Wednesday, February 22, 1989

The dealership called me at work today to advise that the repairs to my Camaro are finally finished. At the dealer, they take us to the car, parked in the back. I'm elated when I see it's been returned completely to the way it looked on the day I bought it.

The service gal says, "We had to put a brand new steering column in there, couldn't rebuild the original."

We leave the rental, sign a few papers and take off with me behind the wheel. It feels incredible to be back in the Camaro. I've missed the new car smell, which is still lingering quite strongly. Making January's and February's payments on it without having it was depressing. I want to enjoy what I'm paying so much for.

We come home to find that the mail has brought a fresh stack of bills and past-due notices. I don't feel like letting them bring me down tonight. For once I don't open the mail, but bunch it together and put it in my day planner.

We decide to go out to GB's for Quarter Night. I enjoy taking the Camaro out for the evening. To complete the evening, I suggest we follow our usual ritual of going to Denny's for breakfast after the club closes at 2:00 a.m. I allow myself to feel good, let down my guard. To be normal. This is refreshing.

Thursday, February 23, 1989

Tonight, Tom and I lie naked in bed after a non-sexual shower together. He holds my hand and says, "Want to try something?"

"Sure," I say, smiling, putting my hands behind my head, closing my eyes. He jumps from the bed and returns with a can of whipped cream.

"What do you think you're going to do with that?" I ask, pulling the covers up and over me.

"Just relax," he says, pulling the covers down.

"The bedding!" I protest, anxious about our relatively new light-blue sheets and mocha-brown coverlet. "Come on, relax," he says again. I allow him to cover my dick with the whipped cream; its stark coldness is initially very uncomfortable. Tom rubs it over my cock, sending a torrent of intoxicating pleasure to my brain. He leans in and further stimulates the joy by licking and eating the cream off of me. It's playful and exquisitely erotic. At first, my body is electrified and I can't stop stirring. Tom says, "Calm down, now, allow yourself to enjoy this." I lean back and enjoy the feeling for a moment, but soon my legs go all over the bed as ticklish sensations mix with pleasure, igniting every nerve ending.

"Okay, okay, I get the object of this game," I say, getting up on my knees, pushing him down. "I have other ideas, though."

I roll him over onto his belly; Tom instinctively rolls on his back, knowing where I'm going with the whipped cream, but I ease him back onto his stomach. He relaxes as I cover his entire butt with the whipped cream. It's so fun to listen to it burst out of the can; and as it covers his rump, I smooth it over with my hand gently. He squirms and giggles as I softly trace it into his asshole and crotch with my fingers. Then it's my turn to eat, and it's really good stuff.

"Love yer hairless bubble butt," I say, licking and biting as I go, exploring his entire sexy rear.

Soon it's Tom who is turning me over and enjoying my ass. As he slurps around my butt he purrs, "You're my little stripper boy. You like to show off this full curvaceous ass? But this perfect butt is all mine, and I'd like to spend the rest of my life enjoying it."

We return to kissing while the sounds of The Boys Club tune "I Remember Holding You," pour from the stereo.

After hours of lovemaking, changing our sheets, and another shower, we watch a movie together, until I start falling asleep.

"I'm so in love with you," he says, massaging my head.

"Me too, my love," I say on the verge of being comatose.

"I'm not tired. I want to go for a drive," he says.

"Why do you want to go out in the cold?"

"It's the drive. It relaxes me. Do you mind if I take the Camaro?"

"What's the difference?" I ask.

"I hate having to shift, and you know the Escort is a stick shift."

I'm concerned about the Camaro in the snow, concerned about racking up mileage for nothing, concerned about where he's going. Yet, I'm totally exhausted, and completely satisfied. I don't have any desire to argue. He's now gently rubbing me with his fingers.

Always suspicious of his motives, I can't imagine Tom is in any need of sex after we each came twice, so I allow myself to believe he's really going out for relaxation purposes. I say, "Sure. Be careful."

I know he'll be gone for hours. Maybe he has a boyfriend on the side. He gets dressed as if he's going out to the nightclub, complete with cologne and jewelry, then bends down to kiss me and picks up the Camaro keys on the nightstand.

Friday, February 24, 1989

The next morning, I wake with nasty thoughts about the mounting debt. Tom is asleep next to me, holding my hand, our fingers entwined. I find myself stricken by rage as I rise and watch him sleep. What burns me up the most is the fact that he can lie there and sleep so soundly with all the bills piling up. Awake or asleep, he never seems concerned that anything has gone awry with our financial situation. After all, it's all in my name, all on my plate. He has nothing to lose; his fucking credit is already shot. I need my credit to keep my job. I scramble around the apartment, furious and miserable, childishly slamming doors and playing music loudly to rouse him. I keep checking on him, hoping he'll wake, but he just rolls over.

As I shower, I think about how I feel so let down and disappointed in him. I mentally scan a list of where our money goes and conclude that after the rent, both car payments and insurance, there's nothing left. I don't see his regular check or the cash he's earned from Mitch. I don't know what he spends his money on. I'm boiling mad, mostly at myself for not having the nerve to just walk away. I send a prayer up asking for refreshing thoughts about the many reasons and things I need to be grateful for. By the time I'm dressed and walking out the door for work, my spirits rise and the depressing thoughts are subsiding.

At the bank, Jon from Glassboro stops in to do a transaction, and he comes over to say hello.

"What brings you here, man?" I ask.

"I'm off today and was in the area, had to do a transaction."

"What are you doing today?"

"Shopping." We exchange lustful glances. I feel a tinge of regret over our sexcapade, but it soon fades. Bobby comes over and sits next to him, smiling. They know each other from GB's.

Bobby says, "What's wrong with you? You look like you're pissed at the world." How right he is. I give him a blank look.

"You want a happy pill?" Jon offers.

I shake my head no and Bobby says, "You're so cranky lately. Maybe it'll help."

Karen walks by, snapping and pointing to the teller line, and Bobby gets up and follows her. Jon gives me a look, lowers his chin and says softly, "Bitch," referring to Karen.

He gets up to leave, winks at me and says, "Catch ya later," as he pulls a pack of gum from his pocket and tosses it in front of me. We're forbidden to chew gum at the bank, but I take a piece and roll it into my mouth.

11:45 a.m.

Tom calls me while a group of four brothers and sisters surround their elderly mother at my desk. While she grieves over their recently deceased father, the siblings circle over her like vultures, eager to get their cash.

"Want to do lunch, lover?" he asks.

"Yeah, we need to talk anyway." Despite knowing how much he hates to talk about bills and responsibility, and despite knowing how he deals with confrontations, I plan for these to be core topics over lunch.

On second thought, I'd be just chasing him away. Maybe next time he'll think twice about asking me to lunch. I love going to lunch with him. I love being with him. What's the matter with me? Shit, I was so mean to Nadine, so tough, so demanding, so regimented. After Nadine, I swore to myself I'd be a better friend to my next partner. Here I am being awful again. What's wrong with me?

As I hang up, all four of the vulture-siblings start firing questions at me at the same time, and their poor mother silently continues her lonely downward stare.

Tom picks me up and takes me to the Stewart's Root Beer place on Black Horse Pike.

What I want to say is only going to ignite a fight, so I stay quiet. Afterward, he drops me back off at work, and when he doesn't offer to give me a kiss, I don't ask for one. We didn't say ten words over lunch.

I'm about 10 minutes late getting back to work. I apologize to Ben for coming back late. He's on the phone, so he nods without looking up. The "King of coming back late from lunch" leans back in his chair, and puts his arms behind his head, probably gabbing with some chick. I walk back to my desk, which I managed to clear off prior to lunch. There's a note from Letitia that reads "See Me!"

She's at a managers' meeting, so I've got some time until she gets back.

I'm typing up loan documents when she swirls in, tossing her keys and pocketbook down on her desk. Almost from the pages of Cosmo, with perfect confidence, her tall, slender figure crowned with her strikingly perfect blonde hair all tied up in a stately uniform of white dress, high heels, earrings, bracelets, lipstick, and suit jacket, she sits back in her chair and picks up the phone. Ben and Karen, like two dogs awaiting their master, scurry over to sit in front of her, tails wagging. I loathe her personally, but watch and learn how she carries herself. I want what she has. I try to see myself, one day, with the knowledge to be a branch manager, let alone the guts to orchestrate the activities of an entire branch office. I purposely wait for the two idiots to return to their doghouses before I make eye contact with Barbie. She motions to me by wagging her index and middle finger in the air as if I have been selected for an audience with the Pope. I get up and carry the pile of completed work for her to review and sign. She motions again, suggesting I hand her the entire pile. Letitia picks up her gleaming gold pen and starts swaying it back and forth as she looks over the pile of loan documents. I sit there with butterflies in my belly, awaiting her nasty comments.

"I told you not to sign the loan checks until I look at the whole package. What's this?"

"It's a copy of their signature card. I thought we'd include it in their package."

"Why? We don't do that."

I say, "It makes it easier at closing." She continues to stare at me, holding the card in her hand.

"Sue had us do that in Mt. Holly," I say. She slams the paper down and continues to roll through the loan papers and signs where necessary, pushing them across her desk to me as she completes them.

As I'm about to remove myself and the documents from her presence to return to my desk, she snaps, "Wait! Call these customers and make arrangements for closings. I want you to do all the closings — not Stephanie and not Matt. I can't afford any loan errors."

I look over at Ben and say, "Certainly, I don't mind. However, Ben told me I could delegate some of the work out to them, so they could get some experience with the entire loan process."

Ben looks up, but Letitia immediately says with sarcasm, "I want *you* to do them, okaaaaaay?"

She's loud enough for everyone to look up and over at us.

Ben says, "I meant I wanted you to train them on other stuff."

Of course, I think. Far be it for you to rush to my defense, jackass.

"Will do," I say, and begin to rise again.

She comes back with, "Sit down, sit down. Where are you going?" She lets out a long sigh and says, "Shit, I need a cigarette, c'mon."

I follow behind her narrow ass into the back, where she lights a cigarette and sits down at the lunch table, crossing her thin legs. The entire movement of our conversation to the back is bringing everyone's attention to the fact that we're going to have a private conversation in the back. This method is to allude to the fact that I'm being "spoken to." Why not just tell everyone? Why not just blast me here in public? No one would dare come to my defense. I notice make-up smudges on her blouse and take pleasure in knowing she's not flawless.

Maureen, our District Manager's secretary, is sitting at the table eating her lunch.

"You need this room?" Maureen asks.

"No," Letitia responds, smiling at her. Maureen is a meek, mousy woman in her early fifties. She poses no threat to the whore in white. Maureen is usually very nice to me and generally keeps to herself. I am somewhat relieved when the hooker proceeds to yell at me in front of Maureen right here in the break room. I didn't know what to expect with her, and now I know this is just going to be a verbal bashing. How lucky I am, I think, trying to tone out her rant about how she's surrounded by morons and has to do everything around the branch. The TV is on and even though I'm making eye contact with the harlot, I'm focused on what's being said on Jeopardy.

"I don't know why you insist on going against everything I say," she bitches.

I'm confused and ask, "What? What's up with you, Letitia? Why do you think I'm working against you?"

"See? This is the type of flippant response I'm used to getting from you." She's clearly out of her gourd. I never say anything to her that's out of line. She's scolding me in front of Maureen for a reason — she wants this performance to get back to Steve, our District Manager. Perhaps she thinks this display shows she's capable of being powerful. She admonishes me for "trying to push my work off on Stephanie and Matt," and "Why did I think I could come back from lunch when I feel like it?" and "I have to keep telling you the same things over and over."

Still confused, but clear on the fact that good old Ben and Karen told her I was 10 minutes late in getting back from lunch, I start, "I don't push..."

She cuts me off with, "I have promulgated this to you in the past over and over."

Infuriated, I take the defensive saying, "I don't push my work off on them. I was just saying I could train them, and we could share in all the work. We could develop them to be supervisors, or..."

Again she interrupts with, "You are not a supervisor. You act like you're everyone's goddamn boss, but you're not."

She's become so loud; I'm embarrassed and retreat back into my shell. Fearful of losing my job, I hang on, because I truly believe there's a future in banking for me. She stands and says, "I need you to clean up your act." I follow her, dazed, as she walks back into the lobby.

Later, a new account brings cause for me to go up to the tellers with a deposit. I approach Bobby. "She's a cunt," he says to me.

"Guess you heard her yellin' at me," I reply.

"Oh, honey, I think the people driving by on Route 47 heard."

There's a message on my desk that Jon called. It's in the bitch's writing. I approach her again: "When did Jon call?"

"I don't remember. I'm not here to take your messages, Tom."

I think to myself that if I failed to write the time on one of her messages, I'd get screamed at. I call Jon and tell him about the day's events. We're not that close, but I feel it necessary to share. He comes back with, "Now you ready for some happy pills? I have some amazing 150-microgram acid. This shit's a throwback to the '70s, man."

"I don't get into it." We stay silent a moment while I process the thought. *What the fuck? Why don't I enjoy a mind-altering drug? For fuck's sake, I've been clean my whole life. What's it matter?* "Can I try half of half a dose?" I finally ask him.

"Man, just do the whole thing. Take it when you get home, so you're safe. When do you get off work?" We agree to meet for dinner.

I leave at 4:00, and drive to Charlie Brown's Restaurant on the verge of tears. Over dinner, we share our hardships off the job and in relationships. He's moved in with someone, and from the sound of it, the relationship is just as toxic yet addicting as mine. Jon and I have dinner and after, in his car, he hands me a small red triangular pill in a little wax-paper envelope.

"What's this?"

"You're better off not knowing. It's perfect for amateurs." He also gives me the acid. "Both will do the trick, regardless of whether you want to erase Tom or Letitia from your life for a couple hours."

We part ways and I head home. When I arrive Tom's not there, so I decide to hit the gym. I leave a note for Tom.

Tom,
Rough day at work.
Going to try and sort things out in my head.
Going to the gym. Be back soon. •
Love you – T

I hit the gym and work my body hard, allowing the stress to drain. I get home to find Tom home watching TV. He smiles as I walk in. "What happened today?" he asks. I told him about the day's events, and he gets up and sits by my side to hug me.

"Don't let her bullshit bother you too much. Try and relax," he says, pulling me down onto his lap and massaging my head. My problems seem dwarfed by his news: "I'm going to have to go to court for R2O Rentals. Remember me telling you about the time when Nelson and I were at a renter's house repossessing some furniture because she hadn't made any payments, and the lady hauled off and belted Nelson right in the kisser? I have to go to court as a witness on Monday night."

I've never heard of a night court, but Tom wants me to go, so I guess it's true. I second guess everything he tells me.

Monday, February 27, 1989

Sitting at my desk, I pull a yellow sticky note off my screen with a message that Vanessa called me. Vanessa and I worked together for a little while in a few branches, and we hit it off. She got promoted to Head Teller in Cherry Hill, and we haven't spoken since. I dial the extension and get her on the phone.

"Hey, Tommy, what's up?"

"Nada. Hangin' in, girl," I say, elated by her trademark jolly tone.

"How's Woodbury? You likin' it?"

"Oh, yeah! It's a pleasure palace!" We talk about my torments and she tells me she's heard similar stories from some of her tellers, who got the Letitia experience when she managed one of our other Cherry Hill offices.

"I wanted to tell ya I'm headin' back to Mount Holly. Nancy got promoted to Assistant Manager. She's taking Tammy's place. You know, Tammy's not coming back." I knew that, but assumed Janet would slide into Tammy's position. "Now you gotta hush, this is between you an' me. I'm goin' to take Nancy's place as Head Teller. You know I'm livin' out in Willingboro, and it's closer and all. I need to get my big black ass outta this place. That leaves the Head Teller slot open here. You know they never post anything, and I was thinking you could apply for it. I know how much you want a Head Teller position. Are you still interested?"

My heart leaps! "Oh, yes, Vanessa! Yes! You're such an angel for thinking about me!"

"That's all you talked about was how you wanna be Head Teller, so you know I got your back. You was the first one I thought to call!"

To say I'm overjoyed is an understatement. Never has anyone in this fucking business been so kind as to think of me without the promise of personal or professional gain. I let her know how much her call meant to me, and put the phone down. Now I'm on my way. I'm a shoo-in for the opening, because I have loads of experience! They can't deny me! It's my time! I'll quit dancing and concentrate on banking full time. Head Teller! Me! I couldn't be more delighted.

Vanessa's had a hard time of it at First Commercial Bank. She's not only black, but also extremely large in a company full of white girls with 24-inch waistlines. To me, it seems she has more obstacles in her way of advancement than I do. Most white guys hurtle through the ranks, while I remain stagnant. It's my fault they found out I was a stripper, and then I let it be known that I'm gay. I wonder if I allowed these aspects of my life to be discovered so I could have something to blame my lack of advancement on. I can reason to myself that I'm not getting ahead because they know about my dancing, my sexuality. But, honestly, why didn't it happen when they didn't know about it all? What is it about me that needs to change? The more I think about how they won't advance me, the more I see morons get great promotions, the more I want to fight for it. I want to win.

I immediately confront Letitia about the Head Teller opening in Cherry Hill. She has a look of surprise on her face, not aware of the opening herself, and says, "Prepare a memo to me officially requesting the transfer, and I'll see what I can do. Danny's the manager there." Yeah, and he's a closet queen, I think. In return, she holds me at work without asking until 8:00 p.m. to help her catch up on all the backlog of loans, as well as to prepare for a presentation to her service organization.

8:40 p.m.

When I roll in, I share the news with Tom and he's excited to hear of my possible advancement. "I'm famished!" I say, seeing he's seasoning burgers for dinner. I creep up behind him and give him a big hug and kiss on the back of his neck.

"You sure are handsome," I say.

"You are, too," he says. He turns around and kisses me on the lips.

"I love you," I tell him, feeling a renewed sense of happiness, purpose and energy. "You have a grill, right?" I ask.

"Yes, it's in the closet. Why?"

"Let's have a winter barbecue!" Tom pushes his eyebrows downward, yet smiles.

We set up the grill a few feet from our small porch, and it turns out great. While I'm flipping the burgers and hot dogs, Tom comes out to offer me a cold beer.

"Thanks Honey. Sure does smell good, right?"

"This is such a cool idea. I have another," he suggests, "After dinner, we can take a bath together. I'll light the candles and set the mood." He puts his arm around me and pulls me in to kiss my cheek, then leans his head on my shoulder. After a moment, he says, "I'm sorry things got so fucked up between us. I didn't know what this was supposed to be like. I've never been in a relationship, like ours, living with someone."

I nod. "For me, it's mostly our money problems that set me off. Plus the fact that I love you so much, and since we've only been together a few months my confidence level isn't high enough to overcome my stupid petty jealousies. I look at the drives you take at night as my rival. My immature need for wanting your attention overwhelms my sense of reason."

The smoke rising from the grill disrupts the scene, and we both break away coughing and waving the smoke away.

Tom sits in the tub in front of me as we enjoy our steamy, sensual bath by candlelight. I put my glass of Cabernet down so I can wrap my arms firmly around him. I lay my head on his back and close my eyes. Tom leans back and I allow my hands to wander, feeling his soft skin under the warm water. I kiss his cheek, bite his ear and snuggle my face into his neck. It's an entrancing mood, full of emotion that takes over my heart.

After a luscious lovemaking session while "When I Need You" by Leo Sayer comes over the radio, the cherry on top of the evening is spending the night together. Falling asleep looking into his eyes, and waking up with him, is something I could never take for granted.

Friday, March 3, 1989

Vanessa calls and gives me the news that another employee was given the Head Teller position in Cherry Hill, and I feel the floor drop beneath me. I thank her for the news and the words of encouragement that follow, and we end the call. Furious, I jump up from my desk and look for Letitia in the back. Finding her in the drive-up area, I compose myself and, keeping my tone in check, ask the same question I have for the past week: "Did you hear anything yet about my request to go to Cherry Hill as Head Teller?"

Even as my words come out, I hold on to some fleeting hope that Letitia may know something Vanessa doesn't. She pauses to take a sip of coffee, and then says, with a smile, "Nope."

I say, "I found out through Vanessa that someone was given the job already!"

"Oh, then you know," she says. I feel my face turn red. She continues, "I didn't even bother putting you in for it. I need you here."

I assemble all the balls I can and, while maintaining my tone, say, "How could you do that? How unprofessional! You *told* me you put me in for it. I've been asking about it every day. Why couldn't you just tell me you didn't think I would be a fit, or that you needed me here?"

In one second she turns from a composed, coffee-drinking, smiling phony to her true self: a fire-breathing dragon with a forked tongue, yelling, "SHUT UP! DON'T YOU DARE TALK TO ME LIKE THAT!"

Heads turn, and a few employees lean over and move in to witness her fit. Without raising my voice, I say, "I can't believe you didn't just tell me you weren't going to put me in for it. You led me on day after day."

She looks around at everyone — my crewmates are now gawking at her in disgust — then at me and snaps, "Tom, go back to your desk. I didn't have a say in it."

I'm feeling more broken up about not getting this position than I thought I would. I get to my desk, fall into my chair, and sit looking out the window. I come to grips with a new reality: *I really love this banking stuff.*

As Letitia struts by on her way to lunch, I pick up the ringing phone. After the call, she blows her top again, admonishing me in front of everyone over my failure to use the proper marketing tag line when I answered the phone.

"Can I talk to you in private?" I ask.

"What do you want?" she asks.

"Why do you have to yell at me in front of everyone? Is this retaliation of some kind?"

Her face turns red as she looks around at our audience. She snaps back, "You're going to find yourself on the outside looking in if you keep this up."

After she leaves, Bobby walks over, stands behind me, and places his hands on my shoulders. He squeezes a couple times and then sits down in front of me, saying, "She's really deranged. Someone should call Main Office and complain."

"Yeah, right, everyone loves the bitch."

Having overheard my comment from his desk across from me, Matt makes a click-click-click sound with his tongue as if to scold me. I make eye contact with him then brush it off. No. On second thought, I look over at him and let him have it: "Fuck off, Matt!" His mouth drops, then he looks right into his computer, embarrassed. I can't count how many times I've taken the blame for his fuck-ups and saved his ass from her over his numerous loan errors.

I reach down under my desk and lift the phone book onto the desktop. "I've fucking had it with that lunatic," I say, flipping the Yellow Pages open to the section on BANKS. The first large ad I see is for Precision Bank of New Jersey.

Bobby says, alarmed, "Don't leave me here by myself." I shake my head, pick up the phone, and dial the main number. Bobby gets up and returns to the teller line.

"Personnel, please," I ask.

I learn they have a couple of openings for Head Tellers, and they'd be delighted to meet with me for an interview on Tuesday.

7:30 p.m., home

I finish debriefing Tom on today's events at work and my upcoming interview at Precision Bank. He offers, "That Letitia is really malicious. What's the matter with her? You work hard and are really into it. All the shit they make you do for such crap pay." He reminds me I've been there three years, and to make sure I'm not letting her chase me out. I assure him that I've given that much thought, and that it's more than just her, but the entire company. My gut tells me that opportunity awaits beyond the gates of First Commercial.

Tuesday, March 7, 1989

The headquarters of Precision Bank in Westmont is a nine-story building faced with ominous-looking dark brown bricks. The lady who's interviewing me is named Debbie. After a brief yet professional conversation about my background and current situation, she says, "We have two openings for Head Teller, Tom. One is in Stratford, and the other is in Pennsauken. Both are very busy offices."

I think of Nadine and me at the Pennsauken Mart, and something makes me say, "Pennsauken?" in the form of a question. Debbie pushes up her glasses and smiles. Then she makes a note on my application and opens a book that appears to be some type of schedule. She stands suddenly and says, "I'll be right back."

She soon returns, smiling broadly, and says, "I spoke with Carmen, the manager in Pennsauken. She wants you to interview with the District Manager."

I can't get home fast enough to tell Tom.

When I fly in the door and call him at work, Cathy says he's out on the road. I spend the rest of the day doing errands and tidying up the apartment. I stop by the grocery store and pick up the fixings for lasagna. I'm in the mood to make Tom a nice supper.

2:00 p.m.

Tom walks in and says, "What smells so good?"

"Lasagna!" I answer, running up to him. I throw my arms around him and plant a big kiss on his lips.

"Whoa! I got a message you called. I'm guessing everything went well?"

"I have an interview with the District Manager, some dude named Elmer, tomorrow at the Runnemede branch."

"Cool!" he replies, putting his arms around me again for another hug. I check my watch and say, "Wait, Aren't you supposed to still be at work?" Tom walks over to the window, moves the shade and points outside. I walk over and peer out the window and see a R2O Rentals van parked outside. I smile brightly, then start shaking my head and walking backwards.

"You're home for a little frolic, aren't you?"

"Shit, my husband's home from work today, and I'm going to take advantage of it!" He comes to me and kisses me while holding my hands. The kiss ignites our passion and excitement as it gets deeper and more intense. Without breaking our kiss, Tom reaches down and turns on the music. As the song "How Can I Fall" by Breathe plays, I'm gushing as he starts moving his hips and dancing with me while we hang onto our kiss.

"Love dancing with you," he says, our foreheads touching while we look down at my hands in the process of removing his belt and undoing his pants. He pulls my shirt off. We stumble and crash into the bedroom door.

"I don't think we're going to make it to the bed," he says. I go down on him in the hallway, turned on by the sight of his underwear and pants around his ankles. I reach around and feel his tremendous ass while I suck. After bathing his cock in my mouth, I turn him around and have at it. We take the action to our bedroom, and Tom is all over me. We've reached a place in perfecting our technique with each other to the point that mutual desires and needs are met with a minimum of instruction and a maximum of pleasure. After lovemaking, he smokes a cig and passes it to me saying, "You've made me feel safe to share my truths with you. I feel very open and comfortable. More than ever before with anyone."

I nod my agreement and offer, "It fits good, you and me. It's comfortable. You've reached a place with me, too, that no one has." After my puff, I hand him the cig back and lie back and play with his hair and think. It feels satisfying to hear those words from him, and to have made such a significant impact in someone's life. He's generally guarded and keeps his feelings locked up. I remind myself again how short my time with him has been, and I will not allow faint shadows of negativity cloud my clear sky. To me, my destination is right here: in the journey. I believe I'm right where I'm supposed to be.

Wednesday, March 8, 1989

I drive to the office in Runnemede to meet the District Manager. In the lobby, a bright large banner over the tellers reads, YOU'RE RIGHT AT HOME AT PRECISION BANK. It gives me a good feeling.

I don't have to wait long. A woman signals to me, and I rise to follow her into Elmer's office.

Friday, March 10, 1989

Around noon, while the bitch is sitting at her desk on the phone, Bobby slips me a note at my desk and smiles. I casually walk to the break room to take the call.

"Hi, Tom, it's Debbie at Precision Bank. Can you talk?"

"Sure, sure," I say.

"We'd like to offer you the Head Teller position at Pennsauken, at a starting salary of $270 a week. If you'd like, take some time to think about it and let me know later." My heart leaps. I don't need any time to think.

"Yes! I accept. When can I start?"

"I'm delighted! Can you be here in two weeks?"

"Yes, I can."

I take all the information down from her as I pull out a piece of First Commercial letterhead from the cabinet and stick it in the typewriter. I hang up with Debbie, and begin typing my resignation letter to Letitia.

"How did it go?" Bobby asks after waiting on his customer. I grin and make eyes at what I'm typing. Bobby shakes his head and leans down to read what I've typed.

"Oooooh!" he squeals, and starts laughing. "Ooooh, I know a secret!" We scoot to the break room like two giddy schoolboys, and start dancing together to the current song coming over the sound system — Dean Martin crooning "Sway." I spin him out of our dance, and he dashes back to his station and starts chanting, "I know a secret! I know a secret!"

I hold my finger up to my lips and say, "Shhhh!" Soon all the tellers are curious as to what's going on. I can't let them know until I tell Letitia so I say, "Never mind!" and shoot Bobby a look. I finish typing up the resignation and take it to my desk. My first day at Precision Bank will be on March 27, so I date it for Monday, March 13, 1989.

After writing it, I fold it into an envelope and sit back down at my desk.

The rest of the day is so incredibly wild. Nothing anyone says or does annoys me. I gleefully do my chores and am exceptionally nice to everyone. Stephanie and Matt walk over to me while I'm filing an affidavit. Matt says, "You're crazy, aren't you?"

"What?" I ask.

Stephanie says, "You're buzzing around here humming and giggling. What's up?"

I tell them I've been paroled from this shitbox, and hooray for me. They appear genuinely pleased for me, probably partly because my vacancy will create opportunities for their own upward movement. They agree to keep it quiet until I slap the bitch with my resignation — which, from the look of things, will end up being on Monday.

4:00 p.m.

Surprisingly, I'm done early today and before I leave, I get a call from Tom telling me he's on his way home now, too. This is too good to be true.

"I'll be right over," he tells me. "I'll follow you home."

"I have some news for you."

"You got the job at Precision Bank, didn't you?" he asks.

"Yes, sir, I did."

"Oh, darling, that's great news. I'm so excited for you! I'll be right there."

Tom shows up with the company van; some nights he ends up getting to take it home, since he needs to leave right from home in the morning to go directly to a client's residence. On the way home, he pulls over at the side of an abandoned donut shop. He pulls the van around so that his window side is next to my window and our cars are facing different directions. I roll down the window and a blast a cold air rushes in.

"What's wrong?" I ask, wondering why he pulled over here.

He says, "I couldn't wait any more to say I'm so happy for you and of course that I love you." We're only about five minutes from home so his incredibly sweet gesture only reinforces the decisions I've made.

Monday, March 13, 1989

I muster up the courage and ask Letitia if I can speak with her. "What?" she asks, rude as always.

"I'm going to resign. I got another job at Precision Bank."

"Precision Bank? They suck! Why would you want to go there?"

"They're offering me an opportunity to be Head Teller."

"Oh, that's what this is all about. Here's some advice — that place is a dump. You'd be better off staying here."

"You haven't helped me advance my career, Letitia."

"Don't blame your inadequacies on me! You're the one who isn't ready to move up. I just didn't want you to fall on your face. You're making a big mistake. You're going to fail there."

"Thanks, Letitia," I say, standing up both physically and mentally, "but I have a news flash for you: I'm not going to fail."

She starts to say, "You…"

I cut her off, "Let me finish. It's rude to interrupt someone. You need to evaluate how you treat your direct reports, Letitia. But I'm not leaving because of you; I'm leaving because of me. I deserve more respect. I won't tolerate another word from you…HERE!"

Disgusted, I throw down the letter of resignation and turn my back on her to walk to my desk. She jumps up and storms to the back, calling Karen and Ben with her. Bobby, Stephanie and Matt run over and Matt says, "She's going to get you fired!"

Bobby smiles, saying, "She can't. He's just quit."

"They might ask you to leave today," Stephanie says.

They're in the back for over an hour whilst I've been back at my desk waiting on our customers. My heart is in my throat, but I don't give a flying fuck. I feel fucking fantastic. Got my new car in the parking lot, got my husband down the street, and fuckin' got my new job waiting for me. I call Janet to let her know what's happened.

I'm met with a negative response. "Man, I never could understand why you want to move up. We've got it made in this position. We can sit back and not have to worry about the vault, the cash and shit."

Janet and I have drifted apart more and more since my arrival at Woodbury. I now see why she and Letitia worked well together: Letitia didn't feel threatened by Janet.

I want more and am prepared to bust my ass to get it.

CRASHING

Saturday Morning, March 18, 1989

T om has a ton of jobs with Jessica today, and he's been irritated by this fact since he woke up. I have a couple of gigs of my own this evening. While I'm taking a piss, he comes in for a shower. "Hey, you look really sexy with that black towel around your waist," I say. He takes it off as he enters the shower, placing it on the rack. "Do you want some company in there?" I ask.

"No. I have to get out of here."

I tell him, "I'm going to the gym, then to get a haircut for the new job. See you tonight."

I get no answer.

I hit the gym, and then stop at the barbershop at Fort Dix. I adore my long hair, but have been debating with myself about getting a military cut for a while. I decide to go for it, both to remind myself to be different in my new role, and to assume a sexy new character in my personal life. After the barber finishes, I check out my look in the mirror. At first it looks a bit severe — like I've got a piece of carpet on top of my head, with the closely shaved sides. As I absorb the image more clearly, I realize the decision was great: the haircut suits me very well. It's exactly the no-nonsense, sexy effect I wanted.

On the way home, I decide to stop into my new branch to introduce myself.

The first thing I notice is a distinct smell of mildew and the '70s décor: orange counters with big green plants, wide-bulb chandelier lights, and lots of wood fencing around the lobby. A beautiful young Italian-looking woman is sitting at the middle desk without a customer. She looks up and gives me a big smile. She's very attractive. "Can I help you?" she asks.

"Yes," I say, gazing at her.

"Have a seat." She motions to a chair in front of her. I hear the song "Sea of Love" by Phil Phillips & the Twilights coming from a radio, and notice that the nameplate on her desk carries the title *Assistant Branch Manager* under the name *Lucy Santangelo*. Her smile is magnetic, and I find myself instantly lost in her eyes.

"Good morning. I'm Lucy, and you are...?"

"Tom Marino. I'm going to be the new Head Teller here on Monday." Her eyes light up. An old, short, gray-haired woman walks by and sits down at the desk to Lucy's left. I'm guessing the old bat is the Manager.

Lucy looks over and says, "Carmen, this is Tom, our new Head Teller." Carmen is drinking some chocolate milk from a straw. She puts it down and looks up to smile. I don't know what to make of her. She has a warm smile and sounds lovely, but there's something about branch managers that I just don't trust. For some reason, I was expecting Carmen to be Puerto Rican and younger, with short, dark hair. Instead, she's well into her 50s, a veteran banker with a pinched face, no lips, a jutting chin and beady eyes. She can't be more than five feet tall. She's got wiry gray hair with just a few strands of its original black; she makes no attempt to color it. Her hair is short, but it looks salon-sculpted, big and bubble-like. Her suit is beautiful, obviously expensive. She reeks of class attained though many years. You can tell she's old school.

I can't stop looking at her hair. It's like frozen tundra. It sits on her head like a basket – rounded, molded, perfect and so right. She's a model in miniature, like one of those manikins you see in department stores, except the hair on this one is like a helmet — almost too big for her body, like a Barbie doll's. She flashes what looks like a genuine smile and asks me to come to her.

As I approach, she rises to shake my hand. I'm still casting side glances over at Lucy as Carmen fishes through her desk for something. Carmen turns out to be a bit like Archie Bunker, as I find out when she launches into a discussion of the people I'll be working with. It's customary that she would share the status of each teller with regard to their work habits, training needs, and difference records; however, she gets much more personal than that. "Three of the girls are Jewish. They all stick together. One is Barb S. Her last name is too long so we just say Barb S. Her husband's Greek, but she's Jewish and part-time. She's thirty-something and heavyset. Barb's real nice. Then you have Nancy. Now, *she's* a piece of work. Always trouble and always asking for something. And there's Judy." Carmen looks over at Lucy and rolls her eyes. Lucy just smiles and looks at me. Carmen gets up and turns the radio up as Susannah McCorkle sings "Night and Day." Back at her desk, she continues, "Judy is a problem. She works part-time as a bartender at… What's that bar Judy works at, Lucy?"

Lucy, now waiting on a customer, looks over and says, "I forget the name of that place." Carmen rolls her eyes and pulls the pencil from her rat's nest hairdo. Her fingers look like the appendages of a lizard — fat wrinkled sausages with nails done and huge gaudy rings that look so crammed on they'll probably never come off. She makes a check mark on some attendance roster she's got in front of her.

"Judy is quite older — she's in her 50s. She's dependable, but always with the mouth. She's been with me for years. Sherry's your best teller. Now, she's fast and always settles. She's an Italian gal but she's always cheating on her husband. I think she's got one or two boyfriends on the side. She's in her late twenties, but looks like she's in her mid-thirties, and has an eleven-year-old son at home. She's so thin, could be drugs. The husband doesn't know anything about her cheating. Shame. She's flirting with the customers constantly and dresses like she's going to work the corner."

I feel myself blush at this last comment. Carmen continues, "There's Donna — that girl lives in Gloucester. She's another one with a mouth on her. She's relatively new. I don't know where they find these girls. She's got a child at home. Doesn't know where the father is. You know the type."

I'm some stranger off the street, and she's unloading this bullshit on me like we've known each other for years. I despise her already, and make a mental note to be careful. I can just hear her now: "He's queer…you know the type." After she finishes the run-down on the girls, she mentions, "There's a part-time fella too. He's Andy. Nice boy. Shy. Quiet. That's a good thing. The male tellers always have problems balancing. He's no different." She moved on to her budget and how she doesn't like overtime, expenses and how the last three Head Tellers were fired, transferred or quit in the last three years due to incompetence. No doubt there's more to the story than she's telling me. I wonder what role she's played in the demise of my unfortunate predecessors. The last one was Marilyn. I got the impression she seemed to have once liked Marilyn, but felt cheated on when Marilyn left the bank to work at a local liquor store as a Manager.

"Marilyn was Japanese or Filipino, she was good and everyone liked her but she went to manage a liquor store. You've heard of 'Over and Out,' the chain of liquor stores? They bank here. So, where do you live?" *Oh, boy, here it comes. My turn to be grilled.*

"Society Hill apartments in Blackwood."

"You married?"

"No, I live with my male partner."

She smiles and says, "He's your roommate."

I somehow get her point. "Uhhh, yes."

3:00 p.m.

When I get home, I'm surprised to find Tom there. He does a double-take when he sets eyes on me. "That hot haircut and tight T-shirt are extremely distracting," he tells me.

I smile and ask, "What's up? Thought you guys had a lot of work today."

"Mitch called. He said Jessica isn't working for him anymore. All jobs scheduled today were cancelled or given to someone else. I get the feeling her leaving wasn't her idea."

"Does that mean you're out of a job?"

"No — he has another new woman dancer called *Noémie*, a French chick he just hired. She's never stripped before, and Mitch wants you to come along with us on the first gig tomorrow to give her morale support. He wants you to call him." I pick up the phone and get Mitch on the line.

"Tombo, look — I need you to go with Tom Jr. to take Noémie on her first job. She's going to go through with it, but I need you to coach her along, give her some advice."

"Mitch, sure, but don't you think another female dancer would…"

He cuts me off. "No, I can't spare one for this. I'll give you $50 of her cut. Can you just go for me?"

"Sure, no problem."

As I hang up, Tom approaches me and kisses me. He trembles when I wrap my strong, thick arms around him. He turns his handsome face to me and looks at me with loving eyes, saying, "Sorry I was curt earlier."

We take our action into the bedroom and in between the sheets. He finds a way to make my wildest fantasy come to life. As I roll him over and kiss his back,

I run my hands over the soft skin on the muscular curves of his shoulders. Dozens of sensations overtake me as we reach another thunderous summit of climax and I give way to the release.

Sunday, March 26, 1989

The spirit hits me today, perhaps because I feel the need for extra graces before I start my new job, so we venture to Queen of Heaven Church in Cherry Hill. Tom isn't interested in going in to church with me; as a matter of fact, he's being quite nasty, saying, "This is ridiculous. Why do you need to go to church today? I'll just wait in the car until Mass is over." I walk inside alone, feeling a need to be close to God. In a way, it's somewhat soothing, relaxing and refreshing to me. Tom changes his mind as I leave him in the car, and after he catches up to me we sit in the pew together. He looks over and smiles at me.

After Mass, we have breakfast at the Denny's on Blackwood-Clementon Road, then head home, where another spirit hits me. We have lustful sex on the living room floor. Basking in the serenity following our session, with my head on his shoulder, he asks me, "Am I a good man?"

I hesitate, take and suck on his cigarette, and mutter a response as I exhale, "In what sense?"

"I don't know. What do you mean?"

I roll over to face him and ask, "How do you define *good*? Good in what way? How do you want to be considered a good man?"

He pauses to allow my questions to land, then says, "I don't know: Caring, nice, decent, hardworking..."

"You're a good man, Tom," I say. We leave the conversation for a short nap.

5:00 p.m.

We drive into Philly to meet and pick up Noémie. She lives in a tiny apartment in University City. Her husband answers the door; they're both here from France and have a little son. Her husband is also a dancer, who works part-time for Mitch and full-time for another agency. He's in his mid-twenties and looks years younger than Noémie, who has to be thirtysomething. After a brief introduction, Noémie feels a need to share that she's a teacher by profession in France, but circumstances have led to having to be resourceful in bringing in cash. We all have a story and reasons to account for why we're stripping for strangers; some we share, some we don't.

We drive to the gig — a house not far from the Ben Franklin Bridge, in Delair. On the way, Noémie mentions the nervous feeling she has, and we talk about my experiences for a while. Along with some tips, I provide her with some words of motivation and encouragement. As she begins doing her thing for the six guys at the house, I'm overcome with a feeling of embarrassment for her as she tries to come off sexy, and it just doesn't work. The straight men don't seem to notice how stupid this looks. They're having a blast as she dances around to them. She pokes her "teets" in their faces while shaking her boney white ass around. When she finishes up, Tom brings her robe to her.

In the car she asks, "How was it?"

"Terrific. You looked like you were enjoying yourself."

"I was, it was fun."

I add, "We have to do something about your music selections."

Monday, March 27, 1989

I'm up and ready early. Tom is still in bed. He gets up as I get dressed, and sits on the side of the bed watching me.

"Good morning, Mr. Head Teller," he says.

"You know it!" I chirp in response.

"I'm going to put some coffee on."

"Already done," I say. "I put the timer on last night, so it's all ready."

He smiles, and says, "Oh, good, I'm going to get a cup. You should have something to eat before you get going. You'll want to be totally energized and all."

"No, I'm okay," I say.

Tom insists, "I'll fix you something real quick. Did you get a cup of coffee yet?"

"Not yet," I say, following him into the kitchen while trying to knot my tie. He fries some bacon and scrambles some eggs for me.

"Excited?" he asks, buttering a piece of toast.

"Very! I wasn't nervous until today."

"You'll be great!"

"Thanks, Tom." After breakfast, I brush my teeth again and check my look in the mirror. "Head Teller," I softly mutter, looking at my reflection. I walk out and approach Tom to give him a soft kiss on the lips.

Later – Pennsauken, New Jersey: 9:05a.m.

Carmen comes over and walks me behind the teller line. As we walk around, I notice another woman on the platform that wasn't there on Saturday. She's waiting on a customer, so we don't interrupt. Lucy is walking out of the teller line as we make our way around, and lights up with a big smile as we pass, saying, "Hi, Tom!"

"Hello, Lucy," I say, following behind Carmen. I tower above Carmen, even with her large helmet-head of hair. Carmen shows me to my new station, saying, "This is your unit. The Head Teller is stationed here so you're close to the main vault." Then Carmen introduces me to the staff. My back-up is Sherry, who is extremely skinny, with a tiny waist. She has a warm, friendly face and is beaming when she lays eyes on me. As she finishes up with her customer, I realize her smile is a whimsical grin that's actually a mask for her own nervousness. She doesn't seem to be able to stop smiling. It's too weird. Sherry has medium-length curly black hair held back with a white barrette. She has to be in her mid-30s, definitely one hundred percent Italian. She's kind of pretty. I can't help but think of what Carmen said about her antics, and how much alike we are.

Carmen then walks me over to the platform and introduces me to Sharon, a Personal Banker. Sharon strikes me immediately as someone with a brain. She's also a bit short, at 5'1, with light-brown hair styled nicely. She has a really cute pixie-like face. She gets up and shakes my hand, offering me a big smile.

Carmen reminds me again that Marilyn left to work at the liquor store. "Marilyn became friendly with the owners and took the manager job there. It's been some time since these girls have had a Head Teller. They need some discipline and order."

"Right," I say, acknowledging her words.

"Sharon will be doing your training, Tom. She didn't apply for the job. She's setting her sights on becoming an Assistant Branch Manager."

"Have you been a Head Teller before?" I ask Sharon, respectful of her, since she holds the position I just vacated.

"No."

"Well, I'll leave you to it," Carmen says suddenly, and walks back to her desk. Lucy follows.

Over the next two weeks, Sharon trains me in the Head Teller position. During the process, I call friends at First Commercial and share my progress. No one but Bobby seems to be happy for me. They're all so punch drunk on corporate brainwashing Kool-Aid, they tell me how disappointed they are that I left First Commercial. Precision Bank is miles ahead of them in technology, processes and maturity.

It doesn't take me long to realize I'm feeling over my head. The branch is very hectic, and joining the team as a leader makes it even more of a challenge, because I'm assuming a role where I'm responsible for directing people who know what they're doing better than I do.

Every night I take policy and procedure books home to study. Every Monday, we have to be at work by 7:30 a.m. to work on over a hundred night-depository bags, mostly from the nearby Pennsauken Mart.

Carmen turns out to be more annoying than smart, and I know I can't draw much from her in the way of either banking knowledge or leadership skills. Sharon is operationally knowledgeable, but inept at leading the tellers. She gives them orders, but if they don't perform as she would perform — namely in the way of speed-of-transaction and bag processing — she displays visible signs of frustration with them. Often, she will huff and puff and roll her eyes at the tellers. Sometimes, she throws night bags down on a teller's counter with a thump. She's been pretty cool with me — probably because she doesn't want the additional duties of the Head Teller job, and feels no threat from me. I'm thinking that she's thinking the sooner she gets me trained, the sooner she can get her ass back on the platform and away from this teller shit.

When I fuck up, Sharon merely shakes her finger at me in a kind manner, gives me a warm smile, and reminds me over and over to relax, stay calm, and stay cool. The cash volume in the branch is just incredible, and the number of transactions is huge. The place really rocks and by the end of the first week, I feel comfortable asking her, "Sharon, is it me, or is this a shitty assignment?"

She laughs in her pixie-like way, pats me on the back, and says, "Yep, it is. Better you than me. You know, it was open for months. No one wanted it."

The position is a major job, and entails a great deal of frustration and aggravation. There's no time to be weak or lazy. By the end of two weeks, I find my skill level has catapulted to expert level in every aspect of teller operations. The new role has reinvented me; by mere necessity, I'm more demanding of others and myself. To make this a cohesive team that functions efficiently, I have to be a leader with a cutting edge: the ability to both inspire drive and propel accountability.

Monday, April 10, 1989

This past weekend, Noémie and I had heavy dance cards. I did nine jobs in two days, and tagged along with Tom and Noémie on a couple of her jobs, which turned out to be really fun. She's cool with the fact that we're gay, and even got into entertaining us on the gigs by undressing some of the guys she was performing for. One job was a bachelor's party for bunch of hot firefighters. The guy for whom she was ordered was one of the hottest of the group. While he was all into it, dancing with Noémie, she removed his clothes after she got naked. He even got a semi-chubby, but soon she was stripping a couple of the others. We stood on the side, arms crossed over our chest, trying to appear threatening, with our straight poker-faces. I laughed out loud when the song for her final number, Fine Young Cannibals' "She Drives Me Crazy," played from her tape over the boom box.

Mitch teamed us up for a joint gig on Sunday, and it turned out to be one of the most enjoyable jobs I've had. It was for a retirement dinner for a fiftysomething guy at this posh restaurant with his co-workers, family and friends. As he was seated next to his wife, Noémie walked in and threw a pair of underwear at him, acting like a jilted lover. Then I walked in and acted like Noémie's husband. Adding the fun theatrics to the usual dance routine was fun. I cooked up a cool music mix and dance routine for us, and it went off perfectly.

Even though my 22nd birthday is this Saturday, all I can focus on is our bills, which continue to mount each week. Tom has a habit of spending way too much money. When I demand his cut at the conclusion of the jobs he does for Mitch, he's great at being evasive on the whereabouts of his cash. I get the credit cards statements, and they're out of control. We continue to struggle with the rent each month. We didn't pay March, and now we're halfway into April. To get us caught up, I decide to cash in the savings bonds I've received from family and friends. It's painful to use the bonds.

Tuesday, April 11, 1989

Tom calls me at work, telling — not asking — me to meet him for dinner at an Italian restaurant in Cherry Hill, not far from my job. "I don't have any cash," I plead, hoping he'll volunteer to pay.

"I got it," he says reluctantly. "It's on Chapel Avenue. Take Haddonfield Road like you usually do to come home, then turn right on Chapel and the place is on the left."

"Why don't I just come home and we'll go together?"

It's out of character for Tom to express frustration with me over the phone, but he does just that, with an elaborate sigh. "Fine, come home and we'll go."

Curious as to why he seems to be having a meltdown, I race to get home after work and, upon entry, greet him with a kiss.

I notice another pile of fresh bills waiting for me, and after quickly perusing them, I ask, "Have you seen the credit card bills? They're getting out of control. You need to put some money in our account — I can't shoulder the entire thing by myself. We can't afford to go out to eat. Just give me the money."

"Are you coming or not?" he asks, picking up his keys to head out.

We remain in silence all the way to the restaurant. We walk in and are seated. Tom says, "I like this place."

"You've been here before?" I ask.

"My ex and I used to come here." He sits back in his chair with an unusual air about him. As the waiter approaches, Tom lights a cigarette, and something about his manner strikes me for the first time as pompous. Despite it being the first time I've sensed this pretentious attitude, I realize it's been there all along and I've never noticed it.

"Gentlemen, can I start you off with drinks?" the waiter asks. I look at Tom, allowing him to order first.

"A very dirty martini," Tom says, implying something to the sexy looking waiter. The waiter, eager to please, smiles and looks at me.

"Manhattan," I say.

He keeps smiling and says, "Very good, be right back with those."

"Is he gay?" I ask as the waiter disappears. Tom holds a finger up as if to indicate he's not ready to answer me, with having a puff on his cigarette taking priority. My irritation festers when he doesn't respond, as if pondering some other important topic in his head. *What the fuck?*

We sit in silence until the waiter returns with our drinks and goes over the specials. I'm sure he's gay. When he leaves, I push the issue again: "Well, is he?" I ask. Tom nods, while slowly sucking in a drag of his cig. He looks so sexy and suave. I do adore how he holds himself, how he looks. He's wearing a silky white button-down shirt with flowing long sleeves; the shirt is neatly tucked into pleated black dress pants, freshly creased. His black shoes are polished, his hair neatly combed and parted. He's never a week without a haircut, so he's salon-fresh and hairsprayed. He's so debonair and sophisticated. Tom looks like he walked off the pages of GQ. As for me, I decided not to bother changing when we got home. I'm wearing what I wore to work, a brown sweater vest over a white shirt and matching tie. I loosen the tie from around my neck. Something possessed me to wear a pair of Tom's cufflinks today – little metallic half circles that took a half-hour to put on by myself this morning.

I force myself to assume the same pose he has — slightly leaning into the table, with a bit more serious look. I have to laugh at myself, trying to be someone I'm not. I analyze him, and he's got the mature sexiness I associate with those soap opera stars on TV. I have to adapt to it if I'm going to improve my image. I'm so silly and gritty. Unrefined. Raw. I feel tiny in his shadow.

When the waiter returns with our drinks and asks about an appetizer, Tom says, "I'll have the shrimp cocktail as an appetizer. For dinner, I'll have the rigatoni special you mentioned."

Angry at his continued lavishness, I think to match him and say, "I'll have the shrimp cocktail too, and..."

Suddenly Tom cuts me off by kicking me under the table and says, "No. I'm paying, and we can't afford it. Just order dinner."

I'm too mortified to respond to this, and at a loss for any words other than, "Spaghetti and meatballs," the cheapest thing on the menu. The waiter, not smiling now, nods, says, "Very good," and walks away. I'm very embarrassed.

"What was that?" I ask, leaning in and gritting my teeth.

"I'm not paying for your appetizer."

I snap, "What the hell, Tom? I never begrudged you anything. That was rude and you made us both look like white trash." He doesn't say anything. Just sits there with a smug look on his puss. I find myself feeling hurt and confused. "This is a very prick-like thing to do," I say.

He snaps loudly, "WELL, YOU'RE THE ONE ALWAYS BITCHING ABOUT BILLS!"

I sit through dinner, very upset and with a hard lump in my throat, ready to explode. His loud remark earned us a look from everyone in the room. The subject of our finances is buried and that, I'm sure, suits him just fine. Fucker. On the way home, he has the balls to ask me if I'm interested in going to GB's. I don't want to do a fucking thing with him. When we get to our parking lot, he says, "Fuck you, then, I'm going the hell out myself. Maybe I'll get lucky and find someone to fuck around with."

"What brings that comment on?"

"You've had a pissy attitude all during dinner and in the car, just because you couldn't get shrimp cocktail. What a baby!"

"Why didn't you let me get what I wanted?"

"Because it's HIGH TIME YOU WENT WITHOUT! YOU ALWAYS have to have everything," he responds.

"Stop yelling and just go!" These hard feelings and heated exchanges always end up in a physical altercation. He's just slinging out anything to get a reaction; it hurts that he's saying it to cause me pain. He ends up taking off to go out and I walk in, go into the spare bedroom, and slam the door. As I fall onto his twin bed in the spare bedroom, I get even more upset, since it's *his* twin bed. It adds credence to his usual mantra that everything in our apartment belongs to him.

8:45 p.m.

I'm sitting at Kurt's, one of Philly's best and hottest alternative dance clubs — a place Tom detests. I'm soaking up a couple of Manhattans. It's busy for a Tuesday night in here. After wallowing in pity for a while, I took a shower and changed into the sexiest jeans I could find – form-fitting around my waist and ass, with a slight hint of bell bottoms. They work like a magnet to pick up guys, and I flirt with a few but leave after an hour, with my mind on make-up sex with Tom when I get home. I turn off Chestnut, then to Market Street, and leisurely walk down toward the prominent City Hall building, taking in the sights of the city and feeling a little better and more grown up than ever. I circle back around City Hall, and walk down toward where my car is parked. Feeling my buzz wearing off, another club, Key West, beckons me in with the promise of more opportunities to flirt and drink. I find another bar stool, and it's only seconds before I spot a short but cute little dude with a nice ass nearby. He has the shadow of a sexy goatee on his face — another plus. Before you know it, our eyes meet. He smiles. I smile back.

He finds his way over and says, "What's up?"

I lost the last hour or two, and this is me talking completely smashed. As it turns out, his car is parked in the same place mine is: on the roof deck of a lot directly across from the Key West. I'm in his car, and we're kissing and fondling each other. He's tugging at my big black belt and the buckle. He's kind of hot, but has a unique smell to him. It's isn't bad — just not Tom. His scent is a different cologne, different soap, or different deodorant. His short, light brown hair is in my face as his head hovers over my lap. I smell his head, and it stimulates me. Love the scent of a man's head. He looks up, and I notice his cute little dimples. Dimples always turn me on. He unzips my trousers and reaches in to feel my cock. He has a pretty-boy face, and I want it on my cock. I push his face onto my dick and feel him suck on it and lick my balls for a few moments. It's dark as pitch out, and all but abandoned outside, so we exit the car; and despite his useless protesting, I find a way to lower his jeans and briefs to the floor, revealing the ass I wanted to see. It's a nice little flawless butt. I take his ass into my face and, finding it spotless, I tear into it with my tongue. He pants that he's got lube back at his place, but I don't want to go there and I don't want to stop. I lube it myself with my spit and position my dick at his hole. Soon I'm fucking him hard and fast until he decides a condom would be a good idea.

"Hey! What about a condom, man?" I realize he's doing more than squirming at this point; he's thrashing about, trying to get me to stop fucking him. I'm so close to shooting my wad, but I stop and pull out. He's a bit shaken but still into it. I console his bitching with some kissing. He walks over to his car in careful steps, with his pants wrapped around his ankles. I laugh, finding it funny. He looks down to see what I'm laughing at and chuckles himself.

"Just take 'em off, for Christ sake."

"Oh, and be a total nudist like you," he replies, shaking his head and using his eyes to gesture down at me. I'm buck naked from the waist down. "Might as well take that shirt off," he says.

"Fine," I say, feeling drunk and free. I stand there, naked as can be. I hoist myself up on two cinder blocks and face the city street. There is no one to be seen down in the dark alley. While he finds a condom, I lose my erection enough to piss off the edge of the building.

"Wow! You should see this!" I shout to him, turning to see him returning. I slip the jimmy on and we assume the fucking position again. It's a long way to orgasm as I fight feelings of guilt and gallons of alcohol. Nameless is bent over, whacking his dick off faster, so I assume I better cum before he goes.

"Harder, fuck me harder," he grunts. I look down at his eager white hairless ass sucking in my cock. I find the right frame of mind to bust my nut, and just as I do, he shouts for it and shoots his own. As we fall into sudden death from our efforts, I roll over and lay on the roof of someone's car. He squats down, holding his legs together — just as a group of guys get off the elevator. My conquest scrambles to his feet, pulling up his pants and yelling to me to get in the car. I find my underwear, and as I pull them on, the group passes by, giggling and snickering about it. My date is clearly embarrassed, and unfortunately not as inebriated as I am. I feel numb to any sense of worry or embarrassment. It's great. Finally, after I shoot a couple remarks back in their direction against his hissing and pissing, I fall into his car and ask for a kiss.

"Fuck, no. You reek of booze, man." He acts like he's done with me, pushing me off and pulling his shirt down. Five minutes ago he was begging me to shove it in harder, and now he's lecturing me about my booze-smelling breath? I stop him from pushing me by grabbing both of his hands. He pulls away and fires a slap off to my face, saying, "Okay, get out."

He suddenly tries to haul another slap at me. I snatch his hair and jerk his head back. He goes absolutely ape-shit, pushing and slapping me. Fuck this. I give him a punch so hard it makes a cracking sound to his jaw on impact. He freezes for a moment, staring at me. I can only hear the buzzing of my brain. He doesn't budge. I grab his jacket from the back seat to wipe my chest and crotch and say, "I'm leaving."

"Oh come on, now," he says, rubbing his jaw, and he actually belts me in the mouth again.

"Fuck you!" I say, loudly and deeply, giving him another slap in the face. He starts freaking out, trying to get out of the car. I grab the back of his head again and push his face into the steering wheel. He says, crying, "Look man, just get out, get the fuck out of here, leave me alone!" There's no reason for me to be here. No reason to behave, no reason for him to be an ass. I don't care at all. I want to slap him again, so I do. He says, "Stop it, man," still crying. I notice he's bleeding from his nose. There's nothing left here to do. I turn his head loose, realizing I'm still holding onto his hair. I get up and out of the car. As soon as I get out, he takes off.

I get in my car and take off myself. Still horny on the drive home, I pull my thick cock out and jack it off again while driving. I toss through a bunch of cassette tapes looking for a song. When I find it, I blast Taylor Dayne's "Up All Night" and fly home at over 80 in my bright red Camaro. I enjoy the lighted dash and its fresh new car smell.

When I get home, Tom's not there. I throw my keys on top of the entertainment center and remove my clothes very deliberately. I feel that my face is wet. Is it blood? I reach for it and wipe. It's water. I've been crying. Numb to it all, I realize I've been feeling ashamed of my behavior. I get completely naked and, after a quick shower, crawl into our bed, right in the middle, throwing his pillows on the floor.

Wednesday, April 12, 1989

When I wake up, the first thing I notice is Tom sleeping next to me. I must have slept right through him coming to bed. The next thing I notice is my aching head and the realization that I've hit the snooze button on my alarm too many times. Now I'm running late, and have absolutely no motivation to work. It's raining on the way to work, and I just know I'm going to be fucking late, given the amount of traffic on Route 42.

8:49 a.m.

I pull into the branch parking lot, anxious and fretful about being late to work. I'm sure Carmen will be agitated. Her black Mercedes is already here. I walk into the branch, holding my head up high, and as I pass Carmen, sitting at her desk, I nod and say, "Sorry I'm late. Traffic was horrible."

She announces loudly, "You're late! We open in 10 minutes."

Sharon is behind the teller line, coordinating everything. She shares that Carmen's been bitching about me being late all morning. I apologize to her, and an hour later I'm waiting on a customer when Carmen comes up behind me moaning about her fucking budget and about how Kathy gave her a list of supplies we need that I had approved.

"Did you approve this?"

"Yes, Carmen."

"These girls need to realize I have a budget. Look here, Kathy ordered three boxes of tampons and last time she only ordered only one box." I nod, giving my customer her change. The elderly white woman looks at Carmen as if she's a nutcase. Carmen carries on, "Don't you know they probably put them in their pocketbooks and take them home? I'm on a budget. We can't be ordering all this stuff. Look," she says, pointing to the supply requisition form, "She's ordered four packs of telephone message pads! What was she thinking? And you, sir, you asked her to order a new typewriter? What's wrong with the typewriter we have? What's wrong with this one?" she asks, going up to it and typing a few keys. I try to speak, but the little witch won't stop.

I organize all the patience I can and calmly state, "Carmen, I ordered a new typewriter because this one doesn't work – the letters E and N are shot. We have to correct everything! They won't send someone to fix it. This old thing is from the 1920s!"

She shakes her head and crosses off the request, saying, "*I'm* from the 1920s! Are you suggesting we 'get rid' of me, too? You don't understand how things work at Precision Bank. You don't go ordering a new typewriter!" She marks up the rest of the form and hands it back to me with her scrawl-like signature at the bottom.

Friday, April 14, 1989

Sharon comes over and tells me, with a grim look, that I have a call from Ellen in Branch Administration. I smile at her and she stands there, frozen, as I pick up the phone.

"Hello, this is Tom Marino."

A very confident and deliberate voice comes back: "Tom, it's Ellen Ryan in Branch Administration. Tom, my man, I heard you weren't getting the incentive for your referrals."

"Oh, yes, right," I say.

"Well, I fixed it and you'll see the incentive in tomorrow's pay, along with the back incentive we owe ya."

"Oh, thanks."

I tell Sharon what the call was about so she can breathe again. She's really spooked about this Ellen, telling me how awful she is.

7:45 p.m.

I come home late from work, and find that the bill for the washer and dryer isn't being paid — and Sears is threatening me with a collection agency.

"Look at this fucking bill! You said you would pay it! You said we needed a fucking washer and dryer!" I tell Tom.

He asks, "Can you shut up? Can't you see I'm watching TV?" I glance at the nonsense music video he's watching and hit the roof.

"How can I get your fucking attention? I have a bill here from JC Penney for new curtains, new shoes, and your little visits to Thrift Drug over and over for candy, candy, candy, cigs, cig, cigs. What the fuck, Tom? There's a bill here from Sears for the fucking washer and dryer — there's one here for Visa with the shit you bought me for Christmas — there's our rent that's coming up again — there's the fuckin' car payments that are now both behind. I'M NOT PAYING YOUR FUCKING CAR PAYMENT! It's on my credit. Where does your money go, Tom? I haven't seen your paycheck go in our account in months!"

"None of your fucking business!" he snaps.

"I want all my cards back NOW! Out of your wallet — NOW!"

He stands up and throws them from his wallet at me one by one, aiming for my face. They fly all over the room. "HERE! HERE! HERE!, he chants, goading me."

"Pick them up!," I say, shaking with an effort not to explode.

"Fuck you! Pick 'em up yourself, and shove 'em up your ass!"

"WHAT A LOSER!" I yell, then turn and bend to pick them up, thinking this isn't what I want, saddened by the whole thing.

He's suddenly on me, punching me in the head and screaming, "FUCK YOU!" I turn and suddenly stiffen up, and within minutes I've got his hands in mine and pin him down and drill my chin into his face. He's twisting and turning now, throwing punches at me and attempting to bite into my hands holding his. I punch him hard in the face until his nose is bleeding. After an intense moment of physical bashing, we start playing the threat game.

"I'm leaving!" I say. Then he threatens to go into my job and tell them I'm gay. That infuriates me even more. I lunge at him again, and we go at it again. We clench each other until fingers are numb. We throw vicious, foul language and comments at each other; nothing is sacred. It's a horrible scene. Love isn't supposed to be this way.

He's gone to the couch and his cigarette, and I'm feeling in need of support.

I call Bobby, and he says he'll be right over. Tom flips out over this news. Bobby arrives and sits in our living room and looks at us. He listens to us bitch about our fight and renders a level-headed decision, scolding Tom for not participating in the payment of the bills — and even admonishes me for not trying to settle this in a civil manner.

Bobby leaves after a while and I go into the little pantry we've converted to an office and collapse onto the floor. Tom soon comes in and sits in the chair to his desk.

He says, "I hate that you brought that queen into this."

I say, "I don't feel like talking."

His eyes, already swollen from crying, well up again.

"I hate to see you cry," I say.

Tom says, "I didn't think we're in trouble. It's none of anyone's business what goes on with me and you. I'm sorry I was an asshole again."

The storm clouds of our fight are clearing, and I'm starting to see the man I love again. He is, after all, a beautiful human being – and he has to feel even lonelier than I do. After all, his parents are gone and he has no one to go running to. If this doesn't work out, he's here — he's not going anywhere. I should know that it's hard for him to trust anyone or believe in anyone, and here I dash his trust and privacy on the rocks. *Shit, maybe the rocks are in my head* — I realize I have to be steadfast in my desire to get this bill situation worked out. Nothing has been resolved; he still needs to pay his share. I tell him how worried I am, and that I can't sleep at night. I certainly don't want to lose him, but he needs to do his part, too. I express that

I want his commitment that he understands what his financial obligations in this relationship are.

"If this is going to work, we have to work together and be closer. I'll give you my checks." He stands up and offers a hand to me. "Come on, let's go lie on the couch together and watch TV." I get up and follow him into the living room. With all the lights off and a blanket of quiet surrounding us, I now feel embarrassed our neighbors had to hear the battle, and regret bringing Bobby into it.

"What do you want for your birthday?" he asks. His arms around me feel warm and comforting. It's as if all I just said went in one ear and out the other.

I close my eyes and shake my head, saying, "Just your love, and let's put the money toward the mountain of bills. I don't want to be alone in this, honey. We got you a new car — and you never mention the status of the insurance situation on your allegedly stolen Camaro. Remember the three grand I gave you? What's up with that?"

"Don't worry, we'll do it. All the bills will get paid. I'll put money in the account tomorrow. Tomorrow is your birthday. Tomorrow will be a better day. I'm planning something, so don't make plans for the evening." He changes the subject. It's avoidance. It can only be a lie. I begin to mentally part with the money I lent him.

My 22nd Birthday, Saturday, April 15, 1989: 8:00 a.m.

A call from Mom wakes me, and when I answer, she's singing the Happy Birthday song to me. She asks what I want for my birthday, and I respond by asking her if we can go to my favorite restaurant, Sky Lodge. I tell Mom that Tom has something planned for us to celebrate tonight, and she sighs. We agree on dinner tomorrow evening, and with another long sigh she ends the conversation with, "I hope you know what you're doing." I don't respond to her, and try not to read anything into what she's trying to convey. After we hang up, an eerie premonition of impending danger sends chills right through me.

I cuddle into Tom, and his sweet smell and soft touch bring me back to possibility, and a peaceful state where I begin to doze again.

9:54 a.m.

Tom wakes me, and what I perceive as his contrition comes in the form of breakfast in bed followed by a nice session of his brand of dessert. His husky hips straddling my chest, his sexy long legs wrapping around me, and his gorgeous bubble butt in my face for munching make a brilliant start to my special day.

1:30 p.m.

When Tom returns from a half-day at work, we take a drive over to Echelon Mall and walk around. We stop in a leather clothing store, and spot a really cool black leather jacket with matching pants. My first thought is that it's perfect for my gigs. I try it on and it's really stylish; with the fringe, it somewhat resembles a western, cowboy-type jacket. The sales dude approaches us and his sexy black goatee and killer smile convincingly offer, "It comes in white, too. I think you would look hot in white." When he finds a white one, I try it on and instantly love it, checking my reflection in the mirror. There isn't one in Tom's size in white, so he tries on a black one. When we see how we look in them and how we look together, it's easy to lust after having them. Tom says, "Just put them on the credit card and I'll pay it off with money I get from Mitch next week." It's stupid, but I do it, justifying the expense by thinking my outfit can be used for dancing. It's a cost of doing business – you have to spend money to make money, I reason. My reasoning doesn't help - in my head I know spending money on this kind of thing is just stupid.

Later, at Home

"I have a pair of white leather boots for you to wear with it," Tom says. When he produces them, I remembered seeing them before when we were moving, but I've never looked at them like I am now. They're really sharp.

Once I'm ready, I join Tom in the living room. He looks me up and down, and after a pause he says, "You are the most incredible-looking guy I've ever been with."

"Wow, thanks," I respond, turning him around as I look at him in his black leather ensemble. I say, "Check you out: your ass looks incredible in those black leather pants."

"We're dressed more for the Bike Stop than Gatsby's," Tom says, referring to the leather-and-Levis bar in Philly.

I'm brushing my hair in the mirror when Tom comes up behind me and gives me a strong bear hug, wrapping his arms around my chest. We catch sight of our reflection in the mirror, and lose our sensual grins for a moment. The mirror reflects something very nice — two handsome guys, clearly in love. This moment will not last forever. I want to engrave this picture in my mind. Seventy years from now, this will be gone; but we have it now, and I take in a deep breath of air and revel in the moment. Tom is big and tall and very striking in his black leather suit. The sight of his soft, shortly-cropped brown hair and handsome boy-next-door face, coupled with his clean-cut appearance, makes him extremely sexy and beautiful. I'm wearing a sheer white tank-top under my white leather jacket, and it does a magnificent job of accentuating my well-defined chest. Tom breaks the silence and says, "We look good, don't we?"

"Yeah," I say, "I was just thinking the same thing."

He takes me by the hand and leads me to the sofa in the living room. Out of nowhere, Tom produces a gift and a card. He hands it to me while I'm sitting and he's on his knees. I open the lovely card and read the caring words. I lean over and kiss him. He grabs me, and opens his mouth to share a kiss with me.

"I really love you, Tom," he says, looking into my eyes.

"These are the moments I crave," I answer, allowing a flood of emotion to drown my sense of reason. I reflect on all the obstacles we've experienced together, as well as some huge hurdles we've yet to clear — hurdles that could stop our journey together dead in its tracks. But during like moments like this, the only reason I need to continue to fall for him is what I see in his eyes when he tells me he loves me. He takes my hand and brings it up to his mouth to kiss.

"You're my life — the best friend I've ever known. I can't describe how you make me feel inside. I'm sorry for all the fights," I say.

Tom nods and kisses me again, saying, "I feel that way too. I'm the cause for most of the fights; I'm sorry I'm not living up to your expectations. You're a dream come true for me. Open it," referring to the gift. I open the gift and inside the wrap, it's a box from JC Penney. I open it and find a delicate yet masculine silver chain bracelet. Tom puts the bracelet on my wrist and kisses it.

"It's beautiful," I say.

"You like it, then? It's okay?" he asks.

I nod, and try to hold back tears as I say, "Yes. I like it, Tom. I do." When I blink, the tears fall down and I look at him and say, "Yes, yes, yes, I do love it. Let's make love. I want to make love with you. I want to taste you."

Tom gets up and says, "No, we've got to get to the club. I've got more surprises for you."

"Oh, please," I beg, "I want to be inside you." We tackle each other, and I end up getting my way. He's very playful. At one point, he's in the hallway, naked, and stands on his head.

"Hold my feet up! Hold my feet up!" he shouts.

"What the fuck? What are you doing, you goofball?" I say. He finally gets positioned on his arms and spreads his legs. He's standing on his head, legs spread open, and says, "Now go for it — eat me!"

"Ha! Okay, sure!" I dig right in. Tom ends up falling over, and I catch him as we pile up in a sexy twisted mess.

We laugh and perform a couple other wild naked stunts and games, like two boys with no rules, so free and so uninhibited.

Finally finished, we take another shower and dress again.

"I'm so spent, I don't think I can stand up straight," he says, giggling.

As we walk to the car, I hold my wrist up to view my new bracelet. "Thank you again for this. I love it," I say. We hold hands as we walk the short distance to the Camaro. Our neighbors, a straight couple and their kids, park as we approach. I see her shake her head and say something to him. Tom must have caught it, too, for he turns to plant a kiss on me. It's a beautiful starry night. I have one of those really content feelings inside of me.

Gatsby's is so packed when we arrive that we have to park in the parking lot of the Chinese restaurant adjacent to the club. I get a nervous flutter of excitement in my belly when I get out of the car, because I hear the pounding thunder of the dance music coming from inside the club. When we enter, the electrifying sound of "Holding Out for A Hero" by Bonnie Tyler greets us. Heads turn to view us, as usual. I feel like a celebrity, so confident and proud holding Tom's hand. I keep my chin up and dish out the small cover charge. In my earshot, I hear complimentary comments and remarks about me and about us. In my peripheral vision I soak in everyone's stares. It feels so good to be sought after, to be wanted, to be desired, to be in demand. Tom leads me upstairs to the piano bar which, to my surprise, is decorated for my birthday. There are balloons, a HAPPY BIRTHDAY banner, and Tom has invited my friends to come for my birthday. Among the group I'm surprised to see that Noémie and her husband are here, as well as Beth — now going by Bet — and her lover Melanie. Pat is here, as well as Bobby and Trish, Jeff, Janet and Billy. I can't stop wondering how much planning and work went into this. After a couple hours, Tom says he ordered a male stripper for me who never showed up. He's clearly pissed over that, and the fact that Mitch wouldn't give him a discount on the price. I lean over and whisper to him, "Don't worry about it, Tom. It was a nice thought, but you're all the man I need."

He smiles and turns to kiss me. Then he stands and says, "Gotta pee, be right back."

I'm in the middle of a chat with Jeff when the lights flicker off and on and off again. Tom appears from around the corner with a big, beautiful white cake covered in twenty-two white candles. He places the cake in front of me, and the dude at the piano begins playing the "Happy Birthday" song as everyone in the room starts singing to me. It feels amazing. I catch the reflection in the mirror across from me, and with the lights out in the room, the white cake with the bright white candles illuminate my white leather outfit. Tom has his arm around me, and I stare at my face for a moment. I look so satisfied. I savor the moment, and send a prayer of thanks for this joy.

I look at Tom, who with this one simple deed has once again ratified and elevated my love for him. He's proven again that there's no one above me in his life, and I'm confident in his love. After the song, I look out at everyone and then at Tom. "I can't explain why I'm speechless," I say. I summarize my many dreams and wishes in my thoughts, then reaffirm my desire to be in God's service. Finally, I send up another prayer of thanks and blow out all twenty-two candles, wondering how this new year of my life could possibly be better than the last.

Then everyone converges on the cake. It's delicious, and Tom looks at me for approval. I take him by the hand and lead him to the bar, finding a quiet moment alone, and say, "Thanks for the great cake, my love." I lean in and kiss him with all my might and passion. "I love you, Tom, I love you. Forget the bad times, we've beaten them all."

Tom rises with a renewed smile and slaps his hand on the bar, ordering the bartender, "Birthdays are a time for excess. Open a bottle of your…" Tom looks at me and then continues, "…cheapest champagne, Keith." I have to laugh at his attempt to help us save money.

Keith the bartender shaking his head, answers, "Sir, yes sir!" and salutes Tom, smiling. He sends a barback to fetch a bottle. Tom turns and gives me a peck on the cheek, grabs my left hand and strategically places it on his shoulder, then puts his right hand on my hip and grabs my right hand, fingers clasped. Now in position, he leads me in a romantic tango-like dance for a moment. He ends the dance with a dip of my head and a long, wet romantic kiss. Soon the champagne flows, and we have a tremendous time sharing, having fun and dancing the night away with our friends and each other.

On the way home, Tom holds my hand while driving, and lifts it to his lips to kiss. This is the Tom I met and fell in love with, and I feel ashamed of my part in the fights we've had. "I wish you could have met my folks," he says softly. "My Mom would have liked you a lot. She was funny like you." Silence for a moment; then he adds, "A good but dry sense of humor." I've never thought of myself as funny, but I know I have a good sense of humor, and I'm laughing all the time. It makes me feel good to know that Tom is equating me with his parents. He always speaks extraordinarily highly of them. He once shared some pictures of them, and I can definitely see his Father's eyes and his Mother's smile when I look at his dashing good looks.

When we get home, we're all about assuming new sexy roles. Safe at home with the man that I love, it's exciting to know we can come home and play together. The stories we heard tonight from friends of astonishing highs from mind-blowing drugs and fantastic hook-ups at the baths can't compare to what we have. Horned up, we strip down and steam up the bathroom to simulate our own tantalizing encounter with each other, sans the need for any lofty drug-induced high.

He's my shameless cock fiend, anxious for a marathon of flesh moving against flesh. With an unparalleled intensity we go at it with all we have for two-and-a-half solid hours. That's when Tom introduces me to a detonation of pleasure and satisfaction that transcends my wildest imagination.

Following our unrivaled session of incredible sex, he slips into bed and turns to me, saying, "I hope you enjoyed your special day."

"Yes, my love. I did. Thank you for everything," is all I can manage as I conk out from sheer exhaustion.

Sunday, April 16, 1989

I must have been really tired. It's 11:20, according to the clock on the dresser, and Tom's missing. I reach for the phone and dial Mom's number.

"Hello," a familiar voice sounds, chipper and upbeat.

"Hi, Mom. How are you?"

"Oh, hi dear, I'm good. What are you up to?"

"I just got up. I was really tired."

"Wow! Wonderful. What did you do last night?"

"Tom had a party for me with a bunch of friends at the club we hang out at."

"Oh, that's nice, dear. Are you going to Mass today, or did you go last night?"

"I went last night," I lie.

"Good. Are you coming over tonight for your birthday?"

"Yup," I say.

"I made reservations for 6:30 at Sky Lodge. Can you guys be here by 5:30 before we head out?"

"Sounds good, Mom."

How can I describe the Sky Lodge experience? It's just a restaurant and nightclub, but as far back as I can remember, it was a tradition for my parents to take me there every year on my birthday. I'd fallen in love with the place from the first time they took me there as a little boy. I found something really magical about Sky Lodge. I was enraptured with the fact that Mom and Dad would get a sitter for Danny; until he was about three, it would exclusively be me and Mommy and Daddy. I'd get all the attention. They introduced me to ice-cold cocktail shrimp, which I fell in love with; and since I only had it once a year, it was an amazing treat. The place had a high ceiling for a little boy, and the lights were in the shapes of little stars. I was in awe at the sight of it. Oddly enough, they also had a big wooden statue of an American Indian in full ceremonial dress. Looking back, I realize it didn't take much to impress me, but Sky Lodge always produced wonderful memories.

Mom continues, "Yeah, that way you can open your presents and then come back after dinner and have your cake."

"Okay, Mom, thanks! I love you."

"I love you, too. Bye, dear."

Tom gets home around 2:30, and he's in an odd, overly-loving and affectionate mood. "Where were you?" I ask.

"Went for a drive." I tell him about the plans with my family, and he's agreeable. He looks at me for a while and says, "I told you I love your eyes, right?" I nod my agreement.

"Well, I can finally describe what it is about them that's so alluring. I heard the song 'Sad Eyes' by Robert John, on the radio while I was driving. All I could do was think about your beautiful eyes."

"'Sad Eyes'?" I ask.

"Sure. They're all sultry and sexy with the half-closed eyelids. It's a major turn-on, and I think it's your best feature."

"Whoa! Whoa! I believed you thought I had *another* best feature."

I get a smile from him and he says, "Well, best public feature. Hey, here's a present for you," he says, handing me two chits.

One is a deposit receipt for our checking account for $1,000. Another is a receipt from the apartment complex for our March and April rent payments. The receipts have Saturday's date.

"You did all this yesterday? Why did you wait till now to show me?"

"I told you I'd come through for us. I made the deposits and rent payments on my way home from work."

I fold the receipts and turn to put them away, feeling overwhelmed by mixed feelings of confusion and relief. He grabs me by the shoulder and turns me around. "How about a kiss?" I move up to him and we share a kiss. I allow myself to park my momentary disorientation with this surge of rain on our parched relationship. I'm delighted, and tell him so. I feel there are negative forces surrounding us, but I cast them off. I abandon my reason and judgment and lie down with him. I trust this moment because it's all I have; something tells me there will come a day when we'll move on, and each find someone else. Right now, though, he's all mine; and regardless of what's right, or wrong, at this moment I'm content and I need to go with it. I trust this moment.

Later

After opening presents, we go to dinner and are joined by Danny and his girlfriend, Debbie. Dinner is fantastic: I savor it all — conversation, company and food. Tom is unusually quiet during dinner, and I prod him a couple times, asking, "What's wrong?"

Mom finally interjects, nudging me and whispering, "Leave the boy alone and let him eat. He said he's fine."

I detect that something isn't normal with him, but shrug it off in hopes he'll come around. Despite Dad's protests, Tom is resolute about paying for dinner. I'm stuffed, and yet we all go back to their place for my ultimate favorite dessert: ice cream cake. I love the crunchy chocolate morsels between the vanilla and chocolate ice cream parts of the cake. I thank God for my Mom. She's bright and smart in so many ways I'm not. I always thought of her as strong. She's animated, honest, loving and tender. She's down to earth and classy when she has to be. She's disappointed me, and I've disappointed her, but that's the way life is. I have thoughts of telling her I'm gay, but something keeps me from it. I know she won't approve. I don't want to lose her. I know the gay thing is a deal-breaker. That's something I just don't want to face. My parents have an absolute hatred of homosexuality. This hatred stems from their ignorance, their lack of understanding it. It's hard to understand something you've been brought up to condemn.

After we get in the car to head home, Tom immediately holds my hand while we wave goodbye. "You did it again," he says.

"What?"

"You called me 'honey' a couple times at dinner and at the house."

"I did?" I say, less horrified this time than when I did it before.

"Relax. I don't think they care. I think they know what's going on between us."

It's second nature to call him "honey." We do it constantly around each other, and it's hard to curtail it in front of my family.

Tom says, "Danny is cute."

"You think so? Yeah, I guess he is," I ask and answer all at once.

Monday, April 17, 1989

I stop by the gym after work. After my workout and stint in the shower and steam room with the boys, my body is so primed and sexy that it's almost a crime not to accept the many invitations to play. But I trust in my love for and from Tom, and that alone makes it easy to behave. Despite not crossing the line, the temptations do wonders for my already-inflated ego.

With the days getting longer and warmer, it feels great to be able to wear shorts outside again; so I put on a pair of dark green gym shorts with a single white pin-stripe on the side, along with a matching white short-sleeve cotton Ringer t-shirt, which takes its name from the ring of contrasting dark green at crewneck and sleeves. By the time I get home, I'm feeling really refreshed and happy.

6:30 p.m.

I finish a call with Mom as Tom walks in and greets me with a smooch. I report, "That was my Mom. Danny dumped Debbie for a new girl named Jane."

"That's nice. I'm hungry," he says.

"I've got some hamburger lasagna mix brewing in a big pan on the stove." He walks up to it, lifts the lid, and smells it.

"Oh, and Mom invited us to Danny's school play. I think they have three shows this week."

"What play is it?"

"*Grease.*"

"Okay, we're going," he says.

"Great. We'll get to meet Danny's new girlfriend — Jane. I can't believe he went out last night with Debbie, knowing he was going to dump her for Jane."

Tom shrugs. "Maybe Debbie dumped him," he offers, walking into the living room.

I follow him, and watch as he plops onto the couch and begins flipping channels on the TV. I sit with him and snuggle up next to him, asking, "What's wrong?"

"Nothing," he answers in a rehearsed tone.

"Something's the matter. I can sense it." He turns to me and shakes his head.

I haven't known Tom long, but I can just tell there's something wrong. He's been a bit out of sorts since last night. He rises and goes to the bathroom and closes the door, so I return to the kitchen and finish cooking. I put a portion of food on each plate with some bread, and bring them to the dining room table. I walk back to the bathroom door and hear him weeping inside.

"What's wrong?" I ask again. I lie down on the floor and peek through the crack at the bottom of the door. I can see Tom lying on the bathroom floor.

"Hey, T," I call, "come on out here. Dinner's ready. Come and eat something."

He gets up and comes out of the bathroom, looking down at me. "What are you doing?" he asks.

"I'm sittin' here, worried about you. Spill it!" I say, offering a smile to cheer him. His eyes well up in tears, and he looks down at a tissue in his hand. I take him by the hand and lead him to the couch. We sit and I say again, "Honey, what is it? You're killing me." His unusual refusal to discuss whatever major issue could cause this strong man to break down causes my heart to jump to my throat. *What could it be? Maybe he found out he's got HIV. Maybe he's had it since we met and he's finally going to tell me. Maybe he cheated on me. What the fuck?!* "Tom..." I say, louder and more direct.

"I got arrested yesterday," he laments, looking me right in the eyes.

"What? What happened?" I ask, concerned and relieved concurrently.

"You know I had that account at United Jersey Bank?"

"Yeah, your checking account?"

"Well, I deposited a check off my closed account at South Jersey Savings in there, and then drew out the money when it became available. Then they got the check back from South Jersey marked 'closed account.'"

"How much was the check?" I ask.

"Seven thousand dollars," he admits.

I organize my thoughts and ask, "When did you do this?"

"About three weeks ago," he says.

"Why? What did you want that much money for?"

"To give you for the bills," he answers.

My breath catches in my throat. "You had to have known they would catch you. Where's the logic in..." I stop and compose myself, then begin again. "Look, I appreciate that you wanted to help with the bills, but that's clearly not the way, Tom. Where's the money?"

He shrugged. "I put some of it in a safe deposit box in your old branch at First

Commercial in Woodbury."

"How much is left?"

"Around five grand."

I sit back and cross my arms over my chest, and know I'm exhibiting facial expressions and body language that convey disdain.

Tom opens the floodgates of confession. "I really have to say this to you, but I'm scared. It's just that I've done this before: when I first met you." He pauses for a moment, looking off into space and interlocking his fingers into a prayer-like fold, then continues: "It was when you lent me the money to bail me out of the First National mess. I told you the insurance company stopped payment on the check for the stolen car while they conducted an investigation. There was no insurance check. The Camaro was repossessed 'cause I didn't make the payments."

He stops to let me digest what he's just said. He appears to expect an explosive reaction after I absorb it, but to me it feels refreshing just to hear the truth. I nod while maintaining eye contact, as if providing absolution for sins confessed. To blow up at this point would only cause him to clam up.

He continues, "That's why I had to take my bike to work at McDonald's."

His eyes water again, and for a moment, I feel pity instead of callousness and offer, "Thank you for the honesty."

"You're so beautiful, Thomas Marino," he gasps, then continues. "With winter approaching, I realized I had to have a car to get to work, so I went to the bank and deposited a check from my closed account at South Jersey Savings into First National, and waited for the bad check to clear."

"Yeah, playing the float," I say, well aware of the illicit practice of kiting. I continue, "How could you rip me off like the banks?"

He shakes his head and now puts his face in his open hands, elbows on his lap. He nods, visibly upset; and with tears falling says, "I'm so ashamed. I have every intention of paying you back. Would you have lent me the money if I'd told you the truth?"

"No, Tom."

"Stop, please, I can't hear any more!" he says. We sit in silence for a moment. I watch as more tears well up and fall down his face, and it hits me hard.

"So what happened with the arrest?"

He looks down into his lap where he's fidgeting with his hands, trembling now, his face wet from tears, and says, "I..." He looks up at me and finishes, "I betrayed you and I'm sorry for that." I nod, my heart feeling very heavy. I maintain a tough front, but his fractured character is tugging at my heartstrings. He goes on, "There's no excuse, Tom, but this gay life has been one of struggle and hiding and self-preservation tactics. I didn't know love and trust until I met you. I'm so ashamed. God, I'm so ashamed."

"That's okay, it's okay, I understand," I say, pulling him close and using my hand to guide his head to rest on my chest. I softly rub his hair and say, "What happened yesterday?"

"The cops came to the door early yesterday morning, around 8:00 a.m."

"I didn't hear them," I say, trying to think back to yesterday morning.

"You were asleep. I had a feeling they were coming," he says.

"You knew? How? You must have known they would catch up with you eventually."

"Yeah, I guess so. I thought it would play out with a phone call like before. United Jersey Bank tracked me down at work, and I told them it was some kind of mistake. I never imagined they would call the police. The cops were pretty cool about it. They told me I had to go to the station with them. They placed me under arrest and put the handcuffs on me." With that, Tom cries again, and buries his face in his hands.

"Why didn't you wake me?"

"I just couldn't," he says, continuing to sob. "We got down there and they took me into a room and they made me undress. I had to go down to my underwear, but it was so humiliating. They took my wallet and keys and asked me what all the keys were for. They went through my wallet and clothes. They fingerprinted me and now I've got a record." He drops his face into his hands and there are more tears.

"They interrogated me relentlessly — wanting to know all about why I did it. What did I need the money for? They asked where the rest of the money was, and after an hour in a holding room, they came in and released me. They actually told me not to leave town. I'm going to get a court date. They said they would probably give me an installment payment plan with the court, or add it to my bankruptcy. No jail time — probably just a fine, since it was my first offense."

I say, "Well, that's good. Sounds like the worse is behind you."

"I just feel like shit. I'm such a fucking loser," he says.

This is my man, and he's really hurting. My gut tells me to be alarmed about the nature of his crime, given my bank job, but my heart tells me he's being honest — and this showing of a vulnerable side somehow ingratiates him to me.

Something deep within instructs me to go into autopilot and do what comes from the heart, so I get up and walk around the apartment lighting all our candles, then walk to the stereo and cue the cassette to our song, "Waiting for a Star to Fall." I turn and say invitingly, "Come here," opening my arms wide. He rises and approaches me. I take him into my arms, and hold him tight as he buries his face in my chest. I tug on his sleeve and find his eyes to declare, "Don't cry, Tom. It's over and you're safe."

He softly says, "I don't care about the arrest. I don't care about what happened. What I'm sorry about, what I regret, is that I hurt you. You're so caring and gentle, Tom. I fucked up, I'm a fuck-up. I don't know how I got so lucky to find someone like you. I can't say how gratifying it is having you in my corner. I'm embarrassed by what I did, and so ashamed."

I nod and return his head to my chest with my hand, saying, "I'm here for you. Remember that." In a moment he lifts his head and our faces meet again. The kiss we share is explosive. It energizes and awakens the initial passions and feelings that sparked our love. I chase away doubt and fear. I abandon reason and logic. I go with this thing in my heart and ignore my gut. I want what I envision: a life partner and husband in Tom. We're soon naked, and in our bed making love. The heat of the candles envelops the room, and we're drenched in sweat as our passions ignite.

"I love you, I love you, I love you," he says over and over, finally smiling as he kisses my face, my cheeks, my ears, and my chest as we open ourselves up to even broader sexual horizons and experiences, taking our trust and thrusts to a new level. Following a four-hour session that results in each of us blowing two huge loads, Tom searches for a cigarette and finds he's out.

"Wait," I say, reaching down for my large gym bag, which is next to the bed. I pull my white baseball cap from the bag and put it on his head backwards. I pull my large weight belt from the bag and toss it aside.

"You have a lot of toys in there," he says. I finally find what I'm looking for and pull them out and lift them up to Tom, saying, "Here ya go, Chief."

He takes my pack of red-box Marlboro cigarettes, saying, "Cigs in your gym bag? Got any candy in there?"

"No, but maybe a French fry or two."

He lights a cigarette, takes a puff and then blows it out, saying, "Christ, these are strong as shit." He hands me the cig. I share a drag and hand it back. "Chief? You and yer names. At least you have a nice body to go along with that tough image," Tom says, stroking my shoulders with his free hand.

"Thanks, *man*," I say, as I roll over and return a compliment to him, "You're fucking hot, too, *bud*."

He volleys back, "Your ass is to die for, *bro*."

I smile and say, "You sure did spend enough time down there, *dude*."

He smirks and asks, "What else you got in that gym bag, *boss*? Can I peek?"

"Yeah, go for it *homey*."

His smirk grows to a full smile, as he roots through the bag. He says, "Oooh, your jockstrap is in here! Here's a new pair of sexy Calvin Klein tighty whiteys with a red waistband."

"Having fun taking inventory?" I ask.

He nods, holding the new underwear up to his face to smell. I shake my head.

"You look so fucking hot in the jockstrap. Love how your ass looks framed in it. Can you put it on for me?," he asks, holding them up with one finger.

I gladly oblige, reaching for them and say, "Nice little smile you got there, Shaw: kind of devious, kind of devilish." I pull on the jockstrap, and it buys me leverage for yet another couple of hours of sex. So we go at it, this time taking our action into the shower and to the point of sheer exhaustion.

We crawl back into bed facing each other. We don't say anything, but maintain a stare into each other's eyes. "Stay with me forever," he says.

"No worries," I offer.

He nods back and smiles lightly. His bloodshot, swollen eyes finally begin to narrow and close. I remain awake until I hear his breathing change to the sound of unconsciousness, and get up to put the candles out. I return to his side in bed, and kiss his cheeks softly, so as not to disturb him. He rolls over on his belly, and I return to his butt under the covers. I snuggle my nose deep into his crack and kiss it. The fresh scent of soap arouses me again, imagining him in the shower. I brush it off and allow sleep to take over, using his bodacious rump as my pillow.

Tuesday, April 18, 1989: 4:00 a.m.

Dreams laden with worry over our mounting debt wake me up. I turn over and find Tom gone. I get up, look out the window, and notice his car is gone. He must have gone out for a "drive." I need my rest, and don't want to worry about anything. I take the optimistic approach, bring my thoughts to imagine a peaceful place and get back to sleep.

6:00 a.m.

After I take my shower and get dressed, I'm walking out of the bedroom tying my tie when I notice Tom in the kitchen, back from wherever, dressed to kill. He turns to me and says, "Good morning. I went to Wawa and got your thermos filled up with coffee for you, just the way you like it."

"Thanks. Where were you? Out all night again?"

"Yes. I had to clear my head." It pisses me off, and I express the feeling by letting out an exaggerated sigh. He lights a cigarette and leans on the counter, drinking a cup of coffee.

"I thought we did that last night," I say. "These nocturnal excursions of yours irritate the fuck out of me."

He snaps back, "Like I give a shit."

I retaliate with, "I'm outta here. Seems I went to bed last night with Doctor Jekyll and Mr. Hyde is back this morning."

He says, "You're an asshole." I give him the finger, and grab my stuff to leave. As I close the door behind me, he opens it and leans out the doorway, watching me. He shouts after me, "You forgot something." I turn and he flips me the bird. I turn back around and trip slightly, but enough to get embarrassed. I'm more pissed off than ever. When I reach the car, I open the door — and the window seems to stick for a fraction of a second before shattering completely into a million pieces, scattering all over the place.

I look up to heaven and mentally ask, *Why me, Lord?* My glance then finds its way to Tom, expecting him to burst out laughing. Instead he walks over in his stocking feet. He takes a drag on his cigarette, inspecting the damage, and smirks. "See what happens when you fuck with me? I used my secret powers."

For a moment, I wonder if he's right. Then I turn in a huff, storm into the house, and plop onto the couch, staring off into silence. Tom comes in and sits next to me. All I can imagine is driving around in a new Camaro with a window covered in plastic, held on with green duct tape. I call Sharon at home, and after listening to my drama, she tells me to relax and take the day off to get it fixed. I hang up and go back to staring into space. Tom, back to Dr. Jekyll, places his hand on my knee and is sensitive to what I'm feeling. I don't even have to bitch about the situation. He's fully aware of where I am.

I turn and look at him and he offers, "I know an auto glass repair place in Berlin that can fix it for a song." He reaches for my hand, holds and squeezes it, saying, "Don't you worry. We'll get it fixed. I have to meet with my attorney today on the

White Horse Pike in Somerdale, so we can drop your car off at the glass place and go to the attorney from there."

I get up and go change into some old jeans and a black t-shirt. I find my sunglasses and keys and we're off.

Later

"This is my last brush with crime. The attorney said the money I spent can be added to my bankruptcy." How that's possible, I'll never know. I feel like asking questions, I feel like asking him how he found this attorney, I want to ask why I'm not more involved in his life decisions. This isn't how I want the relationship to be.

I don't need to know. Just let it go. When we get back to the glass place, the car isn't done so Tom, now starving, wants to get something to eat. We go to the Berlin Diner, and I have coffee while Tom enjoys breakfast, gabbing about what the attorney said. Apparently everything is going to be okay. His fee would be factored into some payment plan. After breakfast, we pick up the Camaro and I get to write a check for $157.13.

Friday, April 21, 1989

I leave work early to go home and change. Tom and I have a low-cost date tonight, courtesy of one of the benefits the bank offers in the way of a recreation program for events such as trips, concerts, bowling and theatre tickets, available with discounted group rates. This evening, we're meeting at the main office in Westmont to take a bus trip to a casino in Atlantic City. Our trip includes a tour and wine tasting at the Renalt Winery in Egg Harbor City on the way.

None of my cohorts from the branch are going except for my boss, Carmen. When we get on the bus she's sitting with Kate, the manager of the Collingswood office. Teeming with confidence, I introduce Tom as my *significant other* — a bold move that earns me one of his trademark winks that cause my heart to float. One of the employees hands us a ten-dollar voucher for quarters at the casino.

The stop at the winery on near-empty stomachs allows us to get buzzed before our casino destination, which happens to be Resorts. After we drop the ten bucks in quarters from the voucher and another twenty of our own money that we can't afford to donate to the casino, we decide to call it quits. We run over to the local gay bar, Studio Six, with the intention of having one quick cocktail before returning to the bus at the designated pick-up time. Well, one turns into three Manhattans for me, as I absorb a very relaxing moment with Tom. While I stare at him, he seems so distracted with what's happening at the club and with gawking at every dude in the place. Some odd sense of strong confidence, or whiskey, swells my heart and I don't feel compelled to influence him to quit his exploration to return his attention to me. Oddly, I don't feel emotionally bruised, which is the usual consequence of his lack of attention. Rather, a calm and easy mood envelopes me and tickles my brain.

We find our way back to the bus, and though I don't remember falling asleep, Tom wakes me at the Westmont Main office parking lot with my head firmly on his shoulder.

Friday, May 5, 1989; Tom's 24th Birthday

April has turned into May, and other than ordering a cake, I haven't done a thing for Tom's birthday. I've been working my ass off dancing and at the bank, while my animosity toward Tom swells due to his continued failure to contribute cash to our bills. I'm feeling our relationship is on the verge of collapse as I struggle to meet the minimum payments on all the credit cards while making the rent payment, the two car payments, and the huge insurance premiums on both cars. For the first time in my life, I'm discovering painful additions to my bills, such as late fees and over-limit fees. The cards have all just about been maxed out, with no available credit remaining. The most stressful bill is from American Express, because they expect full payment each month. Since I was paying it off every month, there was always some available credit on it with no set limit. Over the last couple months, I haven't been able to keep up with Tom's monthly spending, and it's about $700 deep and two months late. They're hounding me on the phone both at home and work, sending form letters almost daily reminding me I'm late. It's brutal. I know I have to get a handle on this.

When I get home from work, I find Tom sitting there watching TV. The thought of getting him a dog has crossed my mind, so I decide to make it a reality. Somehow, I equate the concept with the natural order of progression in a relationship. Despite everything, I still want to build a nest and grow with him.

"You ready to pick up your birthday present?" I ask.

Tom smiles, and asks, "What? What is it?"

"You'll know when we get there. Let's go," I say, smiling back.

I drive us to Deptford Mall and he follows as I walk to the pet store. Tom looks at me curiously. "I could have brought a dog home for you, but I think you should pick one out yourself." He smiles and turns to hug me. His embrace feels warm. Inside there are a dozen little creatures to look at. Selecting one is extremely difficult, since they're all so sweet and cute. Tom finally approaches me as I stand with a puppy barely big enough to fit in my hands, and says, "I don't know what to do. I love them all. What do you think? You like that one?"

"Well, I've always had miniature schnauzers growing up. They're great dogs." I can see Tom has an immediate crush on this little fellow, too. We take turns holding him and kissing his little head. He's so helpless and new, shaking all over yet full of energy and playful. His face is adorable. His little razor-sharp teeth nibbling on me sends chills up and down my spine. The adorable bundle of wagging tail, soft eyes, and warm puppy kisses is begging to be taken home. I hand him to Tom. Tom holds the puppy and stares into his little eyes now. I think we have a match. Tom walks over to another cage with the little baby in his arms. He's looking at a little white puffy dog, one he was holding for a while earlier.

He comes back and says in the sweetest tone I've heard him use, "May I please take him home?" referring to the schnauzer. I give him a big smile and write a check for $275.59. The saleslady goes over the shot record and papers with me. Then she asks who is to be the registered owner. I look at Tom. He steps up and says, "Both of us." We put our names on some registration form, and walk out with him and a bag full of supplies. Even though I offer to, Tom pays cash for the toys and other supplies for the puppy. As we walk through the mall, a couple kids rush up to us and want to pet the puppy. The kids are cute little six- and seven-year-olds, just puppies themselves. They ask what his name is, what kind of dog he is, and so forth. It's a cute scene. I see tall Tom kneeling to share the puppy with the kids, and wish I had a camera to capture the moment.

On the way home, in the car, Tom holds the puppy up to his face and says, "What are we going to name you?" We throw out some names and none seem to fit. Tom says, "I want an old English name for him."

"Tom, he's not an English dog. Schnauzers are German."

Tom says, "That's okay, I just want an English name for him."

I suggest, "How about Winston Churchill?" and Tom loves it.

"That's it! That's great! We can call him Churchy for short," and Churchy is named on the way home from the mall in the car. He's so spry and playful, trying to jump from Tom's arms all the time. Tom cracks the window open and the baby dog jolts up to greet the air with his little black nose. I stop and pick up the birthday cake I ordered for him on the way home. After too much cake and hours of playing with Churchy, we take him to bed with us when we're ready to turn in.

"What if he pees?" I ask, concerned.

"Oh, yeah, that's right," Tom says, lifting the little creature up to put him in the bathroom on some newspaper. Churchy, still anxious and excited from all the day's attention, starts crying and scratching at the door. Tom rolls over and goes to get him. He returns to the bed and holds Churchy between us and leans in to give me a nice soft kiss. He then kisses Churchy.

"I love you. He's the most beautiful gift anyone's ever…" I interrupt him with a kiss.

Tom continues, "I mean it. I look around and see my life so full with you in it." That feels good to hear. I look down at his sexy bare chest and pajama shorts.

"Where's the top to your pajamas?" I ask him.

"I didn't put it on because I like the feel of him on my chest. Feel this…" Tom positions Churchy on my bare chest. At first it feels a little painful with the tiny little claws digging in to get a grip, and then it's neat as Churchy lies down and the soft fur brushes against me. He's panting now; it's so sweet.

Later

The phone wakes me, and I find we must have all fallen asleep. I spring to life immediately, worried that Churchy may have peed or that one of us may have squashed him. Churchy jumps up with me and I feel the bed for any wetness while I reach for the phone. The clock reads 1:00 a.m. I can't find any wetness. I pick up the phone and grab Churchy at the same time.

"Hello?" My voice wakens Tom, who also bolts up, looking for the dog while feeling around on the bed for pee.

"Hey what's up?" a familiar female voice asks. I hold Churchy up to Tom and silently motion for him to take him outside for a pee. Tom nods and grabs our new baby.

"Not much, how about you?" I say, hoping the caller's next words reveal her identity.

"I'm not feeling well. Lucy and I went out to the Woodbine tonight, and I got sick. I think it might have been the shrimp. I've never got sick before there."

It's Sherry and she's talking about the Woodbine, a nightclub near work. Since they bank with us, they always give us passes for Friday night happy-hour office parties where tons of local business people gather to cheat on their spouses, blow off a week of stress at work, or just relax with friends. It's an adult playground — the straight equivalent of Gatsby's. She's always raving about how fun it is there, and how much I just have to go with them. She's a spastic broad, and I wonder what her husband's take is on her late nights out while he's home with their two boys.

She continues, "I don't think I'm going to make it in tomorrow."

Sherry never calls out. There has to be more to it than this. Her words are slurred, so I assume she's a bit tanked. I ask, "You know now that you're not going to feel well in the morning?"

She answers, "Lucy will explain it all to you tomorrow...yeah, it's a long story. But don't tell Carmen I called you tonight. And don't tell her I went out tonight. She don't like hearin' about us goin' out for Happy Hour."

"Sherry, sounds like more than one hour was happy."

"You're gonna join us next week, right?" she asks.

"I thought you were sick, and yet you're already pumped about next week's party."

"I'm serious! Will you come out with us next weekend or what?"

"Fine, Sherry, I'll be there. Can I get some sleep now?"

She gets excited, "That's so cool! Are you sure?"

"Yes, sure, now get some rest!"

"See you tomorrow, Tom," she says.

Confused, but eager to get back to sleep, I answer, "Uh, yeah, see you tomorrow. Good night, Sherry." I hang up and snuggle back into bed, trying to regain the cozy and relaxed feeling I had prior to being disturbed by the phone.

Tom comes in and says, "I took him for a short walk outside." He puts Churchy on the floor and gets into bed. The puppy cries and cries, trying to jump up on the bed with us. Tom lifts him up. I pretend to be sleeping, gazing at them through slitted eyes with the light of the digital clock slightly illuminating the room. Soon I don't have to pretend.

Friday, May 12, 1989

At work, I hang up the phone after a short conversation with Janet, asking me if Tom and I want to join her out at the Concord tonight. It's the third call today. Bobby and then Billy both called to ask if I was coming out to Gatsby's tonight. I suppose everyone has cabin fever after a long winter, and is anxious for summer to get here.

It's been a week of training the new puppy at home and having lunches with Sherry and Lucy at work. At work, Sherry has been becoming more and more excited over my going to the Woodbine tonight, just like a little kid waiting for Santa. It took some coaxing, but I convinced Tom to join us after work for the famous happy hour party. He's negative on partying with my new co-workers, but says he'll meet me in the parking lot of the club after work. When I tell him how excited I am to introduce him to everyone, he persuades me to be hesitant about presenting him as my significant other, cautious of how being gay will affect my banking career. *Where's this coming from?* He's not being the fearless icon of pride I know him to be, especially since I already introduced him as such to my manager Carmen. The dignity I learned I needed by observing him, the self-esteem I gained from listening to him, and the honor I get by having him at my side have made me a new person. I *feel* stronger, and brave enough to dare defying convention.

5:30 p.m.

We all leave work and get in our cars, following Sherry like a funeral procession: there's Lucy, Sherry, Andrew, Dolores, and Judy, as well as Kathy and her husband. Sharon has other plans, so she can't go, and of course Carmen refuses. We get there, all wearing our little lime green circular stickers that pronounce us as Woodbine Happy Hour Party members. I find Tom and fight back the urge to kiss and hug him. I hand him a lime green sticker and ask, "How's Churchy?"

"Fine," he answers in a dismal tone.

"What's wrong?" I ask.

"Nothing!" he snaps.

As we stand in line waiting to enter, we introduce ourselves. Sherry runs up and gives Tom a hug and peck on the cheek as if they've known each other for years, and she looks at me, saying, "Oh, he's cute!" She turns back to Tom and says, "I hear you have a new puppy! Do you have a girlfriend?"

"Uh, no," he says, looking at me, eyes widening.

I blush and smile, shaking my head. "Tom, this is Lucy…" and go down the line introducing everyone. Once inside, our group settles into a couple of plush burgundy couches in one of the several alcoves around the huge room. Sherry almost immediately drags me to the buffet.

I watch Tom flop down on the sofa, looking quite uncomfortable. Starving, I grab two plastic plates and fill them with food: one for me and one for Tom. Sherry says, "Oh, aren't you sweet. You're making a plate for Loo, huh?"

"Uhh," I mutter, then say, "Yes."

Sherry says, "I had a feeling you liked her. She likes you, too."

There *is* some type of attraction between Lucy and me, but I've dismissed it. I certainly didn't think it was that evident to Sherry. "Doesn't she have a boyfriend?" I ask, not sure why I'm asking.

"Bob?" Sherry asks.

"Yeah."

"I met him. He's nothing compared to you. She'd go for you if you wanted it."

We return to the crowd, and I offer one plate to Tom, who takes it and returns a grimace. With that, I turn and hand the other plate to Lucy. She beams and offers thanks. I follow Kathy and her husband up to the buffet, this time for my own food.

Tom can't relax. He refuses to dance, and doesn't even drink. He's sucking down cigarettes and isn't really talkative with my co-workers. I take a couple of walks out to the parking lot with Sherry to share a couple drags on a joint. After a few hours, Sherry drags Lucy and me up to the dance floor and finds a way to leave the two of us dancing alone. The Manhattans I've been drinking alleviate my anxiety. Lucy's got a sweet sense of humor and she's so kind. Still dancing, I find something more in her eyes. Her smile is adorable and her scent is sweet. I'm not certain if it's her hourglass figure, her classy appearance — nails done, soft brown semi-curly hair cascading just below her shoulders, or if it's just that she finds *me* attractive — but there's a connection. It's causing an unexpected stirring in my pants, and the desire to fuck her crosses my mind. I escape the trance of desire for Lucy and announce that we must go, since Tom has to work tomorrow.

"You guys goin' to another party?" Lucy asks.

"No, just gotta run."

Lucy leans over and whispers to me, "You can stay. I mean, with me if you're afraid of driving drunk. I can drive." I respectfully decline, but tell her that I appreciate the offer.

We escape, and I expect Tom to blow up once we walk out, but he walks me to my car and says, "Drive safely. I'll follow you home." I get in the car and think that he must believe I'm stoned or drunk out of my mind.

My mind is on Lucy and the weird feeling in my pants. *This thing with Tom — is it a phase? Is it time to return to women?* I know one thing is certain: I owe it to myself to find out. I can't ignore the feeling. My entire future depends on it. We get home and Tom leaves for one of his nocturnal jaunts. I play with Churchy until sleep takes me.

Tom's nightly "drives" become as frequent as every other night. They start to begin before I settle down to sleep, leaving a gap in my evenings, making me feel lonely, confused and neglected. This, and a burning desire to explore and discover what ignited the spark that night between Lucy and me, causes a shift in my behavior. Lucy and I begin having lunch together every single day. We smile at each other all day, doing each other little favors and talking and listening to each other with more passion and interest than ever. I discover her "boyfriend," Bob, is just a dude she's dated a couple of times and hasn't impressed her. Like me, Lucy has to bat admirers off. She enjoys hearing about my infatuation with going out clubbing, something she also enjoys very much. She asks what clubs I like and I rattle the names of some straight places I've been in Philadelphia, a couple of which cater to non-white crowds.

All this foreplay leads to another happy hour evening at the Woodbine. I keep saying "Woodbine," but the attraction is *Images*, a nightclub club within the Woodbine Inn, an entertainment complex that includes a restaurant, hotel and nightclub. As my friendship with the crew intensifies, I end up going out with Sherry and the gang on a weekly basis and soon it's up to three nights a week after work, taking the place of visits to Gatsby's with Tom. A whole new world opens up with Lucy. I feel like I'm falling for her. It's unimaginable to me, but it's happening. We laugh, dance, drink and talk every moment. She's a delicate flower, and so sweet-smelling, I have the urge to take a bite. Her soft, gentle, effeminate ways make me wonder if I'm bisexual. I assume Tom is just on hold for me; and given his antics, it's easy to put my feelings for him on autopilot while I try to figure this out.

Friday, May 26, 1989

Lucy and I are completely smashed while we dance. She loves to drink as much as I do, and as we get drunk, we get even more fun-loving and relaxed as inhibitions drop. My two tellers Andrew and Dolores have grown friendly during these jaunts, and a love connection has formed to the point that as we turn in our dance, we see them engaged in a kiss. We turn to Sherry, dancing with one of her boyfriends, and she's soaking it up, loving every minute. I shake my head and look at Lucy, saying, "Check them out." She smiles and holds me closer. We stumble out of the Woodbine, laughing at the fact that I need a cigarette at the same time as some fresh air. We make a great pair: I can't walk and she's slurring her words. I don't give any thought to the fact that we hold hands while we walk around the parking lot. Suddenly, everything's funny as shit.

"Is that a purple truck?" she asks, pointing toward it. Sure enough, there's a large van painted purple.

"Am I fucked up?" I ask.

She laughs and says, "How many times did you come out to smoke a joint with Sherry?"

"Who the fuck would paint a truck pur...ple?" I ask, belching between the syllables. We look at each other and enter one of those rare fits of uncontrollable laughter that keeps you giggling and amused every time you look at each other. It's silly and ridiculous but suddenly the funniest thing in the world to us. We laugh and laugh and then notice a few raindrops begin to fall.

"We got to get back in," Lucy says, and I look in her eyes and place both of my hands on her face and gently pull it into mine for a kiss right on the lips. At first it's a soft, closed-lip kiss meant on my part to feel her out; then she parts her lips, and I enter her mouth with my tongue. Her kiss is passionate, soft and appealing. She kisses well. I stop the kiss intentionally by giggling and she pulls away, saying, "What?"

"No, I'm just...You felt this way, too?" I ask. She smiles, her face beautiful in the light from the street, water droplets glistening on her cheeks.

"Can we do it again?" she asks.

"What?" I ask. She shakes her head and leans in for another kiss. By now, we notice the sprinkle of rain has turned into a downpour, and we're suddenly soaked. We dash for her little light-blue Chevy Chevette.

"I left my pocketbook inside," Lucy says, referring to the club. I shake my head, going in for another kiss.

"Keys," she giggles, softly fighting off my natural advances. "Pocketbook!" she exclaims. I laugh at my weakened state from the whiskey and the natural urge to take her. We dart into the club together and Lucy says, "I'm going to the bathroom. Do you mind going to get my bag?"

I nod my agreement and she walks into the bathroom, and I head into the club soaking wet. People look at me while I walk past them. I catch my reflection in one of the many mirrors in the place. Expecting to see a wreck, I'm pleasantly surprised to see that my wet bangs frame the sides of my face nicely. My white silk shirt is see-through, so my white tank underneath is exposed. My face looks bright and refreshed. I'm a portrait of young and hot. Sherry is dancing with a much older man, and stops to notice me grab Lucy's pocketbook.

"Raining out?" she says, acting hyper as usual and rushing over while dragging her partner.

"Yes," I answer.

"You guys hookin' up?" she asks.

"Hookin' up?" I ask, shaking my head. *What am I doing? What does this mean? I love Tom. I'm carrying his love with me. What's the matter with me?*

She smiles, reaches for her own pocketbook, and digs through it while I turn to leave.

"Tom!" she shouts.

I look behind me and say, "See ya!"

She smiles again and tosses a condom at me. As I catch it, she says, "See you later, Handsome." I nod at her and her date and turn to leave. I inspect the condom she threw at me; it's covered in a bright yellow wrapper. I stuff it into my pocket and find Lucy waiting in the reception room.

We make it back out to her car, and I ask her, "Would you like to go out this weekend?"

She smiles and goes in for another kiss. I promise our next date will be official and not at the "stupid Woodbine." She drives me back to my car at our branch, only six minutes away. We kiss again before I leave the car. I can still smell her perfume as I drive, and try to make sense out of the evening. *Where is this going?*

I'm feeling no pain as I fly high with the alcohol streaming through me, while fantasies of a straight lifestyle roam back into possibility: marriage, children, back to publicly-perceived normality with a publicly acceptable relationship, and happiness for my parents. Lucy is, after all, a lovely person. She's sweet, beautiful and sexy. Then I get a little angry at how confused this is making me feel. I walk in the apartment and toss my keys on the counter and realize Tom isn't home. He's trapped Churchy in the spare room. I hear the little baby yelping and crying to be let out. When I open the door and turn on the light, he comes out, wagging his tail, trying to jump up on me. I see that he's taken his rage out on my weight bench by biting and tearing into the leather padding. It's frayed at the edges. There's a newspaper Tom must have left in the room that Churchy tore to shreds as well. His wagging tail involves moving his whole back end; it's cute, and brings a smile to my face. I let him out for a moment then bring him in and find the remote to the TV. I plop down on the floor in front of MTV. I reach down in my pockets to empty them of change and my wallet, and I find the condom Sherry gave me. I hold it up and examine it, turning it as thoughts turn in my mind, reviewing today and looking forward to what tomorrow will bring. Sleep soon takes me.

Tuesday, May 30, 1989

I'm sitting on the floor of the vault with Lucy as we verify the cash shipment. I look up at her as she sits on a metal stepstool looking all sexy and curvaceous in her black business suit; her skirt stops well above the knees, revealing long, sexy legs neatly crossed and covered in sheer pantyhose.

When I ask her if hanging out in Philly together this weekend would be cool, she beams and nods.

Carmen appears at the acrylic day door of the vault, tossing her keys around, trying to find the one that opens the door. She gives up on finding the key and barks, "What's taking you two so long? Sharon and Marilyn never took this long. Tom! Stop fussing over Lucy and talking to her and get this done." She walks away, and I roll my eyes. Lucy blushes and averts her gaze, but her smile tells me she likes me.

I look up and say in normal tone, "I need to stop fussing over you and get this done!" Her smile widens, revealing her bright white beautiful teeth. I rise up on my knees and crimp a canvas bag filled with an outgoing shipment of cruddy mutilated bills and lean in to kiss her. We finish the kiss and I finish preparing the cash shipment.

Sharon comes to the day door, and she's able to find the right key. She enters, not smiling, and stands there watching us with her arms crossed across her chest. "Almost done?" she asks.

"Oh yeah, just finished up," I respond. I can feel a cold aura coming off Sharon, and wonder if my new fondness for Lucy is the cause of it. Sharon has a boyfriend or fiancée or whatever. I get up, toss the bags in the locker, and slam it shut. Sharon remains in place like a warden. I dismiss her attitude and as I walk past Lucy, who is now returning to her feet, I boldly ask, "Lucy, want to join me for lunch?"

Lucy nods and I say, "Noon," and pause to catch my reflection in the day door. Knowing they both like what they see, I purposely tuck in my shirt, then pooch out my chest and ass, preening my hair, pleased with my looks. I have developed quite a swagger.

There's no one in the lobby when I get back to my station. Good old Carmen starts walking over to me again. I close my eyes to conceal rolling them. When I reopen my eyes, she's standing in front of my unit staring at me. I smile and say, "Yes, ma'am?"

She pauses for a moment, her face looking wicked as hell, a pencil stuck in her poofy gray rat's nest hairdo, and says, "I'm on vacation next week. Lucy will be in charge and she'll be very busy, so I don't want you to give her any trouble."

For the remainder of the week, my thoughts try to justify sidestepping my relationship with Tom for this thing with Lucy. My reasoning is that this research must be done. I tell myself I have to pursue this and see where it goes. No regrets. Tom has to drive Noémie around this weekend, so I plan on taking Lucy out Saturday night. When Mitch calls with work for the Friday night, I tell him I made plans for Saturday night.

"Come on, Tom. You know Saturday nights are hot for us." His tone is sharp.

"I want to be able to make plans," I say.

"Shall I run my business around your personal life, Tommy?" I don't know how to respond. The dancing gig has become my saving grace financially.

"You're right, Mitch, you're right."

"Tommy, listen, I'm not going to apologize for what I said. I will say that I'm under a lot of pressure to get jobs filled, and most of you guys are young and want your social lives, but this job is happening around the times you're all into the party scene. I dig that." He sounds fatherly.

I say, "I hear you. Don't worry — you can count on me. Just give me whatever you want, Mitch."

"Attaboy. Now, you've always been one I can count on to pick up the extra work. I'm taking out a couple of new ads and summer is coming. We're going to get real busy. I may have you loaded up on the weekends." It's inevitable that I'll have a job on Saturday.

Friday, June 2, 1989, 4:00 p.m. at work

"Tommy!" Mitch's voice is filled with the excitement that can only mean he's landed another sale.

"Mitch!" I answer.

"Looks like you're free Saturday at this point. But I got another one for you for tonight, last minute. It's at Della's. I had this for Eric, but he's got some funeral, so I'm switching him and you. He can do a job tomorrow and you do this tonight and everyone's happy." I don't argue. It leaves me free Saturday night.

"Great! What's the story on tonight's gig?" Mitch tells me the time and details, and I hang up with a happy feeling.

I firm up plans with Lucy to pick her up at her sister's house right down the road from work in Pennsauken tomorrow evening. Later, she says she wants me to meet her Mom, so I'm to pick her up at her house in Northeast Philly. She writes down the address and directions from our branch.

Tom has been out three nights this week and his excuses vary from "I needed to take a drive to relax" to "I have to take Noémie on a job." It was infuriating when, yesterday, he used that excuse and she called to chat and told me she didn't have a job.

What is he doing? I care, but don't want to know. *What am I doing?* I concentrate on the possibility of going straight. *Is it possible?* I pray on it: *Holy Father, help me find my way. I beg you, please be with me as you always have been. Help me find the truth and the light. I love Thomas Shaw, truly. Why is this so complicated?*

6:00 p.m.

I get home from work and find Tom outside with Churchy. I tell him about my gigs, and he says, "How about I join you, and we hit GB's after?"

"Sure," I answer, eager for his attention.

The last job is at Della's; and as luck would have it, they want me to dance in street clothes, so I put on what I'm going to wear to Gatsby's: faded, light-blue low-rider jeans totally frayed at the bell-bottoms, with a tight black Taylor Dayne concert T-shirt. I feel really sexy and excited about exotic dancing tonight. Eager to mix up my routine, I fish around in my gym bag for a cassette tape of different tunes. It starts with Tony Terry singing "She's Fly," then moves on to the Breakfast Club with "Right On Track" — a super electric tune for this type of sexy dancing — and finishes up with Tony Terry again with "Lovey Dovey." I tear it up on the floor, dancing more for myself than anyone else, and easily flip around, snatching moves out of the air that I didn't know I had. It's more fun than usual, and the girls pour their money all over my sexy bright-blue g-string.

Later

At Gatsby's we dance a little; I drink a lot. Tom socializes with everyone; I talk to myself in my head. He continues to leave me alone while he's off chatting around the bar. We leave early, and Tom drives us across Route 70 toward the notoriously cruisy Cooper River Park. There's an old abandoned seafood restaurant on the lake in the park.

"This would be a great place for a gay club. It would be super competition for GB's. I'd love to have my own club," Tom says, dreaming as he speaks, looking at it. "With all the men cruising around the park, we'd clean up. The location is ideal. Keep the restaurant section up, and offer Sunday tea parties and brunches."

"What would you call it?" I ask.

"Cruisin'," he says, sounding half-sure. "Hey, that's it, *Cruisin'!*" he says, this time confidently.

"That's cool," I say. He parks in front of it and makes imaginary plans for where he would put the sign, some of the events he'd stage, cover charges and what employees he'd hire. I encourage his lofty aspirations with my own ideas. It feels good to brainstorm an ambitious goal with him. As we talk on the drive home, I can feel the momentum of excitement build — enough to transform a dream into reality.

As soon as we get home, my spirits are flying, and I have a major hard-on for Tom. Before I can express one sentiment, he says, "I'm going for a drive and taking Churchy with me." The whole dream goes down the drain.

"Stay home with me!" I protest, my mood flipped like a light switch, angered by his constant need to escape into the night. I'm frustrated with his failure to even ask me if I want to join them. He assumes I don't want to go, and the sad part is, *he's right*. Why should I feel guilty? Why, then, do I?

I pour myself into a Joan Crawford flick and a glass of Merlot.

Saturday, June 3, 1989

After work and tending to chores like picking up my dry cleaning, I do some light housework while I contemplate thoughts of Lucy. A full-blooded Italian, she's my perfect type for the female of the species — at least in a sexual sense. Sensual, curvaceous, sumptuous and voluptuous, she has full, sexy, lips framing a brilliant smile. Couple that with intoxicating amber eyes, and you have a formula for desire. Besides smelling great, she dresses in the most polished, classy way you can imagine. She's warm, sensitive and caring. Under Tom's short influence in my life, I feel more polished. He's got a mountain of faults, but has shown me how masculinity can be strong and confident. Before, I always equated it with being cocky – and with being a bully.

Tom is out all day and comes in briefly, Churchy in tow, about a quarter to five to shit, shower and shave for a night working with Noémie. He tosses me an Australian coin he found on the sidewalk during his daily travels.

"Where were you today?" I ask.

"Couple jobs to attend to," he says, referring to R2O Rentals.

"They never found that missing money?" I ask.

Tom shakes his head and asks, "What are you going to do tonight? You're not planning on going to GB's by yourself, are you?"

"Of course not. I was going to go out with people from work."

"Okay," he says, and gives me a peck on the cheek as he leaves.

Later

I put on a long-sleeve turquoise shirt with a suede finish and a print that looks hand-painted. I wear the shirt untucked and low-rise jeans with an all-over distressed effect. I stop to run the car through a carwash. It comes out sparkling with its bright, fiery red coat gleaming. I make one final stop on the way, to buy Lucy a small bouquet of brightly-colored flowers.

Lucy lives with her Mom in the type of classic brick-face townhome that you'll find across most of the Great Northeast. I park the Camaro and gather my thoughts, searching for a reason to start the engine and take off. *What am I doing here?* I'm only 22, and I have the rest of my life to be gay or straight. This is an experience, and something is telling me to go with it. It's as if my life is a book, the story unfolding as each day goes by, as each page is turned. I take in a deep breath of fresh air as I open the car door and stand up outside the car. I watch some kids walk by kicking a soccer ball.

A woman swings open the door and smiles at me through a screen door. She opens it and with a thick Italian accent says, "Tom?"

"Yes. You must be Lucy's sister, Diane?" I ask, feeling the woman in front of me is Lucy's Mom, but knowing I can't go wrong saying this to either of them. She smiles widely and then the smile fades quickly, hidden as if by some kind of embarrassment or shame.

"I-a-Lucy Mom," she says.

"Oh, hello," I say, extending my hand for a handshake.

We shake hands and she says, "Please come in. Lucy is getting ready. Come, sit down. You're as handsome as Lucy said."

"Thank you. This is very nice," I say, pointing out her wall designs and various statues decorating the living room. It's not exactly my taste, but it's certainly nice. It's like a miniature palace with large paintings with huge gold-painted frames, Wedgwood blue walls with white crown molding.

"Something to drink?" she asks.

"Sure," I say.

"Coke all right?"

"Yes, please."

She returns with a tall, thin glass perfectly easy to spill or drop. We watch the news on TV, not saying anything, until she breaks the silence with, "You and Lucy work together at the bank?" I nod and she continues, "What you do there?"

"I'm the head teller."

"Lucy was head teller at the other bank she worked at, here in Philadelphia. At the Prima Bank."

Lucy walks downstairs and corrects her Mom, leaning down to kiss her, saying, "Prime Bank, Mom."

Lucy looks absolutely stunning, in a sexy black dress that accentuates her shapely figure. She smells terrific. It pleases me that she got decked out just for me.

After sitting with her Mom for a moment, we get up to go. "Where are you two going tonight?"

Lucy says, "To town." I find it interesting that she refers to downtown Philadelphia simply as "town."

"Be careful. There are a lot of crazy people," her Mom says.

When we get to the car I open the door for her, and as she remarks on my newly-washed car, I reach down and pick up the flowers that I'd left on the seat. "These...are for you," I say, proudly holding them up to her.

"They're beautiful!" she says, her eyes lighting up. Her Mom is still standing at the door. "They need to go in water," Lucy says, turning to bring them up to her house. As she walks up to the door, she holds the bunch up and moves her head from side to side. Her mom opens the door and takes the bouquet. Lucy returns to the car, where I continue to hold the passenger side door open for her.

"I asked Mom to put them in water, so they stay fresh." I hop over to my side of the car and get in. "That was so sweet of you. Thank you," she tells me. I smile and turn on the radio.

As we get on Route 95 South, I say, "I hope you don't mind me pursuing you outside of work. I don't usually date people I work with."

"I hope you pursue me *inside* work too," she says, giggling. She leans over and kisses me on the cheek, as we hold each other's hands. I don't know why I'm doing this. What do I hope to gain?

Downtown Philadelphia

Thoughts of Tom cross my mind as I get out of the car and walk to the passenger side to open the door for her. To defer guilt, I frame my actions in my mind as an experimental walk on an imaginary scaffold around a possible different lifestyle. I briefly think of how hurt Tom would be if he knew I was out on a date with Lucy. Then the thought fades as she rises from her seat into the bright lights of the outdoor parking lot. Almost in slow motion, like a shampoo commercial, her silky, beautiful curly hair bounces up as she rises. As we stroll through Jewelers'

Row toward the club, we peer in the windows. Everything has been locked up, and the stores are deserted. We find ourselves at The Strand — a small straight club on Walnut Street.

We enter and take stairs upward to the club. There's a small dance floor and a black bar lit by a white backdrop of lights behind shelves of liquor bottles. As I walk past the patrons, I think for a moment that I'm in costume — some disguise of the real me. *Do they know I suck cock?* I pass for a straight guy, I think, catching my reflection in a mirror. The pride of being gay is shadowed in this new pride of assuming the position of another character. In this role, I realize there's no question as to what we're doing in the sack. I'm the protector, the one doing the fucking. They all know it, and they all look at her and then me and assume our identity. I introduce Lucy to my signature drink, a smooth Manhattan. When the bartender slides them up on the bar, the caramel color glowing with the bright light behind it, in combination with the bright red cherry falling slowly to the bottom of the glass, makes my mouth water in anticipation. Lucy takes a liberal taste and immediately shakes her head and closes her eyes, twisting her lips as if she just got an electric shock.

I laugh out loud, to which she says, "Wowch! That's strong, Tom."

I keep my smile, saying, "Yeah, it's an acquired taste. Puts hair on your chest."

She shakes her head, smiling big, saying, "That's okay. I like my chest the way it is."

"Yes, I do too," I say, bringing my glance down to her beautiful breasts. I finish my drink and Lucy's only half done. I take her by the hand as we listen to the smooth jazzy-type music playing.

"I don't really like this," she says, pushing the Manhattan toward me.

"What would you like?"

"Nothing right now."

I pick up her glass and take her by the hand, leading her in an exploration of the club. We walk outside where there's a crowded deck. A club employee is fanning flames from a grill where hot dogs are cooking. I see a couple dancing together; he has a hot dog in his hand, and she's slumped over with a cigarette hanging down from the hand cloaked around his neck.

"Jeez, she's going to drop ashes on his ass," I say. We walk around the club and up to another floor to find a small, dimly-lit room off the stairs. The room is only lit by the bar and some cheesy light fixtures scattered throughout. There are very few people up here. I suggest we sit at one of the fancy stylish purple couches.

"What do you want?" I ask, proposing another drink.

"Long Island, please?" When I return with our drinks, we sit and allow our eyes to adjust to the darkness.

"Look," I begin, "those tables are set up over what was probably the dance floor." Lucy looks down and around. "Yeah, see, there's a box on the floor that's tiled and the rest is carpet." We finish our drinks and I suggest we take a walk down to the Phoenix.

"Isn't that one of the black clubs you told me about?" she asks.

"I don't see it like that," I say. "The crowd is less pretentious and more accepting. The music is more hip, and the atmosphere is most relaxing. You'll love it." She trusts me and smiles brightly, nodding and taking my arm.

Inside, there's a sea of black folks on the sunken dance floor. We find our way to the dance floor and have at it for about five songs. The songs are groovy and easy to dance to. I follow the example of the black dudes on the dance floor — no one has lavish moves, or jumps around. There's a small, subtle realm of movement which allows you to enjoy dancing to song after song without getting too overheated. Lucy has a few cool dance moves of her own — one is a Charleston-type move — but she keeps it so suave it works with the beat. The DJ is radio celebrity Frank Cerami, spinning the latest round of songs I listen to on Power 99 FM — the top black station in Philly. He plays "She's Fly" by Tony Terry, and I'm lifted high into a trance-like bliss, taking delight in the precision of my moves, soaking up the well-matched lyrics to the tune.

The place is packed, and there's nowhere to sit. Buzzed and feeling light as can be, we decide to leave and drive over to Christine's on South Street, one of the more popular straight, predominately white places in Philadelphia. I park the car on a side street, and we stumble along, clinging to each other, laughing and kissing. It's fun to be able to show each other affection without disapproving eyes.

"The cover is ten each," the beautiful young girl at the box office says when we enter. I fish a $20 bill out of my wallet and pay the price of admission. Guido-types dominate the crowd here as we make our way through to the bar. We order a drink, dance, drink some more. After a while, my legs are numb from standing, since all seats are taken here as well. Village People's "Y.M.C.A." brings us to the dance floor again; this time sentiments of homosexual pride fill my head. I feel like an impostor in here. Looking at her big, beautiful bright smile while she soaks up the fun in dancing with me, I think that I'm cheating on more than just Tom.

"You dance so well," she shouts. Clapping and spinning to the disco classic, I grab her hands and turn her around and then around again with her back to me. I release her hands and we resume our individual styles. The song melts into another great one, "I'm Alive" by ELO. It's time to go to another bar. We walk to Roxy, right down the street, only a five-minute walk. I've performed here a couple times. It's another straight club, but a bit more hip and slightly less pretentious. We enter to the sound of Olivia Newton-John's "Make a Move on Me." Lucy insists on paying the $7 cover charge for each of us, and she looks like a cute little doll, causing male heads to turn as she maneuvers through the crowd, taking control of our tour of this bar.

She takes me by the hand and leads us to the stairs leading to an outside deck, saying, "I know they have somewhere where we can sit and have a drink." I smile, knowing it, too. I let her lead and enjoy the way the various lights accentuate her soft and beautiful long brown hair, hair that cascades straight down her head and face and falls into soft curls just below her shoulders. She turns to look at me, her sexy lips looking moist with freshly-applied lipstick. She walks with an elegant swish, her legs shaped beautifully within their hosiery. She finds the ledge of the balcony and looks out at the city. I come up behind her and bury my face into the back of her hair.

"Smells good," I say, taking in her personal scent.

She turns and says, "Perfume is..."

I interrupt with, "No. Not your perfume."

"Shampoo?"

"No. It's your smell. Your scent. Your own unique scent. If these perfume companies could bottle it, they'd make a fortune." We share a kiss with the moonlight shining down on us. The kiss causes my cock to stir and soon it's raging hard and it feels tremendous to brush it against her. She purrs soft moans into my ear.

After a drink we leave to go to the Savoy for a bite to eat. I park on the ceiling of a lot I usually frequent in the gayborhood. Of course the diner is flooded with the gay crowd. When we're finally seated, it's evident that Lucy is so bombed she doesn't notice the atmosphere.

"Hi Hunny," a stout waitress says, looking at me, "youse want coffee?"

After eating, we stroll back to the car in the parking lot holding hands. In the car, we begin making out. I help her bring her seat down. Her perfume and the feel of her shoulders, her arms, her soft neck, get me excited. I open her top and reach behind her to unhook her bra. Her bra drops slightly and I pull it off, revealing big, round, beautiful tits. I am on them, sucking and licking each breast, and begin mounting her. Suddenly, there's a loud sound, which I make out to be someone banging on the window.

I turn around and a flashlight blinds me. It's a parking lot attendant. To my surprise, my pants are open and I struggle to get them back together. Lucy quickly covers her chest. I roll off her and race to open the driver's side window, where the attendant stands.

"Sorry, man, sorry," I say.

He's a big, fat older black dude and he says, "Hey, okay, no problem. You guys gotta split and find a room."

Lucy laughs and I'm suddenly nervous and off kilter, bumbling to find the keys. In my haste, I drop the keys on the floor. I find them, stick them in the ignition — my own sexual ignition is already turned — and floor the gas pedal to get us mobile. The car zooms toward the half wall and I jam on the brakes to prevent us from flying off the top of the building. I pause a moment and catch my breath.

Lucy says, "Tom, calm down," and places her hand on my knee. I look over and she's still smiling and laughing softly. I compose myself and reach down to my crotch to adjust my erection to a comfortable position in my pants. She's clearly drunk and is attempting to turn on my radio. I guide her hand to the controls and find a song she likes.

After seeing her home safely, it's not thoughts of Lucy that cause me to jack off in the car on my drive home. It's thoughts and images of Tom and his butt that fill my mind. I know he won't be home when I get there, but I intend on reversing tonight's sins in the form of penance paid on my knees to him.

Monday, June 5, 1989

While Carmen is on vacation, work is a different place. The first day is hectic because Lucy is out sick. When I call her, she says it's something to do with cramps that I don't have to be concerned about catching.

I go about my usual routine, helping and guiding the tellers. At one point during the day, I take a moment to stop and smell the roses, so to speak. I stop what I'm doing and drop my hands to my sides and look around and then down at myself. I'm doing it. I'm a Head Teller. Sharon is over on the platform by herself, and I just returned from helping her with a few clients and feel amazing. I'm actually a supervisor and in charge in this bank branch. It feels really good being comfortable and in control.

On the way home, I stop to pick up a couple of bags of groceries for our bare refrigerator. When I arrive, I find a pile of nasty bills in the mailbox. Tom's car is here, so I wonder why he didn't check the mail. I open the door and Tom is lying on the floor playing with Churchy. He had to work all day Sunday, so we really haven't spent much time together.

He looks up and says, "Hello, Daddy!" as he waves one of Churchy's paws at me. I put down the groceries and lie down with them.

I say, "They finally opened the pool. Be cool to go for a swim. It's beautiful out."

Tom turns to me and gives me a kiss. Softly, gently, he opens his mouth to offer a more passionate kiss. He gives me a massage and my muscles melt into his hands to the point I feel myself start to drool. In a flash, we're naked, experiencing the joy of sharing every bit of our sweet nectar with each other. His scent is that of Obsession as I bury my face in his soft chest fur. Tom looks up at me, catching his breath, and says, "I'm devoted to you, Tom, not just for your fiery lovemaking skills, but because you've made being in a relationship with another person more appealing and admirable than anyone else has." I nod and focus on raw sex to avoid the distraction of his words — words that swell my guilty conscience. I put all of my energy and enthusiasm into performing with smooth might and precision. Soon we're climaxing; me first this time, then him, then me again. He's so patient and I'm so greedy.

"You're so sexual. Your appetite is huge," Tom says.

"Ditto, Sport," I say, thinking of but not mentioning Tom's own relentless hunt for possible conquests.

After sex we're both famished, so we dive into the sacks of groceries and build an incredible dinner together of Cornish game hens, Brussels sprouts, and mashed potatoes with gravy. After devouring dinner, with two major human needs satisfied we switch on TV and fall into satisfying a third — sleeping on the couch, holding each other.

Later

The phone ringing wakes us. I remove my arms from around Tom, slowly digging myself out of our love cocoon.

It's Bobby. "Hey *gurl*, whatcha doin'?" he asks.

Bobby and I catch up while Tom takes Churchy out for a pee and poo. When Tom comes back inside, I'm off the phone. "Let's go for a swim!" Tom says.

I focus my eyes on the clock, which reads 11:34 p.m., and say, "It's closed, I'm sure."

"That's when to go!" he says.

"The gate is locked."

"Aren't you up for an adventure, Marino?" he challenges. I smile and shake my head as I rise and walk to the bedroom.

"Where ya going?" he asks.

"Goin' to put my suit on." He puts Churchy down and races behind me. In our bedroom, he pushes me on the bed and helps me take my pants off for the second time today. He's tickling me, and I love it.

We have towels around our necks and are wearing our suits as we walk toward the pool, which is situated on a built up deck, surrounded by a four-foot fence and six-foot bushes. There's a small door to the gate on the side that's got a huge chain on it with a padlock. Tom climbs the gate and lands on his feet.

"Ouch! Shit! Should've worn sneaks!" he shouts.

"Shhhh!" I say, stopping to look around. The complex is quiet, and I hoist myself up and over the gate. Learning from Tom's lesson, I take it slow on the landing, extending my leg so as to reduce the impact from the jump. A minor sting to the foot and we're in. Tom and I put the towels down and realize the bushes don't completely conceal us when we're standing on the deck surrounding the pool. We duck down and slide into the cool water of the pool. The water is invigorating and refreshing as it cleans my body and mind from the stresses of the day. I stay under water as long as I can, then break the surface, gasping for air.

"You were down there awhile," Tom says. I revel in the small pleasure of having the pool to ourselves and Tom uses the advantage to kiss me. "Let's swim naked," he suggests.

"What if someone comes?"

"They won't," he says, shedding his suit. He goes under water then rises and says, "Ahh, feels good." My cock inflates, knowing he's naked. I remove my suit, toss it on the side of the pool, and swim up to him.

When I approach him, we embrace, and it's exhilarating and exciting to hold and kiss him in here.

Having him float on his back in the cool water by the light of a full moon, with his head cradled in the crook of one of my arms, feels splendid. Neither of us ruins the moment with words. I let myself relax and enjoy, allowing dreams to race through my head as I recline into the side wall of the pool, and cast my eyes and thoughts up to the star filled sky while I sink deeper into his arms.

Friday, June 9, 1989

We bring Sherry with us on lunches during the week, and she catches on to our budding romance. She assigns pet names to us. We are now *Tom-Wom* and *Loo-Woo*, she announces one day at lunch. Lucy absolutely adores the new names.

We've grown used to our daily hour-and-a-half lunches, so today, since it's a longer work day, we just go ahead and take two hours. *"Fuck it"* becomes our new rally cry. The branch is operating well, and morale seems high to me. Sharon is the only one who's walking around without a smile. She looks pissed off about something. Lucy and I return from our two-hour lunch, buzzed from a couple cocktails, and sit in the kitchen with Judy, who is eating her lunch. Judy is regaling us with stories from her little dive bar, where she bartends three nights a week. Sharon walks back, clicking her heels on the linoleum floor, the skirt tightly clinging to her short legs coming to just above her knee. She looks as mean as can be, and glares at me with icy eyes, saying, "You have a phone call." She turns and storms out of the kitchen and slams the door, a door that's always open. I can tell she's pissed at my antics, at my attitude. Inwardly, I know she's right, but I don't care.

I take the call and, alas, more frustration: some whore from American Express bothering me about my past-due bill, this time threatening me with legal action.

Despite all the blossoming friendships surrounding me and my new position, Sharon's disapproving looks — coupled with my mounting debt — sap my joy.

Despite my two-hour lunch, I feel myself having a meltdown, and decide I need to leave an hour before closing time to get a grip. I get in the car and slam the door shut. Here I am, almost to the point of tears, and wondering what I'm made of. *Why am I allowing this to get to me? Why am I so angry?* It's all so petty, and I'm letting it get to me. I look up and catch my reflection in the rear-view mirror, and see my eyes well up.

My throat is throbbing, and I have a big lump in it. I pray, *Dear God, come down and sit next to me in the car and give me strength and patience.* I drive home and question the choices I've made. These feelings for Lucy — they just don't fit. Nothing makes sense. *Am I gay? Am I straight?* Regarding Tom, he's been lying from the beginning about so many things — not the best foundation to build a relationship on — and he's been running up my credit cards and not contributing to our expenses. I realize now that I'm in over my head — not just because I'm deeply financially invested in Tom, but because I'm deeply, truly, unequivocally in love with him. I learned from my time with Nadine that when my heart is at the wheel, it's not a good thing. Despite all these things, being with Tom makes me happy, content and satisfied. His words and his sweet romantic ways overshadow the blatant red flags telling me to run away. Like a moth, I'm drawn to the flame. Does he love me? I'm not sure.

I get home to an empty apartment, but Churchy is here, so happy to see me. Tom has locked him in the spare bedroom, where I notice he's chewed the seat of my weight bench to shreds in retaliation for being left alone. He's left a little poop on the floor too. I tuck my tie into my shirt and gag as I clean up the shit on the carpet. Then I pick him up and take him out. After we come in, I take him to the kitchen sink for a bath. After he's clean, I jump in the shower. When I'm all fresh and clean I scavenge the refrigerator and find what's left of Tom's pistachio ice cream. I prefer vanilla, but this will have to do. I take my scoop and the pile of bills into bed with me. It isn't long before my thoughts float back to *Does he love me?*

I'm not sure.

CASUALTIES

Saturday, June 10, 1989, 5:00 a.m.

I must have passed out, because I'm brought back to consciousness by the explicit sensations of a blowjob. I open my eyes and see that Tom is sucking my flaccid dick and rubbing my stomach. He attempts conversation with my cock shoved in his mouth: "I love your abs." I look down to catch his eyes, and he gives me one of his trademark winks. He rises up and positions himself to kiss my lips.

"I miss you, Tom," he says. As he jumps up on the bed, Churchy follows. He grabs Churchy and quickly puts him in the spare bedroom, then returns and climbs on me and starts kissing my neck, chest, shoulders and face. He runs his tongue around my lips and slowly pokes it in my mouth. I lie perfectly still and allow him to lead, letting his darting tongue find its way deep into my mouth. He's kissing and servicing me, and I'm enjoying it. He finishes stripping himself and rips my black bikini briefs off; then he rolls me over on my stomach, and proceeds to spread my butt cheeks wide to rim me. He rolls me over again; this time my penis is rigid. He takes me into his mouth, again, and sucks until I start pumping into him. He pulls away and starts jacking his own cock off for a while, then takes my dick back into his mouth and allows me to resume thrusting it in and out. I get excited and jam it down his throat, causing him to gag. He wants to go the distance with me, and it feels so damn good to have my cock deep in his throat. Looking at his sexy, clean-cut, boy-next-door looks, with my fat dick bobbing in and out of his mouth, is so orgasmic. I get to a place in my head where I'm non-apologetic about how I behave; with sheer animalistic intensity, I grab his hair and shove in and out like a beast. He stops sucking and stops me for a second by grabbing my hands softly, and pulls his face away. He tells me gruffly, "I want to act like I'm put off by it, but keep forcing it until you cum in my mouth. Be rough, okay?"

We've played and crossed limits before, but this is another Tom with me. This is exactly what I like and want, and it's as if he'd performing a penance of some kind. *Maybe I'm not the only one in need of redemption*, I muse. Thoughts of why he wants this cross my mind, but the passion and excitement surpass any guilt. I shove my cock back in and snatch his hair, harder this time.

He plays protest, but I season the sex with hot comments. "You fucking asshole. Suck my cock, you pig." He shakes his head from side to side very quickly, as if saying "No." I pull my fat dick from his mouth and rub it on his face. This time I shock him by raising my voice: *"Suck my fucking dick, you nasty faggot! You like my cock? You're gonna take it. Come on!"*

He opens his mouth and I'm up on my knees now, with his head on the bed. I slap his face a couple of times, this time gently. He opens his mouth and his eyes roll back, so I slap him harder, saying, "You piece of trash. Suck that fat cock!"

Soon the pleasure overtakes me, and I warn him that I'm about to shoot: "Ready to drink my cum, pig?" He nods and I spray my wad deep into his mouth; then, a few second later, he releases his own load. We fall to the bed, exhausted. After a few minutes, he jumps up and returns with Churchy in hand. Churchy jumps over to me and Tom lights a cigarette.

"How was your day?" he asks.

I want to ask where he's been, but all that comes to my lips is "Fine." I put my head on his chest, and Churchy joins me there. He has both of us near his heart.

"You working today?" he asks.

"No. You?"

"Not until tonight. Noémie has a job. You coming with us?"

"Sure, I can go with you if you want."

"Cool," he says. He continues, "We're up now. Want to go get some breakfast?"

"Sure."

6:00 p.m.

I pick up a job from Mitch mid-day, and Noémie is delighted to have me join them. She only has one gig tonight. It's for a bachelor party in Downingtown.

When we arrive at the large penthouse-type hotel room, I take in the looks from the guys toward Noémie and us. I wonder if they think Tom is her boyfriend, or if I am. She's clearly not as pretty and sexy as they expect. That black wig of hers has to go. I told her to ditch it, but she doesn't give up. I suppose it helps her assume the role. During her performance, Tom shares a flask filled with vanilla-flavored vodka with me.

At my gig, we encounter a group of glamorous, well-to-do fortysomething women celebrating one of their 40th birthdays. I imagine the women are wondering who Noémie and Tom are. The party is in the living room of one of their homes, and it's easy to please this crowd. They're a classy and unpretentious group. I finish my work, and Noémie is full of compliments. She and I walk to the car, arm-in-arm, talking about the work.

She says, "You pay attention to everyone. You make them feel good and your dancing is very good." I kiss her on the cheek and propose that the three of us go for a drink, and she's more than agreeable. When I catch Tom's expression, it's surprisingly one of disgust.

Sounding miserable as hell, Tom offers some negative commentary — some audible, some under his breath — about going to a straight club and about going somewhere in Center City. I find his attitude rude and ill-mannered. I don't want him upset, but I don't care either. I'm having a good time, and he needs to grow up and have fun. "You want to go to Kurt's or GB's?" I offer.

"No," he barks.

"Do you feel okay?" I ask, this time more determined.

"I'm fine. Let's just go for a drink."

We find our way to a small, dark bar on South Street, where I had my first assignment working for Mitch. It's relatively loud and there isn't anywhere to sit and talk. I'm uncomfortable, but Tom is extremely irritable. After just one drink, we all decide to call it a night.

Tom is quiet on the ride back to Noémie's apartment and once she's out of the car, I ask again if he's okay. He says, "I really didn't want to go out tonight."

I think it's best to just nod and stay silent.

When we get home, he walks toward his Escort. "What's wrong?" I ask.

"Nothing. Going for a drive."

"Where?" I ask.

"None of your fucking business!" he snaps back.

Without a word, I cast my eyes downward, and walk to the apartment. He gets in the Escort and takes off, burning rubber as he reverses out of the parking space. What the fuck crawled up his ass?

Thursday, June 15, 1989

It's been a week. Sleepless nights over debt, days of arguing with Tom over the bills and his nocturnal excursions. To make it worse, my new-found friend Lucy is on vacation this week. She comes back tomorrow, and we already have plans for the weekend. I'm mostly looking forward to the diversion.

Friday, June 16, 1989

Dressed in standard club garb, I pick Lucy up at her sister Diane's house in Pennsauken. She greets me at the door, wearing a sexy white body-hugging dress, mid-thigh in length, with an alluring keyhole opening in front that accentuates her shapely breasts. She gives me a big hug and we kiss. I enter the house, and she introduces me to her sister. Diane Nuzzi looks a lot like Ginger from *Gilligan's Island*. She isn't subtle about checking me out. I follow her eyes as they travel over my body, and I wonder what she's thinking. I meet her children, and after declining an offer for a soda, Lucy and I depart.

We start at Images to meet Sherry and the gang. After only an hour, we drive over to the Phoenix in Center City, where we dance and drink until we're well buzzed. Then I suggest, "I'd like to take you to another club I think you'll like. It's also a primarily black crowd, but the drinks are better. Place is at 30th and Market."

"What's the name of the place?"

"It's called Vampire."

I haven't been here in a while, and being inside instantly reminds me how much I enjoy it here. The club is dimly lit but freshly air-conditioned, and has the sweet scent of jasmine incense. Instead of big video screens common in gay clubs, the walls are adorned with large, decorative metal artwork. The bartender is really nice to us, and despite a heavy Caribbean accent, makes a laugh a couple of times. He's very complimentary of Lucy. She insists on buying the next round of drinks, and asks for his recommendation. He suggests their "house specialty," called a Zombie.

"What's in it?" I ask.

"Tree-type-a-rum an some brandy an sugar an some pineapple an lime juice."

"Oooh, sounds fun," Lucy says. He puts it together and serves us in fabulous big hi-ball glasses garnished with mint leaves. The drink is amazing. After two each, we're lit.

"I *feel* like a Zombie," I say, taking her for a walk to another part of the club, a cave-like alcove called the Mars Bar.

This area is almost totally dark, lit only by the reflection of blue lights on sphere-like planets in different shapes and colors. One is in the likeness of Saturn, complete with rings, and it's suspended from the ceiling and hanging down in the center of the tiny room. The psychedelic effect is accentuated by our buzz. We find a seat on a big, comfortable purple sofa and take a break from drinking, soaking up the enchantment radiated by the décor in the room. A slow familiar tune plays and we rise to dance in place, my arms around her, my head in the small of her neck and an easy calculated rocking motion, mimicking the position and moves of brothers near me dancing with their women.

It isn't until after three in the morning that I drop Lucy off. We both have to work tomorrow. I'm drunk and have no idea how I'll make it. When I get home, Tom's actually home and asleep on the couch in front of the TV. He begins to rouse as I turn off the set.

"Where were you?"

"Out with the girls from work. We went to Images."

"Was Lucy with you?"

My heart jumps with that question. "Yeah, everyone was there, why?"

He shakes his head and follows me to bed.

"I have to sleep. I have to work tomorrow."

"Lots of luck," he says. The alarm clock reads 3:49. I set it to go off at 6:40 and climb into bed. He snuggles up to me and puts his arms around me. I'm drunk, and it feels odd that he wants to hold me. Moments ago, she was holding me, and he notices, saying, "I smell perfume on you."

A trace of guilt about my reckless behavior begins to form, and just as quickly it dissipates as I consider the number of Tom's unknown jaunts and lack of attention to helping contain our mounting debt. My efforts to respond politely escalate to, "I just said I was out dancing with the girls."

Saturday, June 17, 1989, 7:00 p.m.

The day started with a major hangover, which caused me to leave work an hour early. Tom was up early and off to work when I got up, and he isn't home yet. Venomous thoughts cross my mind about his neglect: no note, no call all day, not a care in the world about the bills. I feel like I'm on a raft, drifting in the middle of a huge ocean. When Lucy calls with an invitation for a night out, I view her as an island oasis.

She's ready when I arrive at her sister's house. "Love that dress," I say, commenting on her black, lacy form-fitting garment.

"Thanks," she says, and returns several compliments back to me about how I look.

I raise and lower my eyebrows and smile. On the way we relive laughs over funny times we've shared, and discuss our desire for another Zombie.

"Christ, it made a zombie out of me," I say. We hit Christine's first – which is packed to the hilt, as expected, on a Saturday night. We find a place at the bar and order two Zombies. They go down, and then we get down on the dance floor to Taylor Dayne's "Prove Your Love." When we return to the bar, I've got a sudden pressing urge to pee.

I force the money into her hand, asking her to order us another round, and eager to pee, dash to the toilet. There's a long wait for the bathroom and when I return, there's a clear liquid in a martini glass waiting for me with a cherry within. Lucy has already swallowed most of her drink.

"What's this?"

"I don't know, I think it's vodka and club," she answers. "The bartender brought it over, said someone bought it for us."

"Lucy, no one buys a drink for a *couple*. A guy will buy a woman a drink but not a couple."

She rolls her eyes and then closes them for an extended pause. When she opens her eyes, her pupils are dilated and her words are slurred. "What don't you like the drink?"

"Lucy, that's scary. Which bartender gave it to you?"

She says, "He's not here. He's gone."

"Well which guy bought it for you?"

"For us," she insists. She can't find the guy who bought us the drink. "He was just here. He was with his friend and they said we make a good-looking couple. I need to go to the bathroom." I follow her to the bathroom and she emerges moments later, looking disheveled and disoriented. I take her by the hand and walk up to the bartender, busy with the crowd at the bar.

He ignores my waving, so I raise my voice. "Excuse me! Yo! Yo!" He puts his index finger up as he finishes making a drink. He hands the drinks he made to someone and when he leans in to take another person's order, I scream, "HEY! I need the manager!"

He looks over, as do some of the patrons. I'm not embarrassed as I raise my voice louder, looking at Lucy slumping over.

"HEY! She's been drugged!" He waves a hand at me and I walk to the bouncer at the door and ask, "Can I see a manager? My girlfriend has been drugged on a drink!"

He looks at Lucy and walks away shaking his head. Was he going to get someone? Lucy is smiling, looking dumb; her eyes are open, but she's far away. My heart jumps into my throat, then all at once, she's a bit lucid again, saying, "Tom, I'm fine. Let's go." She pulls herself together and walks toward the door. I follow, breathing heavy, my heart still racing. She appears fine.

I come close to her and take her hand. I pull her to a stop as we exit the club and I look at her face. She's focused in on me, smiling. She closes her eyes and puckers her lips for a kiss. I plant one on her and pull away. I feel her forehead and cheeks and find them cool and clammy.

We get in the car, and as we drive around the large City Hall landmark, she slumps into the door and hits her head on the window. I pull over and reach to pull her from the window. She's passed out. I gently slap her cheek and say, "Loo, Loo, Loo..." She comes to and says, "I need to throw up, Tom-Wom," looking at me through slightly crossed eyes. I reach over and open the latch for the door.

"You okay? Lean over and throw up outside, Loo." She turns and takes the door handle. As she leans into the door, it opens and out she falls face first down into the street.

"LUCY!" I scream, trying to catch her as she falls. She is unreachable, with her total upper torso out of the car. I jump out and scan the area as I run around to the other side. I pick her up and she's smashed her forehead onto the curb. It's scraped and bleeding. She's vomited, and some of the gunk is on her face and dress. I grab a clean towel from my gym bag in the back seat, and clean her face. I strap her in while she moans, and contemplate driving right to the hospital. I find a Wawa, and run in for a cup of ice and a bottle of water. I sprint back and try and wipe her face up; I tell her to hold the ice on her scrape. She's barely there, just muttering some gibberish.

I decide to head back home. While on the Ben Franklin Bridge, Loo starts reaching for the handle to open the door, saying, "Tom-Wom, need to throw up," and I grab her and hold her from it.

"Lucy, we're on the bridge. Relax, stay calm! Once we're across the bridge, I'll find a place to pull over." We cross the bridge and by then, she's sleeping calmly.

Jeez. I notice the time: 10:30. In what seems like hours, we arrive at her sister Diane's house only an hour and a half after we left it. I exit the car and go to the passenger side. I hoist Lucy from the car and into my arms. I find the balance I need and carry her in my arms up the sidewalk to the door. Diane opens the door as I reach it; she must have been looking out.

"What happened!?" she asks, eyes wide. I tell her about it while putting Loo's feet down and together. She helps me stand her up. Lucy comes to and mutters, "I need to throw up." We take her to the bathroom and lean her over the toilet, supporting her head.

"I have to pee," Lucy says. We lift her and turn her. I sit her down and leave the bathroom. I stand outside, and moments later, Diane opens the door and asks me to help get her onto the couch in the living room.

With Lucy now cleaned up and passed out on the couch, Diane stands and shakes her head, her hands on her hips.

"Whew. Want some coffee?"

"That would be nice," I say, following her into the kitchen. We jointly decide she's probably okay, but that she may have been the victim of a scheme to get her drugged so she could be taken off somewhere for a rape.

"Just madness," Diane says, looking down into her cup.

"Yep," I say, now feeling a bit responsible for the turn of events this evening. We commiserate over the toxic nature of people out there, as we finish our coffee. Finally, I make note of the time and say that I need to go, hoping it doesn't sound careless. Diane vindicates my behavior, saying I acted very sensibly under the circumstances.

11:25 p.m.

I get home and find Tom sleeping in our bed. After a shower, I get into bed. He reaches over and puts his arm around me. Before I know it, he's kissing me and pulling me into him, his hands on my ass. I'm open to suggestion, and giving him what he wants satisfies my need. He keeps his eyes closed during our lovemaking. It feels so good to be close to him. He whispers, "I love you," turning his chiseled face toward me. I purposely don't return the sentiment, even though I do love him, despite all the crap. I just can't bring myself to verbalize it.

Wednesday, June 21, 1989, 10:45 a.m.
Penn Queen Diner, Pennsauken, New Jersey
Over breakfast, Sherry regales us with another narrative of one of her lunch-

time fucks with some guy she's cheating on her husband with.

"You actually have time to go do it on your lunch?"

"Yeah, man, especially when I get a late lunch," she says, hyper as always. I look at Lucy, and she returns my glance with wide, starry eyes.

When work is over, Lucy and I stand in the parking lot talking after everyone leaves. I pitch an idea, half-hoping she'll decline...but soon she's trailing me in her car to the motel Sherry described at breakfast.

The Crestway, on Route 130, is a seedy dump well known for hourly encounters. This fact is confirmed when the Indian owner asks me how long I'll need the room as I register. I fork over twenty bucks and he hands me a turquoise-colored, diamond-shaped key chain with a large, battered key attached. We enter the dark, nasty-smelling room; the curtains are thick and old and heavy. As Lucy freshens up in the bathroom, I turn the TV on and find a music video channel. I turn the volume all the way down and tune the radio into a soothing local station. It's hot and musty, so I find the air conditioner and turn it on full blast. Lucy comes out of the bathroom, and we sit on the bed and look around at the shitty room. We share disgusted looks, and then we grin. The sweet sound of Nina Simone singing "Here Comes the Sun" floats from the little radio, and we begin undressing as we kiss, excited with anticipation. Lucy is down to her bra and panties as we get under the covers, kissing and licking each other's face and neck. My cock is throbbing and excited at the thought of entering her. I roll her on top of me, and she reaches behind to unhook her bra. I smile up at her and say, "You're amazing." As her bra opens in the back, she holds it to her chest with one hand, and holds herself up with the other, leaning down to kiss me.

I grunt while I pump my cock against her panty-covered crotch. I take down the bra, revealing her two beautiful breasts, then roll her back down on the bed and bury my face into her chest, sucking and kissing them. We're down to my white jockeys and her black lace panties. When I come up for air, she kisses her way down my chest to my happy trail – the strip of hair leading downward from my belly button. She pulls my underwear off and compliments what she sees, then gets down to demonstrating her oral skills. After a while I halt her progress on my blowjob, and all but rip her panties off. I mount her, spreading her legs with my knees. "Ready for me?" I ask.

She nods. I rip open a condom with my teeth, and shove my hard dick into it. She pants her desire for my cock, and then I plunge into her. The sensation is warm, wet and wonderful. We go at it for the next hour and a half. The experience leaves me completely satisfied with my performance, pleased with the fact that I was able to deliver pleasure to her — but far from fulfilled. The sex wasn't bland, but something was missing, some ingredient that usually brings more zest to the act.

As we dress, "How Can I Fall" from the group Breathe — a song Tom and I call our own — comes on. Suddenly, I feel the need to quickly exit this scene. I turn everything off and rush Lucy out. While walking her to her car, she asks, "When can we do that again, Tom?" She's full of compliments about the sex. I bid her farewell until tomorrow, citing a need to take care of some errands. I return the key to the front desk and follow her out of the secluded parking area onto Route 130.

In the car on the way home, I continue evaluating the sexual encounter in my head. It was good, not great, and certainly not on par with my experiences of man-on-man sex. *Definitely* not even close to making love with Tom. Lucy is sensual, good in bed; but afterward, I had no interest in being there with her. What am I trying to prove? I ask myself. *Do I think it's somehow going to end up being better than with men? I keep trying it but it doesn't get better. What am I doing?*

Friday, June 23, 1989, 1:30 p.m.

While sitting in the bank's kitchen the next day on my lunch break, I peruse the pile of bills I brought from home. Trying to get a grasp on the total damage, I come up with a total of $39,000 in total debt, with monthly payments due of $1,170. It's impossible to survive, even by liquidating the $19,000 I have in savings.

Judy comes back and says, "Your friend Tom is here for you."

"Thanks, Jude," I reply, standing up, wondering why he's here. I walk out to my unit and find him waiting there. "Hey," I say.

He smiles and replies, "Hello," resting his elbows on either side of the teller window, crossing his fingers into a prayer-like grasp.

"What brings you here? Are you done work for the day?" I ask one question after another.

"I had a meeting at our main office in Maple Shade."

"How did it go?"

"They never found the money that was stolen. They had this investigator interrogate me again. In the end, they said they were laying me off. That's a nice way to say they were going to fire me."

"You? It wasn't your fault. You didn't take the money."

"I know."

"Are you okay?" I'm worried about him, but I harbor doubts about his integrity.

"I'm all right. Did you get lunch?" he asks.

"Yep. You need me to be with you right now?"

"No. I'm going home. I'll see you when you get there."

"Okay."

As I walk him out, he waves at everyone; he knows most of them from when he met them at Images, and he knows Carmen from the bus trip to Atlantic City. Outside, in the small foyer before the door to the branch, I turn to him and we share a cigarette. "This sucks," I say.

"I'll find another job. Besides, I'm still working for Mitch."

I want to tell him everything will be okay. I want to comfort him for losing his job, but I haven't seen a paycheck from him in months. Like the debt, I have mounting doubts and suspicions about him. I want to ask him when he last gave me money from his jobs for Mitch but he says, "I didn't tell you the good part."

"There's a good part?"

"I structured a new scam that proved to be quite lucrative. I was unloading a washing machine last week and purposely let go of it when it was coming off the van. I fell backwards and onto the ground. I complained of back pain and had them send an ambulance for me. At Underwood, they did some X-rays and shit, but couldn't find anything. So today when they told me I was being laid off, they also said I was going to be able to collect disability from their insurance company. I'm going to get a check for $800 a month for the next three months. It's going to be a great summer."

I'm speechless for a long moment, then I say, "Tom, I thought they couldn't fire you while you're on disability."

Tom says, "That's what we worked out. They want to pin the missing money on me, but I'm getting the disability payments."

For a moment I'm dumbstruck. I can't believe all this. None of it makes sense. With his credibility continuing to plummet in my mind, I say, "Tom, there are so many things wrong with what you just told me that I don't know where to begin."

He starts shaking his head and ranting, "You want money, you bitch about bills, *what the fuck, Tom?*" He pulls two checks from his pockets, handing them to me, saying, "Here!" I look down at them. One check is his regular work check, and the other check is the first insurance check. Together they total to just over $1,000.

Now I'm shaking my head, thinking, but reserving my words. I want to tell him, *Tom, the risk of getting caught for an insurance scam would have serious ramifications after your recent arrest for bank fraud,* but I don't. The fact that this just isn't right, the fact that my beloved Tom continues to stoop to these tactics, is disillusioning.

"See you when I get home," he says, turning to go to his car. As he goes, he declares, "Love you," half-heartedly.

Again, I don't return the sentiment, simply waving and saying, "Thanks. See ya." Notwithstanding the situation, I have the money spent before walking back into the branch, thinking of the thousands we owe on credit cards. Talk about stress.

6:35 p.m., Bob's Big Boy Restaurant
Mt. Ephraim, NJ

Tom asks, "Why are you so quiet?"

"I'm confused."

"About what?"

"I don't know what to do about all the debt we have. Car payments are behind, rent is behind. The money you gave me today is nice, and I appreciate it, but it just puts a dent in our debt. There's still a huge amount owed. By the way, I used your money to pay your car insurance, some credit card payments, plus rent."

Tom says, "I have an idea. I'm going to fake a claim on my homeowner's insurance. Say some of our stuff has been stolen, and get them to pay us $2,500."

The thought of that money feels really good, but the idea of the scam doesn't.

"I'll call the cops and stage a robbery. Break some glass."

I shake my head. "This is turning out to be the summer of scams. I don't want to be a part of that, Tom."

"Yeah, but you're sure as hell okay with benefiting from it, right?" he snaps.

I shake my head, but he knows he's caught me red-handed in evil thoughts. "Fuck it," I say, giving into a diabolical urge I'm ashamed to possess. "Sure, why not. Let's do it."

At home I approach the potential crime scene, the outside window of our spare bedroom, and envision myself smashing it. I enter the apartment and find my way to our spare bedroom. Churchy is there, wagging his tail so hard that his entire backside is swaying back and forth. I glance at my damaged weight bench, the seat covering ruined by his regular chewing on the leather. He has to go out.

I pick Churchy up and plant a couple kisses on his head. He's so cute. He affectionately greets my kisses by licking my face with his tongue.

Upon returning inside to the kitchen, I shout to Tom, "Care for a drink?"

"Sure," he answers. I grab two glasses from the cabinet and pull the ice tray from the freezer. I empty several cubes in each glass. I find the measuring cup, and pour two and a half ounces of whiskey into a plastic container with an ounce and a half of Vermouth, and then I drop in a tablespoon of Campari. Where are the cherries? Oh, fuck it. I dump the remainder of the ice into the plastic container and mix everything together. I dump the ice out of the now chilled glasses, and pour the contents into the glasses. *Voila!* Manhattans for two! I carry the drinks into the living room and hand Tom one. He's curled up on the couch watching TV.

After a drink, I test Tom's resolve, daring him by asking, "Are you ready to do this tonight?"

"Do what?"

"The fake crime. Let's do it! Then call the cops!"

Tom shakes his head. I return to the window in the spare bedroom, and return to the vision of smashing it. *See the window broken,* I tell myself.

I look for something to bust it with and spy a barbell. *How to do it?* I have to break it from outside so the glass lands inside. I walk back into the living room with the barbell in my hand.

"What are you doing?" he asks.

I respond, "Get up, come on, let's get this done."

He shouts, "Tom, relax. Stop."

"Were you kidding about it?" I ask, infuriated.

"No, no, but not now. Let's not do this *now*."

"Yes, now!" I demand, anxious to avoid another sleepless night worried about the bills. Tom seems uninterested. Infuriated, I exit the apartment and look up at the night sky. I walk up to the window and contemplate busting it. *What am I doing? Am I crazy?*

I walk back into the apartment and collapse, deflated and defeated, into bed alone.

Saturday, June 24, 1989

I wake and find Tom has left the windows open and the air conditioning off. The aroma in the apartment is a fragrant mix of cool summer foliage and the remains of the incense from last night.

Feeling his big, solid, strong arms wrapped around me dilutes any negatives; and as my prince wakes, he kisses me, and the power of his kiss only solidifies the love I feel for him. Despite all we've been through, or maybe in spite of it, this moment is everything I've dreamed of.

He rolls me over on my back and grasps my hands, interlocking his fingers in mine. As he stares down, we lock eyes and communicate an unspoken shared joy. I feel higher and happier than I've ever felt. Woven deep into the fabric of my being, somehow I have connected to what I've been yearning for my entire life — right here in this bed with him.

He lowers his head and, once again, his lips touch mine. I gaze into his eyes and the passion repels my fury. As we dive into each other sexually, it's as if we're transported to a tantalizing, warm beach with cool and refreshing waves washing over us. The lovemaking has been perfected. It's in this precious moment of bliss that I realize that this is where I belong.

We easily navigate our way to a holding pattern, maintaining an extreme sensation of ecstasy by mutual oral stimulation. The hot kissing while engaged in the most intimate of acts, coupled with the look of surrender in each other's eyes, brings us in for a landing.

4:30 p.m.

After Tom had to head out around noon to take Noémie on several jobs, he just called to say he's going for a drive after their jobs and won't be home until tomorrow. I gently protest, this time telling him I miss him and wanted to go out tonight. He comes back strong, telling me to *relax and calm down*. I resent his bully-like attitude as we end the call.

Notwithstanding our sweet session this morning, I'm left to my thoughts, drawn back to Tom's lack of contribution to the household. I consider his lack of financial responsibility to be a direct flaw in his participation in our relationship. Couple that with these late night "drives" that go unexplained and his contention that I'm supposed to just go with it blindly, and…I don't know. Maybe our love will light the way for us to overcome the hurdles.

Fuck that. I feel so stupid that I continue to hold any hope that this love can survive. He's sucking everything out of me and this relationship, and not investing into it or building it one bit. It could be so great, but I feel he's just killing it. I've shared all my innermost thoughts and desires with him. I feel foolish and terribly confused. I call Lucy to make a date for this evening.

11:40 p.m., The Phoenix dance floor

DJ Frank Cerami announces a Kissing Contest, and asks for couples to come up and register. "Wouldn't that be fun?" Lucy suggests.

"Yeah! You read my thoughts!" The performing, attention-seeking side of me is ignited with excitement. We walk up to the line of couples signing up. We get up to the DJ, and give our names and a song request.

Back upstairs at the bar I ask, "Whatcha want?"

"Hmmm, I don't know," Loo says, beaming. I lean in and kiss her sweet lips. She smells good. We sit at the bar and suck back two Tequila Sunrises. We're well lit when the kissing contest begins, and are lost in each others' glance as we hear the co-DJ announce, "Hey, where's that cute little Caucasian couple?" Lucy's eyes widen with glee and my jaw drops as we jump up and scoot over to the railing, looking down the stairs. We wave our hands toward the dance floor, and the huge crowd starts clapping as we approach. We stand out as the only white couple among dozens of beautiful black people. It's tremendous and outrageous!

One at a time, the couples take turns kissing for two minutes each. We're last to go, and as we do, "Two Occasions" by The Deele begins, cued to the middle of the song. We take our place in the center of the floor. I put my arms around Lucy, and slowly bend to take one knee in front of her, taking one of her hands in mine. I gently kiss her hand and slowly rise and take her into my embrace. With one hand behind her head and one around her waist, I gradually kiss her cheek, then her lips. We part our lips and our kiss takes on a frenzied porn-like pulse as she takes her cue from me and allows me to slide her lower as I drop back to one knee with her on the other. There are sounds coming from the crowd, but they're lost as our performance fades into reality as we truly take pleasure in the kiss. I slowly bring us back up and release the kiss and spin her around in a semicircle. Lucy puts one hand out, and then balances for a curtsy while holding my hand. I bow and they conclude the contest. Applause; we're the winners! Better kissers than five other couples! WOW! *Holy fuck!* We're all smiles as we collect the $100 in prize money, and everyone is just as happy for us.

After a few more hours of dancing and drinking, we stagger out of the club and giggle about winning the contest as we walk. People passing us are all smiles as a very drunk Lucy announces, "We won a kissing contest!" It's cute. Music from a club we pass is audible from the street, and I clap and dance as we pass.

"Feeling good?" she asks.

"Oh yeah," I answer. We swing our arms, hands held, as we stroll into the next club, The Trocadero. "Your Love" by the group Lime is just being mixed in as we fork over the cover charge. We practically sprint to the bar to grab a cold beer before tearing it up on the dance floor until closing.

Sunday, June 25, 1989: 2:30 a.m.

As "Hit & Run Lover" by Carol Jiani pours from the cheap radio on the table beside our bed at the Crestway Motel, I find myself deep inside her again — and condomless. Pulling out of her inviting warmth at climax totally wrecks my satisfaction. Lucy has gotten off a couple times, and my one and only time is lost when I have to substitute my hand at the last minute, disappointing my anxious cock. Sex for me is now all about getting it better than before. Coming like this is like paying for a bad meal.

It's really late when we get back to her sister's house in Pennsauken. Lucy is spending the weekend with Diane. I decide to take Lucy's invite and spend the night on Diane's couch, given that my head is now pounding, I'm too tired to drive, and I'm still feeling fucked up.

I'm barely asleep when the shocking sound of a ringing phone pierces the silence. I hear some rustling upstairs and it doesn't faze me until I hear Diane's voice. "Who? Tom? Wait, what? Tom is gay? No, no. Look, no, okay, don't call back. I have kids sleeping here."

It suddenly becomes horrifyingly evident that *my* Tom is on the phone, and I can feel the adrenaline flow as my heart goes into my throat. I jump up, and my ears perk up for more dialogue. I can tell Diane is doubly pissed off at being stirred from sleep, but probably more so from harboring a hatred and suspicion of anything male due to the recent collapse of her marriage. Looking toward the stairs, I see the light come on and Lucy is soon following Diane down the stairs. Diane speaks in a stern yet low tone, sounding like an overprotective bitch: "Tom, I have kids here. This is the second time tonight your roommate has called. Is Tom your roommate?"

Before I speak a word, she fires off another question, "Is he your roommate, or exactly what is going on here?"

Lucy, looking panicked and brought to an uneasy sober state by this drama, tries to speak. "Tom, he's on the phone, and do you know what he's saying?"

Diane puts a finger up and hushes her with, "Shhhh, Lucy, please." The phone rings again.

"That's him again!" Diane announces.

"I'm not getting it. He wants to speak to you!" Diane says.

Lucy announces, "He was saying you're gay, and he's your lover. What's going on, Tom?"

I lower my brow and shake my head and begin acting. "What?" I ask.

Diane rises and answers the kitchen phone with, "What?!...YES! YOU NEED TO STOP CALLING HERE. I HAVE KIDS SLEEPING.... YES, BUT... *STOP CALLING.*"

I'm certain her screaming exceeds the damage the ringing phone did to her kid's sleep. Displaying award-winning high drama, Diane holds the receiver up and says, "You need to talk to him." Diane shouts to Lucy, "What's going on, Lucy?"

Lucy and I rise. I take the receiver, and Lucy takes Diane to the stairs. I hear Diane say, "Lucy, if he's gay, you can't be getting into this. What's going on here?"

Lucy responds in a hushed tone, "Go to bed. I'll get it sorted out."

Diane lets out a huff and puff and storms upstairs. I hear Tom on the receiver shout, "TOM!"

I answer, calmly, "Yes, I'm here."

He whips back, "What the fuck are you doing? Are you fucking her? What's going on?"

I instantly go into character. "What are you talking about?"

"Don't act like you don't know why I'm calling. I'm on to you. You've been fucking her, haven't you?"

"No! Are you drunk?" I ask, conscious of Lucy's proximity, while holding the receiver tightly to my ear so as to block the sound of his words.

"You know I'm not drunk."

"Calm down."

"Stop *acting* for them!"

"What do you want?"

"I want you home *right now.*"

"All right, I'll be right there." I'm thinking I'll probably go to jail tonight when I get my hands on him.

"You're damn right you will. You better fucking be here within the hour, or my next call is to your parents — and I'll tell them what you've been up to."

Uneasy and extremely embarrassed, I smirk a little and say, "I'll be about 20 minutes. Calm down and lie down. I'll be right there."

I hang up the phone and pause a moment. Lucy, sitting on the stairs, rises and walks up to me, putting her arms around me, and says, "What's going on, Tom?"

I'm searching for the right words, and begin to speak when Diane comes down the stairs again, arms crossed.

I say the wrong words: "He's drunk off his ass. I don't know what's wrong with him. He's talking crap."

Lucy leans in and says, "Tom, is what he's saying true?"

"Oh God, no," I begin, again calmly. "Listen, I gotta go. I have to sort him out."

She holds tight to my arms and pleads, "No, Tom, stay here and go in the morning! You've been drinking all night and shouldn't be on the road." She looks at Diane to support this.

Diane, still standing with arms crossed, her face looking staid, says, "Lucy, let him go."

Lucy loosens her grip, kisses me and says, "Call me when you get home. We need to talk."

"I will, don't worry. Gotta run."

I think about apologizing to Diane, but when I look at her I can't find the words. I know she can see through my façade, but her quest to protect Lucy comes off as hatred.

The drive home is the worse 20 minutes of my life. I'm nervous about what I'll find, what I'll do. Why do I feel guilty, like I let Tom down, when he's been out every fucking night doing God knows what? Of course, I have no real hard evidence that Tom has strayed. *What am I doing?*

I must be dreaming, because this shit can't be happening. Christ, Lucy fucking works with me. What excuse can I give her? Why don't I just come out and be done with it?

I was out at the other bank. I'm angry with Tom, yet confused and humbled by this demonstration of jealousy when he's been an absentee landlord in our relationship. I feel like I've reached a new low, and the hurt reaches to the pit of my heart. I turn my thoughts into prayers and cast them at the Lord, pounding the Almighty like my own personal sounding board. Begging for help, asking for forgiveness for only visiting when I need something – rarely praying to pay homage or give thanks for favors granted, that's me. I'm embarrassed with my side of my relationship with the Most High. I pray to Mary to beseech Christ on my behalf. *Mary, I need your help now more than ever, I pray. Please come to me, be with me, and guide me through this situation.*

Before opening the front door, I remind myself that I can control the consequences of what's happened. The outcome remains in my hands. *Relax, be calm, be steady, be confident.* I arrive at home to find Tom lying on the floor in front of the couch, watching TV.

Thoughts I had on the way home of beating his ass subside when I see him. I feel I've hurt him, and tears well up in my heart; yet my eyes remain dry. I toss my keys on the table and say, "Well, what the fuck are you doing?" I force myself to be angry and direct. Finding a way to approach this mess is difficult.

Without removing his eyes from the TV screen, he says, "Don't act, Tom, don't act. I knew you were fucking her. You don't know what you are yet, Tom. You're a fucking faggot, man. There *is* no other life for you. What are you trying to do?"

"Have you been following me?" I ask.

"Well, there you are. No need for you to say anything else."

"What?" I ask, realizing my response to his allegation divulges my guilt.

"Just shut it," he snaps, shaking his head. He looks up, with sad eyes that turn to finally soak in the sight of me. He adds, "You're fucking this up, Tom," and looks back at the TV.

I want to scream, "ME? *I'M* THE ONE FUCKING IT UP?" but I catch myself and don't. I was caught; I need to stop. For a moment, we both watch TV together. I try and gather my thoughts, preparing my defense. He finally brings his eyes back to mine and says in a frail tone, "Isn't there anything between us anymore?"

How dare him. Rather than defend, I go on the offense: "I can't believe you're saying that." I pause to organize the delivery of a rapid-fire series of thoughts. "You go out every fucking night and do God-knows-what with God-knows-who. I'm supposed to believe you're just going for a *drive*? You gave me a bunch of cash on Friday for the first time in months. Months! Do you think that helps put a dent in the charges you've ran up on my credit cards? Or the insurance or the car payments or…"

Tom cuts me off with, "Don't start that shit, because I'm not going to talk about it. What you *assume* I've done doesn't give you a license to perform your antics."

When faced with my misdeeds, my reaction is to bolster my cockiness. "Why did you call there and embarrass me like that?"

He rolls over as if to ignore me, but I will not be ignored. His insolence will not be tolerated. I'm not about to chase his face by moving where I am. I stand my ground and contemplate pouncing on him. I take a deep breath and say, "You essentially ruined me at work. I can't go back; Lucy is going to tell everyone I'm gay." He remains silent.

I feel another rush of adrenaline and raise my voice as I complete the next sentence, "Now she and her sister THINK THAT I AM GAY! ARE YOU LISTENING TO ME?"

Tom turns back and uses his hands behind him to hoist himself onto the couch.

He sparks up a cigarette and takes a drag as if coming up for air after being held underwater. He declares, "I got a news flash for you, pal; you *are* gay. None of these dopes are going to be on your side. Why don't you put your energy into being the best homosexual you can be instead of chasing shitty little hopes of pleasing everyone else?"

"Fuck you, Tom. If, when, how and to whom I choose to reveal my sexuality is up to me," I assert. "You're unaware of how much you've damaged my reputation."

He shakes his head stating, "Damaged? You're not damaged. Being gay is a gift. When are you going to embrace it?"

I plop on the couch and think: *I am gay. He's totally right — being gay is a gift, and I've already concluded Tom was more than I could dream for.* I mentally remind myself, *You've never given a fuck what people thought before. You actually enjoy the attention your looks bring from both sexes. So why now?* Inwardly, and cowardly, it could be that I'm truly using Lucy for many reasons that don't connect: to see where it goes, to make my parents happy, to make babies, as a substitute for Tom's friendship when he's not around. In my own selfish way, I've rationalized that having sex with a woman isn't really cheating on Tom, since it's not with a man. Honestly, I'm less worried about *people at work* knowing, and more worried about Lucy's feelings.

Maybe I'm looking at this all wrong: maybe I should be delighted that he's so jealous and into us. Then my thoughts turn back to the embarrassment and shame of it all. *What will I say to Lucy?* I'm still so angry at Tom for calling there that I can't bring myself to feel bad for what he's feeling and dealing with at this moment. Tom is probably going out for another drive, and it's so late. All I want is to be unconscious. I walk into the bathroom and chase a sleeping pill with a shot of NyQuil. As I throw myself on the bed I feel tearful as negative, self-defeating thoughts flood my mind. It's not until Tom comes to the bedroom that I realize I've been sobbing. He attempts to soothe me by taking me by the hand and leading me into the living room. He positions us so he's sitting on the floor, leaning on the couch, and I'm lying down with my head face-up in his lap. He uses his fingers to wipe my tears and then gently massages my head. He asks, "Do you love her?"

"No," I answer honestly.

He asks, "Were you fucking her?"

"No, we're just friends," I lie, looking into his eyes. I'm upset that I allowed myself to go as far as I did with Lucy. I'm confused and over my head. Tom must believe me, because he says, "Nothing will happen. Just call her and tell her I was drunk. Tell her to get over it." He tells me everything will get fixed in the morning. I roll over, and he continues to gently rub my head while flipping through the TV channels. I'm about to doze off when he offers, "I'm sorry for upsetting you with that call."

Sunday, June 25, 1989, 8:01 a.m.

I wake to discover that we've both slept on the floor in the living room all night. "I'm calling her now," I tell Tom. "Remember, you said you were going to fix this mess." Tom nods, in a surprisingly obedient manner.

Thankfully, Lucy answers, and not her sister. "Hello," she says, sounding tired.

"Sorry about last night. Tom wants to talk to you."

She says, "I don't want to talk to him. I don't care what that was all about. I really like you, Tom."

I hand Tom the phone. He holds it to his chest and widens his eyes at me.

He gets on the phone and says, "Lucy, is it you? Look, I'm sorry for calling last night. I don't know what to say. I was wrong to —"

Lucy obviously cut him off by asking a question. Despite straining to hear her, it's inaudible to me. Tom's face reflects nervous tension as he searches for an answer to her question. He counters with, "No, no. I had a fight with my ex-girlfriend, and was tripping on some bad drugs. I was passed out when he got home and didn't realize what I did until this morning." Tom lifts his cigarette and takes a quick puff inward. "Hold on Lucy, hold on... Tom, can you get me two aspirin?"

"What?" I ask. He snaps his fingers and waves the questions off, shaking his head, rolling his eyes.

"Yep, and I sure hope you and your sister aren't too angry with me." He hands the phone back to me, nodding and smiling.

I say, "Hi, it's me."

She begins, "He really sounds far gone."

I don't have it in me to carry on a conversation with her. "Sorry about all that, but I'm gotta go for now."

She asks if we'll see each other tomorrow. I say I have to go, because I'm not feeling well, and end the call promising to call her back later.

I storm into the spare bedroom, angry over my behavior, over Tom having to lie to Lucy, over the entire situation and how our once perfect relationship has deteriorated. I fall down on his other bed. Churchy jumps up and joins me, licking and gently biting on my head, since I'm covering my face in my arms. He pushes his nose into my arms, trying to get me to raise my face.

A range of emotions builds within me; soon, my feet hit the floor and I walk back into the living room. Anger has surfaced as I enter the room, furious again about the entire incident, and I snap, "What were you thinking, calling her last night? You are such a serious fuck-up!"

Tom's jaw drops; clearly, he's baffled by my hostility. He says, "I have every reason to be pissed off at you. You messed around with a woman, Tom. What were *you* thinking? Your blatant unfaithfulness gives you no fuckin' right to call me a fuck-up. How dare you! As a matter of fact, why don't I call her back and tell her you suck cock? I'll tell everyone in that bank you're a faggot. How's that?" That said, he reaches for the phone. I feel myself go into reaction. Rage takes hold and I charge toward Tom and, with a piranha-like frenzy, we tear into each other in a brawl that is our nastiest to date. This battle of fists leaves us both bruised and bloody at the end of the match. Tom has sustained the worse of it; his nose is flowing red.

Breathing heavily, we exchange vicious and revolting remarks until I storm back to the spare bedroom, where I collapse and fall asleep on the spare bed. After what seems like seconds into a therapeutic REM sleep state, I'm shocked into consciousness by a physical attack. When I realize what's happening, it's too scary for words. Tom is fucking beating me with the huge metal buckle part of my massive leather weight belt. He's slamming it down with all his might, without regard for anywhere it lands. I curl up and protect my face and genitals, fearful he'll strike them. All I can do I hold one hand up in defense. With one whip of the belt, he hits my hand so hard it stings every part of my body. Virtually defenseless, I lie there and take the beating, hoping he'll stop. I envision my retaliation and it terrifies me.

Tom doesn't stop his assault. I realize I need to be strong. With everything I've got, I seal my mind and assume the role of a tank as the metal crashes into my skull. I grit my teeth and find a way to snatch the belt from him. I'd forgotten that I had undressed before getting into bed, so I'm standing in my underwear, fighting him. He and I begin fighting again, this time with even more intensity. I take a moment to look at my hand, which is swelling up like a balloon. He's pounding me, and while I feel the ignition that could trigger certain calamity, I realize I have to control my actions. I need to stop this. I notice large welts on my hand, and am more enraged with Tom for this.

He's gone berserk, and I need to stop him. We resume our fight and it takes us from one end of the apartment to the other. He enters the back den and slams the door in my face. I turn and lean against the door and slide down to the floor. Tom opens the door, and I don't budge. My muscles tighten and prepare for the next round of fighting but I can tell by his expression that he's done. I walk into the bathroom and sit on the side of the tub, running my hurt hand under the cold water. Tom enters and clenches a fist, banging it on the wall. He addresses me but stares at the wall, "Look, I'm sorry. I guess I'm just about as jealous as they get. Can you find it in you to make up with me again?"

I tell him something true but amazingly difficult at this moment to say, "I love you, Tom."

"I love you too," he says, nodding.

I don't make eye contact with him. I'm disappointed in both of us. I share my thought, "This pattern of arguing, fighting each other, it has to stop. It's lethal to any hope we have to having anything permanent together."

"I'm sorry," he says. I don't speak.

He walks up and begins cleaning me up. He nurses our wounds and puts me in the tub for a bath. I am shaking and moaning. He obviously wants to make up and inwardly, I just want peace. I am just as responsible for this chaos as him. I tell Tom I need to be alone for a while so he departs and lets me be.

After soaking for an hour and half, I check out my face and body in the mirror. Black and blue marks everywhere, and my hand is swollen and sore. In the medicine cabinet, I find the acid Jon gave me, still wrapped in wax paper. I think about swallowing it, but don't hesitate and drop it down the drain. I tell myself, *Get a grip. And a plan.*

Monday, June 26, 1989

Tom will get one hundred percent of me when we're together — no more fights about bills or his mysterious drives at night. He can do his own thing by day, and if he wants me at night, I'll be there. I'll have a talk with Lucy, and set things straight. In between waiting on customers, I spend most of the morning calling my credit card companies to cancel cards. To my chagrin, I learn what I suspect — that most of the cards are maxed out. I knew Tom was calling to have the card limits increased, and I discover every limit has been raised to almost double the original credit line. I obtain a copy of my credit report and am thankful for the fact that nothing else unusual is going on.

Wednesday, June 28, 1989
The Crestway Motel

This is getting crazy. My intention was to fess up to Lucy about my relationship with Tom. I wanted to come clean and work to transition our budding romantic relationship into a platonic companionship. Needless to say, as I sit here sucking on a Marlboro in post-coital remorse, that plan didn't happen. As we share a couple beers over pizza, discussing taking a course together at American Institute of Banking, I contemplate my fear of pulling the plug on the sex because I risk losing the friendship.

Tuesday, July 4, 1989, Independence Day

Summer is the height of the stripper season, and Noémie and I each have over a dozen jobs each weekend in addition to several during each week. Tom was able to swing things so he could accompany me on two I have scheduled this afternoon.

Before we leave, he watches as I put the finishing touches on my cop uniform by polishing the black shoes till they shine like mirrors. "Uh, ya know your ass looks so fine wrapped in those tight black polyester pants. Bet you can balance that can of hairspray on it."

"Hmm, so glad you like what you see," I say, adding, "I'll increase my regimen of squats at the gym." I turn back and look at how neat the blue shirt looks, freshly pressed and creased. I position the hat on my head and stand at attention for a moment.

Later

Before knocking on the door, I put three sticks of gum in my mouth and don the shades. A cocky gum-chewing cop with sunglasses enhances the costume.

They let me in and I enter the living room, surrounded by women sitting on chairs. There are a bunch of presents around, and about another half-dozen chicks in what looks like the kitchen on the other side of the small house. As I enter, I go right into character; nerves aside, I have a job to do. I love how my internal auto-pilot takes over and I just begin acting. I tell myself it will all be over inside half an hour, and I'll leave $75 to $100 richer.

I walk right to the center of the room of women and immediately earn everyone's attention by calling out, "Alicia Wo-jo-ko-witz" trying unsuccessfully to pronounce her Polish last name. A tall, slim model-type with beautiful blonde hair and a pretty, sexy smile walks toward me. Despite her high heels, she glides as she walks.

"I'm Alicia," she says, extending a French-manicured hand. Rather than shaking her hand, I take her by the hand and turn her around to initiate the charade of the whole phony arrest racket. I situate us in the center of the living room. There is no need to collect up front on this one; it's prepaid to Mitch with a credit card. My cassette is already cued up, so I press play on my boom box after finding a place to plug it in. I take Alicia by the hand and gently guide her to have a seat. She's pretty playful as I perform for her and her group of friends. At the conclusion of this gig, I leave with Alicia's phone number along with $90 in tips.

In the car on the way home, I ask Tom, "Mom asked me if we wanted to join her, Dad, Danny and Jane in watching the fireworks on Fort Dix. Wanna go?"

"Sure."

"Cool. We've been going to see the fireworks at Fort Dix for as far back as I can remember."

"Family tradition thing?" he asks.

"Yes, it's been a perennial favorite for us." We stop home, pack up the doggie, and Tom gets a bottle of wine to share with my parents.

8:30 p.m.

This evening, sitting on the blanket watching the fireworks with my family and Tom, turns out to be just the kind of pure and refreshing diversion my psyche was craving.

As I cast my eyes to the starry night sky, my thoughts float to dreams that I carry: taking the power of this love with Tom to the next level in order to make all our ambitions, aspirations and goals come to life. I scan my own hopes — one day having a baby, one day writing a book, one day becoming a District Manager in a bank...I don't think that's asking too much of the Creator.

I look at Tom and think to myself, *You need me, I need you. I'll remain just a little longer, until you grow into this relationship.*

Intuitively reading my thoughts, Tom leans over and surprises me with a whispered, "I'm so happy that you're mine. Let's wait for each other."

10:55 p.m.

Holding hands on the ride home, we explore a wide range of topics unrelated to the current stressors in our life. I'm unsure what initiates our conversation on threesomes.

"Some couples do them with the understanding that there's no anal sex, no kissing on the mouth, and they get to open up their relationship, so they can experience new things," Tom offers. I allow the thought to cross my mind for a selfish reason, in that there's one component of his plan that *is* a turn-on: the thought of watching him with another dude.

"I thought you didn't want to do them," I say finally. "I remember you saying you didn't want to share me."

"Dig this: we can each have fun. I know we're together and we're tightly bound. Nothing will jeopardize our relationship. Is that cool?"

"Tom, no more of this conversation in front of the child," I say, pointing to Churchy, sitting on my lap. We chuckle, then I say, "I'm not playing with you. I mean, I don't want to share you."

He ribs me with, "Tom, the couple that plays together, stays together."

I shake my head and say, "The saying is *the family that prays together, stays together,* you knucklehead."

"Let's pick up a guy and see what happens. If you don't want to do anything, we won't. Listen, you may like the guy and want it to happen. I'm just saying don't lock out options. Let's have some fun. Let's pick up a straight boy and terrorize him," he says.

"What? Are you fuckin' nuts?"

"Let's just offer to blow him or something. Straight guys love that. What's the difference between a straight guy and a gay guy?"

I chuckle and answer, "Isn't the answer something like a six pack of beer?" Tom returns a chuckle and nods. He pulls into a bar on the White Horse Pike in Oaklyn called Rebecca's.

"Go in and get one...Just go in and see if any want to party."

I contemplate acquiescing for a moment, then say, "Shut up."

We continue driving and Tom just drives and drives all over. I'm starting to fade into sleep from the comforting hum of the car when he nudges me and says, "Oh, look, there's a cute guy hitching." I sit up and realize we're on Route 130 right outside Camden in Collingswood. The guy looks younger than us, but I'm unsure. As we approach, the dude jumps into a jog toward our Camaro.

"Aww, cute dog, guys. Thanks for the ride."

"Where you headed, man?" Tom asks.

"Over Fairview," the dude says. Cute as a button, I like his small frame and bubble butt. "What are you two up to tonight?"

Without hesitation, Tom says, "Looking for some fun. Lookin' to play."

"Oh, that's cool," the kid says, looking out the window, bobbing to the music on the car radio.

"How about you?" I ask.

"Uh, headin' back to my girlfriend's place."

I nod and peek over at Tom, who is rolling his eyes and making a face. "Cool," I say, smirking. "Does she give good head?" I ask, stunning even myself. Tom's eyes widen. Even he is amazed.

"It's cool," the boy says.

"You ever get head from a guy?" Tom asks.

"Whoa! No thanks, man," he answers quickly.

Tom retorts, "I didn't offer, Bud."

We drop him off at his girlfriend's house and head home. Alone again in the car, I ask Tom, "Is this what you get up to when you go out for drives at night?"

"What?" he asks.

"Trying to pick up boys."

He shakes his head.

We ride in silence until we reach Blackwood. "If You Don't Know Me By Now" by the group Simply Red comes over the radio. Tom breaks the silence as we cross the bridge over Blackwood Lake by asking, "Hear that?" referring to the part of the lyrics that go, *"Oh don't get so excited when I come home a little late at night, cos we only act like children when we argue, fuss and fight."*

He adds, "Hey, that's it, honey. You've got to learn how to deal. I do love you, Thomas." I turn my head and look out the window, feeling ashamed of my thoughts about him, and definitely embarrassed of my actions with Lucy.

Saturday, July 8, 1989, 2:00 a.m.

Being off from work isn't fun when there's a ton of annoying chores to accomplish. It takes all day to tidy up the apartment, iron a couple of shirts for work for next week, and pick up some food for our empty refrigerator. Tom had to work with Noémie today and it isn't until now that I awake to find him next to me in bed.

"You were gone all day," I say, recalling that he was gone when I awoke this morning. "It was such a beautiful day. I was hoping we could have had a picnic over at Fairmount Park or Valley Forge today."

"I had an evil plan earlier this week and it blew up in my face. I'm going to tell you because you're going to find out any way."

"What are you talking about?" I ask, irritated to hear about another scheme.

"I went over to Philadelphia last Monday and bought all kinds of shit — a TV, a VCR, a watch and some tools. Then I went back today and tried to return it all for cash because I was going to tell the credit card company that the card was stolen. Then we could get the cash to pay bills, and we wouldn't be responsible for the charges. Well, when I went back to return the shit today, they would only credit the card, they wouldn't give cash."

"You're kidding me, right?"

"No. Why?"

"That's so *stupid*, Tom. Like, they have cameras in the fucking stores. They would see you returning the shit for cash, you dope."

"Well, I'm not the cardholder, *you are*. You could say you don't know who I am."

"Tom, that's fuckin' risky and stupid. Don't do anything like that. Why did you do that without talking to me first?"

"I wanted it to be a surprise."

"Oh, surprise: you're in jail. Real smart."

He's quiet. *How the hell did he get the cards to work when I stopped them all?* I want to fight, call him a jackass, yet it's no longer in me. In his own warped way, maybe he *is* trying to help. I've lost steam for his level of intelligence, unsure if he's exhibiting survivalist techniques I should applaud or just being plain ridiculous. I roll over, then roll back to face him.

"Did you return everything you bought?"

"Yes. Took all day."

"Didn't you have a job with Noémie today?"

"Yeah, but I got it all done."

I roll back over. He gets up and turns on the light of the neon clock he bought me for Christmas. It illuminates the room in a dim blue hue. He gets back in bed and I turn back to face him. He smiles and says, "You." He puts his hands on my face and says, "I *love* this face," stressing the word love. "I'm sorry things have you upset lately, honey. If you equate love for someone with the money situation in a relationship, then you're not really in love."

"I…" I start, but he silences me with a long kiss. He caresses my lips with his. His hands find mine and he squeezes. His tight grip incites my erection. I try so hard to push loving feelings out of the way and with one touch, he brings everything streaming back. He looks into my eyes and says, "I love you. I would like to hear it from you. I hate asking, but I need to hear it. It's been a while."

Then I hear myself speak the words, "I love you, Tom."

I continue, "It was such a good day today. So bright and beautiful; why can't…" I stop, breathing heavy, thinking hard about the emotions welling up inside as memories of Nadine and Tom flash though my mind. "Even though we haven't had much time together, I feel we've been through a lot. Most it has been trying. I want us to spend time making happy memories. Sure, I want to travel around the world and eat at fancy restaurants and party every night. One day we can do these things, we can make all of our dreams come true. Right now, we need to economize, but that doesn't mean we can't have fun. I have a lot of ideas of things we can do."

Tom peels off my white tank top and tugs my blue briefs down and off. He kisses my neck, shoulders, chest and stomach. I can't shake this complete feeling of sorrow, can't separate the gloomy outlook I have for our relationship. There's a cloudy vision of us in the future. I want something I can be sure of, but it seems no love is invincible.

We roll into making love and the thoughts of bills, fights and work blur into warm, sensual feelings and erotic thoughts as we express our love physically. With his face in my ass, I bring him to orgasm with my hands and then he returns the favor with my face buried in his soft, shapely sweet ass.

We finish and clean up and Tom takes my head into his lap and massages it for a long time — my favorite thing is getting my head and hands massaged, and he does so, willingly and lovingly, until sleep takes me. It's the best feeling in the world to be sexually satisfied so completely, followed by being brought in for a sleep-landing with such tender attention and care. Tom has mastered the ability to relieve the tension my hyper-drive and insatiable passion for achievement can sometimes bring to both of us. In a simple, yet magical way, he's made me feel on top of the world.

Saturday, July 15, 1989

This week has been severe – I cashed in more CDs and savings to satisfy the ravenous appetite of bill collectors who are now calling me at home and on the job almost daily. I missed several minimum payments, and presume Tom must have intercepted the bills in the mail before I had a chance to see them. Now they've imposed "penalty rates" to point where it would be cheaper to borrow from the mob. I spend time getting all of them reorganized again and create reminders in my calendar to remind me of payment due dates for each card. At this point my cards are all useless now anyway. I have no access to credit. *How did I allow this to happen?*

Tom has continued his nightly expeditions and came home this morning with an announcement – he has a new job as one of the managers of an adult bookstore in Berlin, N.J. I was stunned with that news and review our conversation in my head. "You're not working in a cruisy adult bookstore!" I protested, yet what could

I do? I've been nothing but supportive of him since Day One. It's a just a job, after all; I should just digest it. He says it pays $400 a week, and we certainly need the money. *Why do I feel like I'm losing him?*

Monday, July 24, 1989

Carmen's acting fucking weird today. She came back all refreshed from a week-long vacation, and her good mood is quickly deflated by the news of $200 missing from a night bag, Nancy's resignation, and the final straw: when she turns the radio on, the station has been moved from her precious AM dinosaur oldies station to an easy rock station. To Carmen, this one thing implies that we were slacking all week. She keeps walking behind the teller line, asking me to clean my station.

"When are you going to lunch?" she asks on her third visit to my teller line today. I shake my head and say, "Noon today, why?"

"Can you go now?"

"Sure, Carmen, why? What's up?" I ask, looking at my watch, which reads 10:40 am. She pulls the pencil from her nest-like hair and bites on the eraser. I finish the transaction I'm working on and assume she wants me to get her something, so I wrap up the crap in front of me and lock my station. She's standing behind me, watching, so I hurry. "Did you want me to pick something up for you?"

She shakes her head and says, "You'll be back by noon?"

"Yeah. 11:40, actually," I say, suspicious of the way she's acting. I yell over to Sherry, "I'm headed out. Be back at quarter to." Sherry waves her hand without breaking an amusing conversation with a cute customer.

The old hag follows me as I walk off the teller line, asking, "Are the tellers all under their cash limits?"

"Yes," I answer, thinking I shouldn't let her bother me. She's not Letitia, after all.

On the way to lunch, I stop by Lucy's desk to see if she can join me. She doesn't look happy.

"What's up?" I ask, smiling.

"I can't go to lunch with you. She wants you to go now because Ellen Ryan from Branch Administration is coming here to meet with us about the missing money from that night bag."

I almost break my neck turning around to find Carmen. She's standing on the side of the teller line, arms crossed, with a flat line for a mouth – and an evil look on her face. I turn back to Loo and say, "What the fuck? That bitch couldn't tell me? Is that why she's been riding my ass all morning?"

"Yeah, I just found out."

Sharon walks over and places a blank phone message on Loo's desk and says, "Customer complaint, Loo," in a loud voice while making bulging eyes at and pointing to the note that reads, *"She's watching and listening to you guys."*

I smile and laugh, saying loudly, "Oh, listen, I'll be back. You're both sure you don't want anything?" They confirm that they don't, and I head to my car. I'm furious that Carmen didn't tell me Ellen was coming.

Noon

Ellen walks into the branch, and even though I've never seen her before, I recognize her immediately. Her presence is prominent, and her authority is captivating when it fills the room. She's taller than the average woman and her long, straight blonde hair falls halfway down her back. The top of her hair is scary looking. Her bangs are brushed almost straight up and appear to be hairsprayed to stand up until they lean over slightly. She's wearing a bright fire-truck red silk dress that accentuates her wide hips. Her shape is otherwise lean. She's not unattractive for a dame who's well into her thirties. She wears bright red lipstick to match the dress; it's got a zipper collar zipped half-way up her neck. She strides in like she owns the place, and Carmen rises to greet her as if Ellen were royalty.

After Ellen and Carmen spend two minutes chatting and looking over at me and the teller line, another dude walks in. He's shorter than Ellen and obviously works for the bank, but isn't wearing a shirt and tie. He has a sports coat on with a sweater underneath. He's got to be in his late forties. He joins them and then walks into the conference room directly next to Carmen's office and slams the door.

Ellen comes over and stands behind me while I'm working. I turn and offer a smile. She says, "Ellen Ryan, Branch Administration, Tom. This unit is a mess. I need your dumps from April and May."

Host dumps are these huge computer printouts that come to us from the data processing department and contain a record of all transactions tellers perform — right down to the cash count we enter when paying customers back or taking cash in. She has a sharp pencil and a yellow highlighter stuck in that weird frozen wad of hair on top of her head.

"They're downstairs in the basement. I'll go get them."

I turn to put my pen down and she snaps, "I need to audit you. Send someone to get them. Hurry up." I turn and ask Sherry, who's overheard every word.

"Sherry, could you..."

Sherry interrupts me and says, "Sure, Tom," and takes off in her usual hyper fashion to go fetch them.

When Sherry rounds the corner of the teller line heading across the lobby, Ellen says, "Her skirt is way too high," and she sighs and grunts, cracks her tongue against the roof of her mouth and says, "Move." I scoot out of the way and she audits my drawer and verifies the count against the system. It's a perfect match. Sherry returns with the host dumps and Ellen snatches them, and says to me, "Close your window and come with me. Put your drawer away." I put the drawer away and she's waiting for me at the end of the vault with the huge host dumps tucked under both hands.

I follow her into the conference room where the older dude is on the phone. He's saying, "We're in the branch now. Yeah, we're just about ready to interview him. I will, okay, right," and hangs up.

She says to the guy, "You want to talk to me first before we bring him in?"

"Yep," he says.

She looks at me and says, "Sit in the lobby a minute, Tom."

It's uncomfortable sitting here. Everyone looks at me and I feel awful. I feel like I'm waiting to go into the Principal's office. Lucy, Sharon and Sherry sneak glances at me and offer smiles and eye rolls when Carmen isn't looking. After a half hour of waiting in agony, Ellen comes out and directs me to sit in a chair opposite from them in the conference room. She sits and looks at the dude for a moment. Before sitting, I extend my hand to him and say, "Tom Marino."

He shakes my hand without rising and says, "I know who you are. I'm Rich from Security." Ellen reaches down to grab her purse. She lifts it to the table and digs through it to find her pack of cigarettes. She shakes a cig loose from the pack till its tip is slightly out. She picks the cig from the pack with her lips and tosses the pack down in her bag. She finds her lighter and lights the cigarette.

As she blows the smoke out, she says, "Rich, you need a cigarette?" The host dumps are covered in highlighter and some amounts and dates are encircled. I'm thinking, *What the fuck is this all about?*

I try to keep from shaking. *Why am I shaking? I have nothing to worry about.*

She slaps down a copy of my last personal checking account statement with the deposit amounts highlighted. She turns the statement toward me and asks, in the most irritatingly rude and negative tone, "Where did this money come from?" I know immediately what is happening. This is my dancing money, and she's wondering if I'm stealing.

"I have a part-time job," I say, knowing the bank's code of ethics requires employees to obtain approval for any non-bank employment, like part-time jobs. They don't want us working for another financial institution.

"Where is it?" she asks.

"I don't — I mean, I would rather not say." She produces another document and slaps it in front of me. It's a copy of a check from Mitch payable to "cash."

"What the fuck's this?" she asks.

Her cursing hits a nerve. It stings. I say, "It's a check from a guy who owed me some money." She looks over at the security guy. She slaps down another photocopy of a check I deposited into my Precision Bank account, drawn on my account up at Chemical Bank.

"Why do you have an account at Chemical in New York?"

"Aren't I allowed to have accounts at other banks?" I ask. She pushes one of the host dump printouts to me and points to an amount. I pull it to me and see that it's a cash deposit I made to my checking account for $300. She's got it circled about a hundred times and it's covered in highlighter.

She barks, "Your take-home pay is $180 a week. Where do you get time to work another full-time job? Look at this one and explain this." She flips the page on the host dump and points out another well-highlighted and circled amount on a page with several paperclips she's plugged into it. The amount is $110. She starts again, "We've added up the deposits since you opened your account when you started here in March and they're over $10,000. How can you explain that?"

The security guy Rich says, "Did you steal this money from customers or other tellers?" My eyes widen but before I can even find words, he continues his question. "Or night bags?"

I sit back and try to digest the insinuation of theft.

"I have a part-time job," I say.

She asks, "You said that. Where is it? We need to know!" I don't really know of any way out without exposing what I do. I know my explanation will dissolve all concern over stealing, but I don't want to tell them I'm a male exotic dancer. The guy Rich sits back and looks me right in the eyes.

"Look, Tom, we have to know what's going on here. I have no problem getting the police involved."

This is an absolutely ridiculous invasion of privacy, and I'm furious. I feel my fucking head heating up, ready to explode, ready to yell out every obscenity I can think of. Instead, I close my eyes and compose my thoughts. "Why do you think

I'm stealing? I haven't given you one reason to think that."

Ellen turns to Rich and they look at each other. She stands up and says, "Get up, come on." I rise and follow her out.

"Sit in the lobby," she orders. She walks over and talks with Carmen; and over the next hour, she marches Sharon in for an interrogation, then Lucy, then Sherry, and finally Dolores. Dolores comes out looking like she's been crying. Her face is red and wet from tears and she won't look at me. Then they call me in. Ellen produces a copy of the Incident Report I prepared on the day of the missing $200 from the night bag. She has a sentence I wrote highlighted, *Dolores processed the bag while Sharon observed.*

"Why did you put this lie in there?" Ellen asks.

I respond quickly, while looking her square in the eye, and say, "It's not a lie. That's what happened."

She leans in toward me and screams, "OH, YEAH, RIGHT! COME ON, TOM! You and Sharon coerced Dolores into signing this fucking document. You both forced her to sign it with this lie in it. Sharon confessed. Now you need to."

"If we didn't observe Dolores, as you're suggesting, then she's fired for stealing the money," I say, sounding like a smart-ass.

Rich flips out, raising his voice, "YOU AND SHARON JEOPARDIZED HER INTEGRITY. HELL, YOU BOTH JEOPARDIZED THE INTEGRITY OF THE ENTIRE FUCKIN' OFFICE, TOM!"

"What? I don't get it," I ask, shaking my head.

Ellen says, "You and Sharon were responsible for observing Dolores. It's not Dolores' fault you failed to have her observed. You set her up! If the goddamn bag was short, you and Sharon didn't provide Dolores a back-up. That's why this procedure is in place. You have to respect that, Tom."

"The procedure makes sense, but regardless of that, you can't pin the theft of the money in the bag on me."

Rich yells again, "WE ARE NOT TALKING ABOUT THAT!"

Ellen says, "Dolores is beside herself. She finally told us that you and Sharon told her to sign that report with the lie in it. There is nothing protecting her here. You, as Head Teller, are in place with Sharon to protect her and make sure policies and procedures are followed. Instead, you manipulated the system and forced her to lie to protect you and Sharon."

I say, "I was doing bags myself. How am I supposed to watch everyone?"

She shouts, "IT'S YOUR GODDAMN JOB. IT'S FUCKING POLICY, TOM. If you weren't absolutely certain that she was observed, why lie on the report and say that she was observed? What's the matter with you?"

I sit back and cross my arms. I say, "So, what's going to happen?"

Ellen screams again, "WHERE IS YOUR PART-TIME JOB?"

"I'm a dancer," I say, thoughtfully, "a male exotic dancer."

A smirk finds its way onto Ellen's face as she sits back and crosses her arms, clearly reaching a sense of success with herself. "Oh, and what's this got to do with checks payable to cash and accounts up in Chemical?" She asks in a more condescending tone.

"That's how I'm paid," I answer.

She continues chirping, "My girlfriend's a dancer at Pin Ups and she doesn't have to deal in checks and shit like this." Pin Ups is a local female stripper joint on Route 130.

"I don't know. I just get paid by check sometimes when the customer pays by credit card."

"Well, we're going to have to call them to verify this," Ellen declares firmly.

I'm so sure Mitch is going to love having the bank call him, considering the nature of his business. Rich pushes the phone toward me and I dial Mitch's number. There's only the machine.

"Machine," I say, handing Rich the phone. He grabs the receiver, listens and then hangs up. "Dolores told us that no one was watching her count that bag. You and Sharon forced her to sign this piece of shit report," he says, arrogantly, glaring at me.

Ellen says, "How horrible that we have two supervisors working for us that jeopardize the integrity of the poor tellers. You and Sharon are bad employees. You two absolutely acted on your own at the bank's expense."

I shake my head.

"We're placing you and Sharon on probation. You have no business being in banking. In the future, you better make goddamn fucking sure you have someone observe the tellers processing the bags. You better never lie again on a bank document or entice one of your tellers to participate in a cover up."

I still haven't admitted to anything. If they had evidential proof that Sharon and I really lied, we would be fired. They don't play. That would mean we couldn't be bonded.

Wanting to crush both of these bastards, I defy them with a look and announce, "I am *not* being placed on probation for lying. I didn't lie. I prepared the form the way things happened."

"Go home, Tom. Before I have to fire you," Her voice has a chilling tone, a mix of anger and impatience. Then as I rise, she rises and says, blowing smoke out of her face as she does, "I didn't get to be Assistant Vice President in Branch Administration for nothing. I know exactly how things work and I know something's up. You're on my radar and you better not have me out here again!"

I head onto the kitchen to gather my stuff. I encounter Sharon in the room and she's surprisingly cordial. We are both visibly shaken from the torture session. Sharon offers a smile and asks, "How'd it go?"

I answer, "It sucked. They didn't believe anything I had to say. How about for you?" Despite the tension, she said she held herself together and demonstrating courage says, "If you can't dazzle 'em with details, baffle 'em with bullshit."

We enjoy a laugh together and I leave the branch and drive all the way home with my heart in my throat, pondering the horrid experience, but thankful I still have my job. I have to get the hell out of there.

Tom is home when I walk in the door. He's been cooking something and the apartment smells like garlic.

"How was your day?" I ask, humbled by the day's events, eager to get a hug.

"Fine," he says, somewhat detached and distant, not making eye contact. He sits on the sofa with his feet up on the coffee table. Churchy is positioned in his lap, and he's petting him while watching television. I stop to hang up my coat in the closet behind the front door. The dryer is running, and I absorb the calmness of my own home for a moment. The chaos of our financial situation seems dwarfed by today's traumatic events.

I run to the gym for a nice long workout to kind of wash today's events out of me. It does the trick, and I enjoy an extra long hot shower in the locker room after an extended visit to the steam room. When I get home, I'm feeling a lot better.

Tuesday, July 25, 1989, 6:30 p.m.

When I get home I find Tom in front of the TV again. I greet him with a half-hearted kiss. Today was his day off, and I notice the laundry wasn't done and nothing is made for dinner. My day was so fucked up, I am just grateful to be home, so I put down my things and walk in the kitchen. I defrost four chicken thighs, apply seasoning and deposit them in the oven. I break open a package of vegetables and put together a packet of mashed potatoes. I fix us both a cocktail and attack the bills. The mail used to be such a harmless and enjoyable event but now it's a vicious enemy, bringing nothing but more demands for payment and threatening letters. They're all critical and all late, but I give myself a pat on the back for being able to get through it. The last piece of mail is an alarming letter from the bank financing Tom's car. The caption across the top of the letter, in bold print, underlined, reads NOTICE OF REPOSSESSION.

The letter indicates payments are three months behind on the Escort, and the bank is considering repossession if a payment equal to three monthly payments plus late fees isn't made. I want to enter into a rational and civil conversation with Tom about the situation. I make a mental note and promise to myself not to become unglued or outraged by his usual manner of responding to these issues. I will be patient and calm; *I will be patient and calm; I will be patient and calm,* I chant to myself as I get up and walk over to him.

I approach him and ask, "Can I talk with you?" He puts down his cigarette and picks up a piece of black licorice to chew on. He so much loves his candy.

"What's up?" he asks, not turning his head from the TV set.

Here goes, "You know we have a lot of bills racked up, and it's become quite serious. I'm really worried."

He rolls his eyes and looks at me and says, "Don't worry about them. *We'll pay them. We'll do it."*

I take in a breath of air and say, "I'm concerned about my credit."

He says, "Well, I'm sure that's fucked up by now." His comment delivers a sharp, painful blow, rendering me almost unable to speak. I'm beyond enraged. What hurts most is how callous and uncaring he's become. He was so sensitive and caring. *What the fuck changed?* I'm beginning to believe *nothing happened or changed:* he was always this way.

I hand him the letter from the bank financing his car and say, "I got this today."

He doesn't reach for it right away. He sparks up another cigarette and then grabs it. He takes a moment to review it and argues, "I can't be three months be-hind. I mailed them a payment in March."

"Tom," I begin, trying to keep my tone calm and my composure in check. "It's now July. That would be correct. They are stating that they didn't get April, May and June from you."

"Well, I don't have it!" he says, looking up at me. "I reached a settlement with R2O's insurance company. Now they're going to pay me $1,000 a month instead of $900."

"What? Wait. I thought they were paying you $844 a month or something."

"Yes, it's $844, but they figured they owed me more, so I get a cool grand a month." Tom continues, "Wait, wait, wait. I gave you my first check last month. Why didn't you pay the car payments with that? I also gave you my last paycheck."

"That went to rent and card payments!" I shout.

"You should prioritize and pay on the car before the cards." He's kind of right, but what does it matter when there was less than a hundred left after rent?

"Where is *this* month's check?"

His mouth turns downward into a frown and he scowls, "Didn't get here yet. Should be $844. Next month's check will be $1,000. Everything will be okay."

"What do you do all day? Where do you go?" I ask.

"What?"

I answer, "You go out, decked out in a nice shirt. The type you'd wear out clubbing with your best jeans on, shades, and those new shoes you bought." I collapse into a chair and allow my head to droop.

He asks, "Tom, what's wrong?" He comes up to me and lifts my chin. "You don't look good."

"Tired. Hungry."

"Did you eat today?"

"I had a long day. I couldn't eat anything for lunch. Just walked around the Mall."

"Let's go to Chi-Chi's for dinner. You're famished and I feel like Mexican food," he offers.

"I cooked. Got money?" I ask him.

"Yes. Now, go put that stuff away. I'll take it for lunch tomorrow," he answers.

"What about this?" I ask, lifting the letter from the bank. Tom waves his hand in the air and motions toward the door as if to distract me from the issue. Driving to the restaurant, while I have him as a captive audience, I suggest he pay the past-due car payments with the disability check when it arrives. In the most gentle and compassionate manner, I dip him again into my own version of a line-in-the-sand discussion, hoping to induce Tom to save our relationship based on a financial commitment — one that I feel he'll never keep. After he agrees, probably to pacify me, more likely to shut me up, I declare, "I'll call the bank and tell them we'll pay April, May and June's payments and their fee, and we'll pay July's when you get the check from August. Listen, Slick, you better come through or you'll be without wheels." Knowing that I'll probably end up going into my savings to solve this, my heart feels like it's heaving.

The fact that I'm able to focus on food and ignore everything has to be purely primal. I drown my sorrows in three large and very potent margaritas. I lean with my head resting on my palm as I stare down into a glass with a much-salted rim. Tom has been leading the conversation, and finally stops to ask, "Anything I can say or do to make you feel a little better?"

I look up, suddenly filled with emotion. "Just hold me tonight. Hold me tight. I don't want this to end. I feel like I'm losing you — like you're drifting away from me." I do enjoy his company. Looking at him, into his eyes, I realize he is reaching out to me. I still love him, and he holds my heart. He still has a way of catapulting my confidence, given the fact I can capture a hot, well-dressed guy like him. It's strange what impact he has on my ego. After dinner, as we drive in silence on the way home, my thoughts wander: I wish he could understand how much I care about him, and that this time has been the best time in my life. The bills are a fire on our stage, the stage of our life.

"Do you love me?" I ask.

"Yes, I do," Tom answers.

I don't know what to believe. This relationship is slowly turning into one huge, stinking pile of dung. I know he *needs* me. But does he love me, really love me? As he drives, I look up at the sky. It's still light out for 8:30, and I ask God for direction: *Lord, I'm so stupid. Lead me. Guide me. I make so many mistakes. I'm so weak. Only with your help can I survive this life. Is this right or is it wrong? What do I do? Please, I beg you. Guide me. Slide an answer my way.* After a moment another thought comes into my head: *The writing's on the wall, Thomas. Look at it and accept it.*

If Tom doesn't make the payment to update and take care of this loan for his car, I'm going to have to leave him. That's it. It's all down to one event. I've given my last best hope, and am calling in the bet. I'm risking everything by taking this down to this one action. His willingness or failure to take care of the car obligation will equal his commitment to or the demise of our relationship.

After dinner, I walk in the apartment and, to Tom's dismay and disapproval, find my way to the spare bed.

"Why are you sleeping in here?" he asks. I wave him off, since he already mentioned on the drive home he'd be going out for one of his "drives." So much for being held. My day was horrible, and these feelings of loneliness in the relationship have overshadowed a desire to share even an ounce of what's going on at work with him. In some strange way, I assign him all the blame.

He shakes his head and leaves. I roll over, and feel myself overwhelmed with emotion. I resume my thoughts, trying to be confident and see the brighter side: *What have I learned in this relationship? I've learned that I'm really a gay man. No question. Not bisexual — gay. I'm happy to be part of something bigger than I am. This homosexuality thing, it's part of my DNA. It runs deep down to the core of who I am. It's the inner most part of me — the part of me that is weak and vulnerable. The part of me that is strong and successful. I am proud to be gay.*

I turn my thoughts to prayers: *Please help me through this time of hiding and discovery. Guide me through this time of learning and progressing in my own evolution to be the best homosexual I can be in every measure.* Peace comes over me, and another thought comes into my head, *I will pass this test of time with flying colors. I just know it.*

Tuesday, August 1, 1989

Things between Tom and me continue to deteriorate, to the point that we just avoid each other. I've been spending every evening in the company of Lucy, and the latest development is that Tom has informed me he's got a new "friend" called Bert. *Little Bert the Bodybuilder*, to use his words.

Another summer day has come and gone away when I get home after a couple of happy-hour drinks at the good old Woodbine. I find Tom seated on the couch, feet crossed on the coffee table with the telephone anchored between ear and shoulder, he is conducting a serious phone sex conversation while watching a porno. He's stroking his cock through tight dark blue jeans. I see the bulge and immediately desire it. More than the bulge and his cock, I desire his love and commitment to this thing we share.

When he hangs up, I ask, "Did your check come?" He shakes his head to the negative. It's a lie. He got the check and is keeping the money. He's not making good on the car payments.

"Want to have sex?" I ask, sounding needy and desperate even to me.

He sighs, looking up at me, and says, "You're still laying the pipe to her, aren't you?"

I nod, unsure of what his reaction will be.

"Well, I'm with Bert."

I'm angry and sad, but what can I say? I'm not surprised.

What can I do? The pain of defeat stings, but it's not as excruciating as I thought it would be. Somehow, someway, when I suffered through the experience of torture when Nadine cheated on me, my heart must have scarred over and I can't feel the same devastation. No matter how much I try to find the same sharp pain, it doesn't exist.

"You're still hot, even though you're a mess, Jack," he says.

"Jack? You mean *Jackass*, don't you?" He does a half nod, lifting his chin, and his smile curves up in a lackluster grin. I look down to see what he sees as "hot." Nothing great: me in a white work shirt under a blue sweater vest. A yellow-and-blue striped necktie loosened and lowered. Tan, pleated pants.

He says, "You can jerk off with me, but don't kiss me and don't touch me." As much as I don't want to, I lean down and drop my pants and sit next to him. He drops his pants and we jack off together, watching a cheesy, grainy, old VCR-taped porno that skips and barely shows a faded and blurry picture of a dozen guys in an orgy. It's so hard to concentrate on coming. My thoughts are the enemy of my orgasm. *Doesn't he want me anymore? Is Bert better than me?* We finally reach climax and I pull my shirt off to wipe up. I don't care.

"Those pants look better on you without a shirt," he says.

"Yeah," I answer, then get up and walk into the bathroom. I close the door and turn to face the mirror. As I wash my hands and face, I look into my eyes for answers. They are miracles, my eyes. I thank God for them and enjoy looking at their color and design. God's handiwork. I return to Tom's side and say, "I want to be together." He nods, but I think the end is near.

Wednesday, August 2, 1989, 2:35 a.m.

I can't sleep. I rise and find that he's out. I pick up the phone and debate calling Mom, feeling so alone. What would I say to her? Jeez, she'll hit the roof if I call now. I hang up and take a swig of Nyquil. It allows me to relax and sleep takes me.

5:00 a.m.

"Tom, wake up," I hear him say. I rouse and turn to him.

"What are you doing in my bed? Go sleep in the spare bedroom." I realize I crashed in what used to be the bed we shared. His words sting but without arguing, probably because I'm eager for a few more precious hours of sleep, or maybe because I just don't have any fight left in me, I go.

7:00 a.m.

When the alarm goes off, the first sensation I experience is that it's balmy and sticky. I wake to notice I'm in the spare room. With a lucid awareness I haven't had in months, logical and strategic thinking dominate my brain, and I'm clear on the compulsory measures crucial to my new mission. I spring into a task-oriented mode and walk into the kitchen. I take the watermelon I bought for Tom out of the fridge and slice it in half. I pause for a second and then plunge my face right into the middle of the refreshing red fleshy center of the fruit.

The first call I make is to Mom. "What do you think about me coming home?" I ask.

"We'll have to discuss that with Dad." Her response sends me into a tail-spin.

"What? Why? What's to discuss?"

"Well, Thomas, you keep deciding to pack up and go, and it just never works out. We can't have you coming and going whenever you feel like it. You can't use our home like a hotel."

"I'm —" I start, but she cuts me off.

"Dad and I feel like you're irresponsible, and we knew this was coming. Are you broke? Because the only way you'd want to come back here is if you were out of money."

"I'm more than broke." I figure I might as well just get it out. "I'm in debt — deep in debt. I think it's about $30,000." She lets out a sigh, the type that expresses the worst kind of utter disappointment.

"What happened? Need I ask?"

"I have money in the bank and a lot of it's going to pay down several credit cards."

"You mean there's more than $30,000?"

"Yes. I've tallied it all up and it's about $42,000. I have $12,000 left in the bank, and that leaves about $30,000 in the hole." She's right to be angry. I need to pay for this mistake and learn my lesson. I will. I know I'll work my ass off to clean it up; I just need her to tell me I'm welcome to come home and maybe that she'll always love me and everything will be fine.

On second thought, the hell with that. The "everything's going to be fine" attitude is what got me in this mess. Everything will not be fine. I have to contend with this shit. *She's right, she's right, she's right.*

9:30 a.m.

Usually, when the world is crashing in my life at the bank, my personal life can be a terrific distraction. Today, it's the other way around. This place is great for changing my thought patterns. Despite how nuts and annoying it has the potential of being, it can also provide moments of comfort and stability.

Lucy approaches with a grim look and walks behind me. Earlier today I debriefed her on my call home requesting the move. I told her I was done with Tom's antics, leaving out, of course, the whole relationship piece.

"Your Dad's on the phone," she says.

"Hello," I answer.

"Yeah, it's Dad," he says.

"Hi."

"Mom tells me you want to come home."

"Yes," I answer, confident she's told him everything we discussed.

"Well, that's fine with us. As I always told you, Thomas, the screw you get today is nothing like the fuck you'll get tomorrow."

"Yep, I know." However, I really don't know. *What the fuck is he talking about? Could he know I'm in a sexual relationship with Tom?*

"When were you thinking of coming home?" he asks.

"Next week?" I ask, now realizing I'm making a commitment to something I haven't yet really firmed up within myself. *I'm talking about leaving Tom — abandoning this wonderful man, this amazing experience.* Then the logical part of my mind steps in again, thankfully, to remind me Tom is with Bert now. It's time to go.

"Thomas, I need to know what you're doing."

I hear Mom shouting in the background on the phone, "If he's serious about this, I need a date. We can't be waiting around for him to decide on this. We're going to need to plan this."

Dad pipes in, "You hear that? You need help moving, don't you?"

"Yes, okay. The 12th. Saturday the 12th," I say, looking at the calendar. It only shuts Mom up for a second while she checks their calendar. She starts babbling again in the background about how she's warned me about all the mistakes I've made, how she's had it with my antics and secrets, my shortcomings, and how long the drive to work is going to be for me when I move home.

"I've thought of that," I say.

I don't say, but also think, of what life is going to be like living back home. I recall an argument Mom and I had when she made a few really distasteful remarks and called Nadine a couple of offensive names while Nadine was just outside the door listening. *Am I fully ready for this bullshit again?*

I don't have any options.

After concluding the call with my parents, I execute the next tactic toward cleaning up this mess. Tom never made good on his promise to bring the car payments up to date with his August check. My next call is to the bank. I get an associate on the phone and let them know the situation. They don't have any other suggestion but for me to do a voluntary repossession which, according to them, will not affect my credit. "Bring the car back to the dealer where you bought it and we can process the return for you."

In my bank-trained mind, the connotation around the word *repossession* sends up a subliminal red flag, despite the suggestion that this will be transparent on my credit record. Rather than explore the subject with Lucy or anyone, I just ignore it and move on, anxious to make the problem just go away. *How could I possibly explain the second car to my parents?*

4:55 p.m.

I get home early and place the statements for each bill and credit card out on the kitchen table. A tally of each comes to just over $41,000. With huge regret, I conduct a letter to Isa at Chemical Bank asking her to liquidate my CDs and put the money in my checking account. Years of dancing, scrimping and saving — all gone. *I sincerely hope you enjoyed this relationship, Thomas*, I tell myself. As I write out checks totaling about $11,000, I think, *How in the fuck will I ever recover from this?* I save about $1,500 for an emergency. The one emergency that comes to mind is if I have to make an unplanned escape from the place where I'm seeking asylum — a.k.a., my parent's gulag.

When Tom walks in he asks, "What's all this?" I'm surprised at first, since he can tell they're financial statements, and usually he avoids the subject of finances and bills like the plague.

"I'm about thirty thousand in debt." He makes himself a cocktail and hands me a glass with ice and my bottle of orange MD 20/20.

"Thirty fucking thousand," I continue after a short pause, "and not a goddamned thing to show for it. Your car has to go back. I called the bank and I can do a volunteer repo. They say it won't harm my credit."

"You don't want to do that," Tom says. "They'll fuck up your credit anyway. You're 90 days late."

"It's going back," I state firmly.

"What am I supposed to drive?"

"You should have thought about that before now. We're going to return it Friday. Oh, and by the way, I'm moving home with my parents." As I say it, tears pour into my eyes. I am flushed with emotion and feel my face heat up.

"Don't do that, Tom. Why are you going to leave?" he asks.

"Why should I stay? How can I? We're broke. I'm broke. You only wanted me for money. You've moved on to another guy."

He moves to sit across from me at the table and says, "And you and Lucy? What's that all about?"

I say, "How can I live here when I can't afford to pay these bills? I can't do it, Tom."

He says, "What's going back with your parents going to do for you? What if you didn't have that? What about growing up?"

"I know. I do have it, though, and I need to use what I have. I can't claim bankruptcy and stay employed in banking."

"I told you to forget about that banking shit. There's no future in the branch banking jobs. You're not some Wall Street hotshot investment banker, just a lousy Head Teller. If you'd dance full time you'd make more money. With your body and looks, you could model in porn magazines or do videos. Have you considered that?"

I put my glass down and stare at him in disbelief. *Who is this guy?* I quickly remember the last conversation we had about threesomes. *Am I being too prudish?*

"Don't go, Tom," he says almost pleadingly.

"Why should I stay?" I ask.

No response.

"I've set the date to move as Saturday the 12th."

I don't believe in him anymore. He may hold onto the belief that this thing we share is worth saving, but his desire and belief don't matter when his actions and commitment are worthless. I get up and walk into the spare bedroom and fall on the bed.

He comes in and says, "If you return that car, I'll consider *us* over."

Without turning to face him, I say, "Oh, look at you. Now you're drawing a line in the sand. I did the same thing with regard to you bringing the car payments current, but I didn't tell you. I told myself that single act would be the deciding point of whether you loved me and wanted to invest in our relationship. You got your checks and you got paid from Mitch and didn't give me a dime towards the car."

He blinks, then says, "You're making a mistake," and leaves, slamming the door so hard it pops open as he stomps away in disgust.

I start to cry, so I bury my face deep in my pillow to muffle the sound. I don't want to care about him. I have assess the damage and plan my recovery – this is for the best. Thinking of Nadine and now of Tom, I realize I've bombed out in a relationship with both sexes. *How big of a loser can I possibly be?*

Thursday, August 3, 1989, 6:00 p.m.

The nasty, horrible feeling that began yesterday has settled into the pit of my gut like a lead weight. This depression far outweighs the broken-heart syndrome I experienced during and after the Nadine chapter in my life. The feeling is one of having "missed the boat." I feel like I'm some misfit, left on the pier as the party boat pulls away from the dock. After all, Nadine and Tom have their new men and lives and I'm the one being forced to leave. I can't fight. I sit at the bar at Images with Lucy — her treat tonight. It has to be. I told her I couldn't afford to treat us. She doesn't mind. She's hooked on me. It's nice to have her friendship, but now I just need her money to help drown my sorrows in liquor. A Manhattan burns going down but warms me within, and it's the medicine I need to wipe the depressed feeling from my brain.

Much later

We dance and drink and kiss. I find some solace in her arms at the motel with her beautiful face and body pressed to mine. I focus on where I'm going — going to get her pregnant and have babies and get married. That's cool. That'll solve everything. I take the condom off my penis during our fuck, saying, "Fuck this!"

She asks, panting, "Wait, Tom, what are you doing? We're drunk. You won't be able to stop."

"You want me in you?" I ask. I give it more gas and pump her harder and faster. The beat coming from the lame little motel radio finds a way to match the rhythm in my hips as I pound her like a fucking jackhammer, causing her to moan and groan. I grab both her hands and shove them up on the sides of the bed while I grind into her over and over. I turn her over and take her from behind. The sex is hot and she's coming again. I've lost track of how long we've been going at it but she's getting dry, so I allow myself to let go. I pull my cock out at the moment I burst and spray my seed all over her chest and face. What a frustrating experience! I collapse into dreamland and Lucy leans up against me. I'm immediately put off by it — by her smell. I don't want to snuggle with her. I push her off, but gently, so as not to indicate my repulsion. I roll over and pray, *God, please be with me and help me rise above this. Take care of me and help the agony of losing Tom pass. Give me a new day.*

Friday, August 4, 1989

I took off from work today to do the voluntary repossession. As I drive to the dealer, Tom follows behind in the Escort. I can't help but wonder if this is the beginning of a new chapter in my life, or the end of an entire book. *Am I doing the right thing?* It feels like there has to be another way, and I can't stop second-guessing myself. I feel so totally alone, unable to confide in a soul.

The day began with a heated argument, but then, out of nowhere, Tom got agreeable about returning the car, as if he had received a revelation from above. He turned strangely icy, but not rude. I don't hesitate when we arrive, taking the keys from Tom and walking into the dealership. I feel the heat of the sun and the sensation of my feet walking, but my mind is just along for the ride. I turn once to look at Tom, who is now standing next to the Camaro having a cigarette. I look up to the sky and pray, *God lead me, Mary help me, I need strength now. If this isn't right, then please stop me.*

I approach a guy at the service counter and tell him, "I'm doing a voluntary repossession."

He asks, "Which car?"

" The '89 Ford Escort. The gray one," I say, pointing to it out in the lot.

"Silver," he says, and then says, "You're turning your car in, then?"

"Yeah."

"Okay." I turn over the keys and promptly walk out. I am so naive and trusting; I don't even get a receipt for it. I should probably sell the fucking thing privately, but I feel backed into a corner. How would I explain the car to my parents? They would go berserk. Plus, this is a large part of the divestiture process with Tom.

We don't speak on the way home. I concentrate on holding back tears.

During the rest of the day, Tom is obsessed with buying a car. Surprisingly, he still has over $4,000 from his white-collar bank heist. He drags me from one shady dealership to the next. He wants to go to less-than-reputable used car places where one can pay by the week for a car. Despite how livid I should be that the $4,000 could have not only saved us from having to turn in the car, I reason that I'm better off not benefiting from that money. All I can contemplate is how I'm going to live without him. He's acting like a rat, feverishly trying to escape a sinking ship. It's as if he has blinders on and is focused solely on getting a car. I'm just the vessel being used to fill that need. Things are coming clear in the logical part of my mind, but my heart is still punch-drunk in love with him. Since Tom has atrocious credit and would never qualify for a new car or bank financing, he drags me to visit nine used car places trying everything and anything to find something decent.

At a dealership in Camden, I sit on the curb in the hot sun while he walks around and meets with a slick salesman. Tom must not have liked what the guy said, because here he comes, looking quite cross. "Let's go," he snaps. "I'm not paying four grand for that piece of crap," he says, referring to a nasty-looking maroon Nova. "These dumps are known for unscrupulous practices like painting engines to make them look new. Let's go to Pizza Hut."

I'm weary of pizza but weak from sadness, so I nod my agreement, lifting my eyebrows to accentuate it. Pizza is always on the menu with Tom. As we sit in a booth at a table covered with a red-and-white checkered tablecloth, I trace one of the squares with my finger and ask, "What kind of car are you looking for?"

He doesn't want to discuss cars. He says, "You know the four grand I've got?" I nod, wondering why he needs to keep rubbing my nose in this shit. "I don't plan on giving it back, you know. I mean, fuck them."

"What if they order you to pay it back to avoid jail?"

"They're including it in my bankruptcy. The lawyer is handling it. Fuck them anyway."

"What about giving me a couple grand toward what I lent you when we met?" He looks at me and I swear I can read his thinking. He chooses his words carefully, probably cognizant that I'm driving his ass around, and says, "I need it for a car, thanks to you."

What the hell is the matter with me? Why do I stay? Why do I still care? Why can't I just walk away? The writing is on the wall, I know. It's over. What is this morbid curiosity with following this out to the bitter end? There's only agony and heartache ahead.

Lost in thought, I'm startled when he continues, "I got a job as manager of the adult bookstore in Berlin. Night shift manager. Four hundred bucks a week."

I glare at him and ask, "You told me that before, don't you remember?"

"Did I mention that I'm the manager?" He acts so pompous about it. It's amusing to hear him make it sound better than it is. "I know Mario, the owner. You see, that's why I need to have a car. I have to be able to get to work." His grandstanding erodes the refined and classy character I created in my mind.

"Is that where you hang out at night when you go for your drives?"

He shakes his head, eyeing up a breadstick.

I explain to him the reality of me moving back to my parents. He's not resistant any more. He asks, "Can I keep the Guess jean jacket suit?"

"It was a gift you gave me, Tom," I plead, caring more about the sentiment than the outfit.

He sits back, looking reflective, then says, "So was Churchy. I'll give you Churchy for it."

"What?" I ask, amazed at him.

He smiles and shakes his head, "No, I'm just kidding." I feel a sharp pain in my heart, then think deeper on his comment: I can't take Churchy with me anyway. My parents have two dogs and have already made that clear. Churchy belongs to Tom. There's nothing I can do about that.

Later

I'm standing under a "Buy Here, Pay Here" banner on the lot of a used car dealership in Pine Hill. Tom seems satisfied with a dark blue Buick Skyhawk. It's pretty quiet when we take it for a test drive, and it appears to be in decent shape. Tom agrees to plunk down $2,800 on it and finance the rest in some weekly payment arrangement worked out in their shed-like office on the lot.

"What do you think?" he asks. I like the car and tell him so. He's not able to pick it up until he gets the money from the safe deposit box.

8:30 p.m.

When we get home, he makes a call and hits the shower. When he comes out he's dressed up and smells great. As he departs, he says, "I'm going out. Bert is picking me up." The thought of him with all that cash in the safe deposit box while I'm saddled with his past-due car loan continues to infuriate me. He's clearly done with me, and I'm confident I made the right decision to evacuate.

Saturday, August 5, 1989

I'm dressed up again in the baseball outfit for a high-value repeat customer all the way down in Cape May. Mitch asked me not to shave for the past couple of days to create the shadow of a goatee for this gig. He's been asking me to grow my hair and it's long for me now, hanging down over my ears.

I'm in a semi-panic because I misplaced my fucking car keys. Since I'm usually quite organized, I get worried when I lose something. I offer up a little prayer: *St. Anthony, please help me find these keys.* Just as I locate the keys on the floor, noting that they must have fallen off the entertainment center, Tom walks in with a guy behind him. The short, muscular flat-topped blonde is introduced to me as "Bert."

He grips my hand firmly and in a deep voice asks, "What's up, man?"

I look him square in the eye and say, "Hey, Chief."

Bert wears a black tank top and jean shorts. Tom must have caught my eyes roaming Bert's amazing arms and says, "Bert, take off your shirt. Tom has to see your chest."

Yeah, right. Bert and I size each other up in seconds. He smiles as our eyes meet, communicating what I perceive as unspoken desire.

Bert's shaking his head, but Tom's tugging his shirt up from behind. The little Adonis gives in to Tom's prodding and lifts off his shirt to reveal a beautiful hairless chest above well-shaped washboard abs. I look at his naked chest, smile, and nod. I say, "Well, gotta go. Running late."

Tom has no doubt probably already told Bert what I do on the side. When Tom reaches for and holds Bert's hand in my presence, it's like taking a bullet. I put my baseball cap on and head for the door.

When I get in the car, I pop in a cassette tape with one of my favorite, albeit sad, songs and listen to Debby Boone sing "If Ever I See You Again," and I shout out in disgust, "FUCK!" I follow it with another gem, "Nothing's Gonna Change My Love For You" by Glen Medieros. Thoughts of regret invade my mind, uncontrollable tears fill my eyes, and I'm choked up on a tidal wave of emotion I can't even grasp. In an instant I'm weeping and sobbing with audible sounds and a level of agony I haven't expressed in years. The anguish is real and aches to the core.

Rather than think, I pull over at a diner in Vineland on the way and use a payphone to call the Mt. Holly branch, hoping to reach Janet. She answers, and sensing grief in the sound of my voice, says "Sue is off and it's slow enough to talk." Janet and I have been drifting a bit, but I crave her candor and reason. Within fifteen minutes I bring her up to speed on the Tom situation in the type of conversation of blunt sincerity that has always been a hallmark of our friendship. She listens intently and then, in her usual way, offers no snug or sugar-coated bullshit to validate my vanity. She doesn't side with my parents, or Tom either. Her priceless words of advice wash away my tears and shatter my state of feeling fragile. Like a tough coach, she reminds me of the best part of youth — the fact that there's value in the anticipation of the next exciting adventure. She tells me to use the experience to formulate a plan, design a new aspiration for what I really want, and mostly that the Nadine and Tom chapters should help build the confidence and faith in myself. We finish the call, and by the time I arrive at the site of the gig, I'm back in possibility.

Dancing for the group of affluent women in a small B&B is fun, and the moment provides more opportunity for my troubles and cares to dissolve. As fate would have it, this is a small "divorce party" of only six, and the women are lovely and eager to participate. They're in their mid- to late-40s and the one I'm to dance for, Audrey, is "celebrating" a divorce. She's sweet and has a wide, pretty face. I can instantly tell she's led a pampered life, given the lack of stress in those baby blues. She has beautifully manicured nails, a salon-fresh 'do and professionally-applied make-up.

"Wendy, check out that butt. Wish Harv had an ass like that." I smile, thinking and knowing women that are just as, if not more than, sexually driven than men. I rise and begin the routine. As I gyrate and break into my routine, they move in while digging in their pocketbooks for tip money. I find the groove and deliver an exquisite experience, dancing up to each and allowing them to touch my butt, my chest and my face.

Rather than go home, I decide to drive my car onto the ferry and head to Rehoboth, Delaware. Standing on the deck of the boat on the way, I look out into the sea and continue to assess my situation. In the vast cosmos of emptiness, I find solace in prayer, turning my thoughts to thanks for what I have and asking for faith that tomorrow will bring new aspirations and dreams that I'll see come true. Somewhere, somehow I process a command to relax and let go of the pain for now. I take heed and find my way to the Renegade Nightclub, where I spend my time partying until near dawn.

Sunday, August 6, 1989, 3:30 p.m.

It wasn't until just after noon that I woke up in a hotel in Rehoboth Beach with an intense pain in my chest — one of absence for the one I love. The pain followed me as I drove back home, and it is with me now as I walk up the stairs on the side of the building that's connected to a produce store and find a dozen or so women celebrating a bachelorette party. This one is easy; I get to wear street clothes. When I tell them who I am, the girls burst into screams and laughter. Some are noticeably buzzed.

Throwing my all into the escape of the dance routine is something I've been craving. When I'm down to nothing more than a black baseball cap and my g-string, I notice a container of chocolate syrup on a nearby counter. To the sound of a new song, "Turn Around and Count 2 Ten" by a group called Dead or Alive that I previously recorded off a TV video, I pour it over my chest and allow two of the chicks to lick it off of me. This is over-the-top for what's probably permissible on a gig, but I'm too far gone to assume any sense of reason.

The women are delighted with me and before leaving, they ask me to judge their "contest," which is to create the best decorated banana split. Of course the bananas are decorated like a variety of cocks. I enjoy the little naughty toys used to build up the fun. I select the most innocent-looking one, and the winner gives me a big hug.

My Last Week with Tom

As I pack and make trips back and forth from my folk's house with my belongings, the week is a blur of crushing depression combined with consistent lambastes from my parents. The drawback to this move is that I'm going to have to listen to them tell me repeatedly how poor my choices have been. I can almost recite their speeches.

I'm ashamed of my mistakes, but have enhanced regrets because I'm not certain that leaving Tom and running home is the right solution. I was proud of the money I had built up in the bank, and furious with Tom, but mostly with my own stupidity for allowing it to happen. I have no choices. I have to endure the sentence. I have no options. Dad's "paying respect to the hand that feeds you" speech is delivered again with agonizing intensity on Tuesday. Knowing it would be delivered again and again leads me to invest what spare change I have into purchasing a cassette tape of Gloria Gaynor's "I Will Survive," the anthem that victims of every tragedy share. I'll need this in my car if I'm going to make it. A beacon comes in the form of a comment from Mom on the eve of the final day. She tells me she'll help make my small room in the basement really nice, saying we can decorate it together.

Moving Day
Saturday, August 12, 1989

I rise to the sound of "A Little Respect" by the group Erasure, feeling a strong spirit of confidence and intention in my decision. It fades quickly as I jam the remainder of my stuff into the Camaro, ready to make the final voyage home. I fight tears as I remove my things from the drawers and closets. I stop frequently to pick up Churchy and hold him close to me, burying my face into his fur and kissing him. He's got no idea what's happening.

As an added bonus to make the day even more painful, Lucy is in Cancun and good old Bert is around to "help" me move. It's a barrel of fun while I wait for my

Dad to arrive with his truck to carry my desk and chair back. That's the only large furniture to take. He's also going to take the washer and dryer to sell for cash to help retire some of my debt. Tom and Bert offer to carry the weights and weight bench back in the back of Bert's truck. How grand.

"I want to keep the washer and dryer," Tom says.

"I don't want to get into this again with you. The Sears bill is still past due for over $700."

"I'll pay it. Just leave the bill coming here."

I roll my eyes and say, "Oh, like you've been doing? How about you give me cash for it now?"

In the back of my mind, I worry that with nothing to lose, Tom may tell Dad about my sexuality. Always one to surprise me, Tom then produces $450 in cash and offers it for the washer and dryer. I accept it, figuring it's probably more than Dad would get selling them.

As the day progresses, I get more sick to my stomach. The reality of the voluntary repo of the car, the break-up with Tom, moving back to my parents in defeat, and the debt hanging over my head — it all sets in so sharply, and I don't think I can handle it. A stern but caring voice within tells me to stay focused. *There is no other way, Thomas. You're strong. You can do this. You're stronger than the average person. You have power that can't be explained or defined. You know you do.* Looking around at what will soon be my former home, I continue to listen to the voice in my head that says there's nothing here for me anymore. *This is an empty future. He doesn't love you. Turn the corner and follow the rough and rocky path out of here.* I envision a drawing I once saw in one of my catechism books as a child, of a road to Hell covered in roses and beauty — and stairs leading to Heaven covered in thorns and dark clouds. The concept being, of course, that the road to righteousness is neither easy nor comfortable.

After what seems like an eternity, Dad finally arrives, and Tom goes through the stupid formality of introducing him to Bert. As they shake hands, I shudder with disgust. Dad and I move the desk out of the den toward the door. It's evident Dad is operating on auto-pilot: task-oriented, alert on getting done quickly and efficiently without fooling around. He barks out, "Careful! Easy! Lift it higher!" as we maneuver it out of the apartment and onto Danny's Silverado truck while Tom and Bert look on. It's extremely painful, and I feel as if my heart is going to burst out of my chest. Dad doesn't go back to the apartment. He asks, "What about that washer and dryer?"

"Tom gave me the money for it."

He nods and asks, "Anything else?" I shake my head, and he turns and leaves as quickly as possible, telling me he'll see me at "home."

I walk into the apartment again. Tom says, "We'll follow you back with the weights."

I nod. I take the key to the apartment off my key-ring and hand it to Tom, saying, "Here you go. I guess I'll see you around sometime." I don't want to start crying in front of Bert. It's so hard having him here.

Tom says, "Can I see you in the bedroom a minute?" Bert sits down on the sofa and switches on the TV to a ball game while I stand there looking at Tom. He turns to walk in the bedroom, the place where we shared many nights together, many magic moments of lovemaking. After I enter, Tom closes the door behind us. Part of me wants to drop to my knees and beg him to change, beg him to be better. I have to keep cool, *stay focused.*

He says, "Can I get a hug goodbye?" I walk toward him and as I put my arms around his soft shoulders for the last time, I can't hold back tears any longer. I love him very much and don't want this to end. Tom is truly a free bird, and I'm not meant to own him. I don't think anyone is. We release our embrace and he kisses my cheek. He holds both of my hands and looks in my eyes.

"We've had some really great times together."

I say, "Yes," answering in a gravelly voice now muddled by emotion.

"If it makes things any easier, I know now that you made the right decision for yourself. You have to figure things out and find your way." Tom stops to offer a smile, and places his hand on the side of my face. He says, "Who knows? This time next year, you'll probably be a Daddy and you'll be in the bookstores." With that, I start breathing heavy again as I reach my arms around, holding him tightly, and bury my face into his chest for the last time. After a moment, he pulls me from his body and looks at my face, wet from tears. He softly says, "I think your nature is to be deliberate but mature in your ways, Thomas. You seem to thrive in chaos. You allowed yourself to be subordinate to the process of love during this turbulent encounter, and that gave you a chance to experience something extraordinary. Always remember; you're a good homosexual. Our tribe needs more like you."

Leave it to Tom to say something deeply profound at this moment. I want him to tell me to stay. I want to tell him I'm not leaving. I can't go through with this.

He wipes the tears from my face and says, "Maybe someday we'll be together again."

I blink, and more tears fall down off my face to the floor. All I can say is, "Yeah, maybe."

He lets go of my hands and says, "It's been great. Lots of luck with Lucy. Stay in touch."

I can't find anything to say that wouldn't result in more tears, so I wipe my face, swallow hard and bid Tom goodbye by nodding and punching him gently on the shoulder. "I love you," I offer, still feeling the flame of our passion and romance burning within. He nods and I go out and pick up Churchy to hug and kiss him. I figure he may now be wise to the situation.

"Can I come visit him?" I ask Tom.

"Sure."

The drive to my parent's house is painful. A thunderstorm falls upon us, and I torture myself with a cassette tape of some of Tom's Christian music. The words actually talk about asking God to lead me through the storm on the right path. I think of the time we made love during a similar thunderstorm. I pop the cassette and put another in, to inflict even more pain with George Michael's "Kissing a Fool."

Why do I do this to myself? I reflect back to his last statement, and ponder his assessment of me as *deliberate*. He's right; I *am* very task-oriented, very directed and intentional in what I'm trying to cause in my life. I direct my thoughts and prayers to heaven and scream in the car, "YOU MADE ME!" God made me; only God can help me.

When I arrive at my parent's house, I find the strength to move the shit in my car back in the basement. It's somehow smaller and darker than I remembered. Tom and Bert take turns coming downstairs with the weights. At one point, Bert and I are alone in the basement. He looks around and asks, "Is that your room?"

"Yep," I respond.

"Can I look?" he asks.

"Yep." I say, busy unpacking. Bert walks in and walks out. I don't know what he's up to.

"Low ceiling," he says.

"Yep," I say again. He's trying to be nice, but since he's now with the man I love, I find it impossible to return any kindness.

He must've read my thoughts and asks, "Why would you ever want to come back here?" Tom must have told him the break-up was my idea. His comment is meant to make me feel miserable, and it does.

"It's free," is what escapes my lips as the desire to shout "FUCK YOU" burns within. Bert walks back upstairs, looking at the other side of the basement that isn't finished, with its gray and dismal cinder block walls. He's shaking his head. I'm depressed. Soon after, Tom comes half way down the stairs and bends over to look for me. His eyes meet mine and he says, "We're leaving now."

I go upstairs to see them off. Tom hugs my parents, and I watch as they pull away in Bert's truck. I stand and stare as the truck turns the corner and disappears from sight. My heart is in my throat. Mom is standing in the yard having a cigarette and asks, "Want a BLT?"

"Sure," I say, anxious for one, since she makes them great. "What did he say to you?" I ask her, curious as to what her conversation with Tom was about.

"Oh, he said I would like Lucy a lot. Said she was really nice."

I'd been feeding my parents updates and news about Lucy, but she hasn't met them yet. Somehow I think they're in tune with who I am, and in some small way, they know I'm in turmoil and feel for me. I long to tell them more of the conflicted feelings I have coursing through my mind. They have never been receptive to any notion that strays from the bible's formula for how things are supposed to be. I feel for them, too. They evolved in a world where this beautiful thing called homosexuality wasn't at all understood or welcomed.

Midnight

I've been tossing and turning for the past hour. The sheets have a familiar clean smell. My space is quieter and darker than at the apartment. I feel like I dreamed I was a man and free, and now I'm awake and realize I'm still a boy. It's like I've returned from some adventure or field trip, and now the harsh reality of the mundane has returned. My head is pounding and my heart is aching. I find my old friend, the bottle of Nyquil, mixed in with my things. I pour two doses of the nasty-tasting liquid down my throat. Despite the horrid taste, I consider the stuff a blessing. I lie back down and allow it to knock me the fuck out. I think of how good it's going to be to pass out, and as the medicine pumps through my system, I sense the beginnings of detachment — and ever so slowly, the weight of thought is lifted and I'm floating.

9

SEARCH & RESCUE

Sunday, August 13, 1989

When I wake up, I'm immediately immersed in the landscape of my new reality. I can't undo what's been done. I recall the events of yesterday, which permanently and irrevocably severed me from Tom. All day, the memories of my behavior and actions burn in a stabbing sense of regret — both while I attend church with my family in the morning, and as I spend the afternoon unpacking. In the evening, I have a gig right outside Vineland. I feel so lonely, but like sex, the dancing takes all the worry away for a little while. Back on the road on the way home, it sets back in, so I stop at a payphone and call Lucy; but she's still not back from Cancun. Something makes me call Tom. I get the answering machine. *Where is he? What's he doing? Who is he with? I am lost.*

I reach Janet, and she allows me to unload. I imagine what my call must feel like for her, and empathize with the agony. Janet has always been a great listener and provides an objective yet compassionate response. She effectively talks me off the ledge, and I resume my drive home. Something tells me the healing process is going to take a long time.

My parents know and accept the fact that I do exotic dancing, so there's no reason to rush back home right away. I'm not ready to set foot in the clubs again. I'm so lonely. I have Lucy to look forward to, but I really don't want her. I drive by the apartment to see if Tom is there. His car is gone, and when I approach the door, it's locked. I peek in the window of the spare bedroom and through the blinds, I see and hear Churchy. I leave.

At home, I torture myself by playing the Dirty Dancing soundtrack, and the song "Where Are You Tonight?" The feeling of despair rises and makes me crazier as I think about the fact that Nadine and Tom are both out there, moving on with their new lives. They're not waiting for me. They don't love me anymore. There is no Nadine and no Tom out there coming back to take care of me.

The sadness of loss is overwhelming.

Monday, August 14, 1989

By the middle of the workday, after two restless nights at my parent's house, I can't take being apart from Tom. I can't rely on Nyquil to put me out every night. Thoughts of him consume my every moment.

I close my teller window and go into the bathroom. I barely make it before emotion overtakes me. I can't stop the tears from running down my cheeks as I reel through memories of us. My fingers want the softness of his skin, my lips want the softness of his mouth, and I miss the smell of his hair. I want to see him sleeping in the morning. I want to watch him take a shower. I want to see the beauty in his eyes when he comes. I don't think I can live the rest of my life without seeing those things again.

Despite Lucy and Bert, despite money problems, I realize I am truly, honestly, deeply in love with Thomas. When lunch comes, I sit in the kitchen and compose a letter to him:

Tom,

You are the love of my life. This love has been the best I've ever known. I knew from the start it was the real thing.

Too late, I realized our love runs deeper than I could have ever imagined. I love you more than I have ever loved anyone else in my life, and now I can't do anything but regret leaving.

I was afraid, and guess I lacked the courage to stay and face the debt. We've both made mistakes over the last 10 months. I was reckless with your love, impatient and unfaithful. I was hurtful, callous and impetuous. I am sorry for that and ask your forgiveness.

You saw the fear I was feeling but didn't seem to want to contribute to building our future. Your words gave me hope and confidence, but your actions left me defeated and confused.

You've shown me how to live my beliefs. You've helped me be a better homosexual and a stronger person.

Now I can't eat, I can't sleep, I'm a mess. Being without you is excruciating. All I keep thinking is that I had you to touch and hold whenever I wanted. Now we're apart and my arms ache to hold you.

I'm asking if we can place our faith back in each other and rebuild our life together. Relationships fall apart, but I want to fight for this one because I believe in the power of us.

Tom, I need you, and I love you very much. I beg you to let me know if we can just start over. Let's get back together and start something new.

Tom

I reread the letter and realize how needy and pathetic it makes me sound. Of course, I *am* needy and pathetic. I'm not sure about the piece where I call him out for not contributing, since I already regret what I've done; but as I analyze each phrase I'm confident it conveys exactly the sentiments I want him to hear. If he doesn't take me back, at least he'll know how much I feel. I wish I could press rewind and go back a couple of months, a couple of weeks. Shit, to go back to last week. If only. My heart is breaking. Fuck the money, fuck everything. I miss Tom.

3:00 p.m.

"Hi, it's me," I say.

"Oh, hi there. How's it going?" he asks.

"Not so good. I was wondering if I could stop by and see you today. Are you going to be home after work?"

"Yes. Why? Anything wrong?"

"I miss Churchy, and I miss you, too. I wanna talk to you about something. I…" I can't finish my thoughts.

He says, "Okay."

"When do you get done? When can I stop by?"

"I'm done at four," he answers.

"Okay, I'll come meet you at the bookstore and follow you home."

I bust my ass to get the branch settled and am out the door just after 3:30. I race to see Tom.

I enter the bookstore and catch sight of Tom behind the counter. I have a short wait until he finishes.

"Why did you want to come here?" he asks as we walk out, putting on sunglasses as his eyes meet the bright light of the summer day after being in the dark bookstore.

"I'll follow you home," I offer, avoiding his question. He doesn't say anything, just lights a cigarette and goes to his blue Skyhawk and takes off with me following him. He's dressed so sexy with his emerald green shirt and dark blue jeans.

Tom makes a stop at the Bradlees department store in Stratford on the way home. It's so fucking hot out. I remove my tie and throw it in the back seat. I also rip off the bank's blue sweater vest with their logo and toss it into the back seat along with the striped tie.

I follow Tom into the store and from aisle to aisle as he selects several items, including a framed piece of artwork. I catch our reflection in a mirror and am immediately delivered back in time. My heart feels heavy as I yearn to return to the couple we were. I think on that and remind my heart that the relationship was not a sustainable option for my future. In the next mirror we happen to pass, this time I notice only me. I look vibrant and sexy in the bright blue dress shirt tucked into black pants that accentuate my youthfulness as they cling to my shape. I catch a look into my eyes and spy a ray of hope. Tom spends over $150, paying in cash, immediately causing me to go into an emotional reaction. Driving, I dismiss the rage I feel as I follow him to my former home, our apartment, which could have still been my home if I had avoided racing out. Now I have to fight to keep him. After letting Churchy out for a pee, we sit in the living room and I hand Tom the letter I wrote and he reads it. After reading it, he hands to letter back to me.

"What do you think?" I ask impatiently, convinced he'll want me back.

"Nothing. I'm not thinking of anything."

"What do you think about us getting back together? I love you and I'm sorry I left."

Tom closes his eyes, lifts his brows and then opens his eyes again and says, "It's too late. I'm with Bert now. I've moved on and I believe it was the right thing to do. You should do the same. I thought you wanted out."

"Don't you miss me?" I ask, sounding pitiful, even to me, in my desperate state.

"I'm actually getting accustomed to the idea of living alone again. It was for the best, Tom. I don't have to put up with your shit, your constant bitching about bills and all, and you don't have to put up with me. I always pissed you off."

"I have to — I mean, I need to know if you still love me," I say, sounding completely forlorn.

"I like you, but I don't love you anymore. There's someone else in my life now. Bert and I are very happy together."

"Very happy? How can that be? You just met!"

Tom lowers his chin and looks up at me as if to remind me of how fast we fell for each other.

"Tom," I groan. "I can't live without you. I love you. Please take me back." I don't get a response, and can't believe how I just poured my heart out to him, begging shamelessly as I realize I really expected him to take me back. I thought this was in the bag – and didn't see his rejecting me as a possible outcome. I had not prepared a plan for this. I was so ready to move back in with him, and had dreams and visions of confronting my parents, telling them he that was my man, that I'm gay and that this is what I want. Now I have to endure time away from him, knowing it is really and truly over. It's almost too much to take. I hate being here as a guest. This is my home. Churchy is crying for me the whole time I'm here. Tom has already changed some things. He's added a picture in the living room — an English theme with dogs and horses on a fox hunt. I can't find it in me to be upset with him; I'm upset with myself for leaving. He doesn't say anything, just turns on the TV.

"So there's no chance of us getting back together?" I ask. "Things just aren't the same. I know you've changed my life forever."

"No, remember you telling me about Nadine? She'd been a big impact on your life, too. You got over her and onto me. Now you'll get over me and onto — or rather *into* — someone else," he says, with a smirk.

"I can't, Tom," I say, starting to cry again.

Emotionless, Tom shakes his head, not saying a word.

"I'm in love with you and ready to make this work — whatever that takes! I'll come out to my parents. I'll leave my job if you want me to be away from Lucy. I tremble inside at the thought of being apart from you."

He just gazes the TV.

"I can't get through another day without you, Tom. I'm so sorry I left. I hope you don't think I gave up on you."

"Just get on with your life," he says again, this time with absolutely no feeling or eye contact. After a long moment, he says, "Listen, I'm expecting Bert and I'd appreciate it if you could just go."

"I miss Churchy." I don't believe he's expecting Bert; I think he's tired of me, and I catch the cue. It's time to go. My head is telling me to rise and depart, but my legs won't listen. I finally give in and rise. Tom doesn't budge. I say, "All right, I'm leaving. If you change your mind, call me." I want to say so much more, but it's useless. It is fucking over and he's done with me. He waves his hand and I know I won't get a hug and kiss.

Driving home, I notice the letter I wrote, still in my hand. I re-read it and think of how idiotic it is. I look to Heaven and send a prayer for guidance. Just then, a surge of confidence and hope is delivered in the form of a song over the radio as "Tenderness" by the group General Public is played. I tear the letter into a dozen pieces.

Friday, August 18, 1989
In bed, 11:40 p.m.

Losing Nadine was nothing compared to the pain of losing Tom. *Why do I allow myself to fall so hard for people?* Lucy came back a couple days ago and has provided some company, but there's an unbearable emptiness in my life without Tom. I rely on the ways Tom taught me how to be strong, for lonely times like now. I miss confiding in him my most intimate thoughts and desires. I think of everything that's happened and every moment we've shared. *I miss my friend.*

Friday, August 25, 1989
In bed, 12:30 a.m.

This night, no different from every night, I hit the sack lonely and wondering about Tom's whereabouts. Facing the mountain of debt — the depletion of every ounce of savings I'd amassed over my time dancing, with the attendant squeeze on my freedom — adds to the agony. Tom is free of it all and out there enjoying life as it was, and I'm in this prison of restriction. I want to leverage all I've learned to help me weather this pain, but I keep coming up empty when I try to find inner strength.

In my mind, I go back to the time when I lost Nadine. I reflect on how lost I was, how desperate things seemed. I kept thinking there would be bigger and better things in store for me. It came true: I found Thomas. I tell myself to try and relax and stay in possibility.

At work this week, I got slapped on probation 90 days for some bullshit charge of having excessive *overages*, based on the fact that year-to-date I have a cumulative amount of over $700. They also discovered I'm banging Lucy, and transferred her to Marlton and me to Mt. Laurel. It's no real surprise to discover my new branch manager is tons worse than the previous two.

God, this is so hard. If I keep telling myself that leaving was the right thing to do, then soon I'll believe it. Soon I'll look back and know I made the right choice.

But I miss Tom's scent, his blazing deep brown eyes, and his kiss when we made love. I miss his deep, sexy voice, which had a way of giving me goosebumps. I yearn for one of his trademark winks. I even miss our stupid fights, but most of all *I miss my friend.*

Wednesday, August 30, 1989
At work

My spirits aren't soaring, but have risen slightly as I reflect on the nice birthday I helped create for Mom this past Sunday. It's now, when I'm only thinking about Tom every twenty seconds instead of every two, that I get a call from him.

"You got transferred," he says, then explains how he called for me at the Pennsauken branch and got the new number from Sherry.

"Yeah," I answer, my heart holding onto the hope that he's ready to get back together. Pride aside, I blurt out, "I want to come home. I love you, my heart aches for you. I can't stand this. I miss you, honey."

"Oh, okay. Listen, I was calling to see if you want Churchy."

"Why?"

"I'm probably going to move soon, and I can't take him with me."

"Where are you moving?"

"I don't know, probably in with Bert."

"Why can't you keep Churchy?"

"If you don't take him, I'll find him a nice home." His words sting. He adds, "I just can't take care of him anymore."

All I can manage to say is, "I'll let you know." I hang up and have to excuse myself to go to the bathroom. I fall to the floor and sob like a baby, more upset at being emotional than at the state of my affairs. *Where is this coming from? Where is my strength? What happened to me? Where is the old Tom Marino? Come on, now.*

The next two days of begging my parents to allow me to take Churchy bring more crushing agony and results in more disappointment, since they refuse.

I reach Tom at the bookstore to tell him, but he's got news for me: "I gave him to a guy in Willingboro. He'll take really good care of him."

"What?"

"I can give you the guy's name and phone number so you can go visit Churchy. He said it would be cool if you wanted to visit him."

It's too much for me to take. I write down the information from Tom, and barely make it to the end of the day.

Thursday, August 31, 1989

This awful month can't die without a final punch in the gut. Mitch calls me around noon and bitches about me going on a gig in my tux outfit wearing a white tank top instead of the tux shirt, then about another gig I totally missed because I couldn't find it in time. "Who authorized you to cut corners?" he growls.

Then I have to hear his wife Lisa blast me on the other line at the same time about how they're very disappointed in me lately.

"Where is your head?"

"What were you thinking?"

Both are questions I seem to be fielding from everyone lately, including myself.

Driving home, I assess:

First, Tom — what a disaster; I've done a number on my credit, not to mention my emotional state.

This relationship I've started with Lucy — another debacle. A wicked little part of me toys with using her to achieve one of my life-long goals, which is having a child. The idea of impregnating her, optimistic that this could be a way to have a child, has crossed my mind more than once. *This poor girl doesn't need her heart entangled in someone who can't give back everything she's capable of giving. Need to find a way to land this jet without crashing.*

My job at the bank — another clusterfuck; I feel like it's where I belong, but I have to get stronger and focus if I'm going to survive there.

Dancing for Mitch — what was once fun is now necessary if I'm going to pay off the debt and break out on my own again in this century. *Mitch is clearly pissed off. I need to buckle down and do what I'm supposed to.*

Options? I come up empty.

I stop at our St. Ann's Church in Browns Mills and go into the confessional. I unload my story on the poor, unsuspecting priest. He neither condemns nor scolds me, simply offers, *"The power is in your hands. Your success, happiness and redemption depend both on how strong your resolve is and how you go about achieving it. Time passes quickly, so let yourself feel joy on the way. Don't be afraid to continue to seek God's help. What else is there to do?"* And then he assigns me a penance of saying the rosary. I sit in the little chapel and complete all of it on my knees. When I finish, as I walk out into the bright sunlight, I experience a sense of clarity and calmness I haven't felt in years.

Saturday, September 23, 1989

When I finally assemble the courage to go out again, I call Billy, once the only person I could talk to about my gay experiences. In such a short time I feel I've traveled far in my journey of self discovery. He tells me our club, Gatsby's, has been demolished. It was sold, and a new straight club is being built in its place. I ask Billy what the fuck happened, and he tells me that the same owners own Wok-n-Roll and they've converted it to Gatsby's. The location, on Cuthbert, is right near the old location. Driving over, I think this may be a good thing, since memories of Tom and me don't exist there. Then I remember the night I danced there, with him along with me. *I can't win.*

When I enter the place, which has been redesigned inside to look a lot like the former GB's on Route 70, it strikes me that I'm alone. I had built a lot of pride and comfort into entering the nightclub with Tom. I walk around the club as a single person for the first time in almost a year. I notice many of the same faces, and a lot of new ones, as I walk around. It's festive in here, and as I pick up looks from some attractive new guys, my mood lifts. *Maybe I'll be all right.*

I can't stay away from the gay world. It means too much to me and, right or wrong, Lucy is only a project. I find a seat and have a drink, watching men as they circle the bar. I'm still thinking of Tom, constantly reliving the times I was cruel to him and all the nasty things I said. I blame and hold myself highly accountable for the demise of our relationship. Something has to be done about this heartache; I can't live with it anymore. All the faces that stream by are a blur to me. I can't stop thinking about how much I love Tom. He's everything I want in a lover. There has to be another like him, another who could be even better than him.

I did it before — nabbed a hottie from the man-tree. I can do it again. I feel convinced my lifelong soul mate has to be a man.

I run into Beth in the unisex bathroom, and we discuss what happened with Tom. She doesn't offer a reaction or render an opinion. Her only remark is like salt in a wound: "He was nice." She asks if I want to smoke a bone out in her van. Following her out of the club, I run into Randy, a colorful gay pothead from high school who used to ride the bus with me. He knows Beth and joins us, eager to partake of the weed. After two joints and another Manhattan back at the bar, Beth and Randy meander off on their separate ways with different crowds, and I'm alone again. I'm relaxed, so I dance a bit and then stand on the side of the dance floor, hoping I don't see Tom and Bert. That'll kill me. Imagine him seeing me here alone — no man, not off doing something with Lucy. *What a fucking loser.*

I find one last cigarette in my pack and smoke it. It's a nasty habit so I decide it will be the last. And just like that – it is.

Then, when I think I'm in my darkest hour, feeling isolated and abandoned inside, I spot a tall, well-built, handsome dude dancing with another. I make eye contact, and he whispers to his dance partner something that causes them both to look over at me. Oh, shit. They're probably a couple. Just then, I notice a hand come out from behind me and pinch my nipple through my shirt. It's John. He smiles and offers, "Look at you flaunting that fine posterior in those sexy jeans. Don't you know I'm a sucker for a guy in a baseball cap?"

"Hey, Chief, *thanks*. You're a sight for sore eyes." I greet him with a hug as he extends his hand.

"Whoa, a hug, that's out of character for you. I guess you've been merging well into our culture." He looks good. He's got to be around 36 or 37 now. He looks the same as the day I met him over 2 years ago. I finish a short chat with John, and when I return my gaze to the dance floor, the stud and his pal are gone. I walk around the club to see if I can find him, and as I round the corner of the bar, I see him sitting with a group of men. I look in their direction, and one of the guys whistles at me.

I get a beer from the bar and stand back up on the edge of the dance floor, with the beer in one hand, moving to the beat. The dude and his buddy emerge from out of nowhere and are back on the now-crowded dance floor. He's built like a linebacker, and I figure I've got absolutely nothing to lose. Fuck it. I cast my line out with plenty of bait on the hook as I throw more looks at the guy and take a deep breath. I have the power inside of me to land whatever I want.

After the song, he comes over by himself and says. "Hi, I'm Ed."

"Tom," I say, shaking his hand. "Sorry for staring at you. Are you here with that guy you were dancing with?"

"Yeah, he's a friend. You like him?"

"No!" I say firmly, pleased they aren't together. "You're pretty hot."

His eyes light up and he says, "Thank you!" with a smile as perfect as his manly shape. He's very cute, actually a few inches taller than Tom, which makes him tower over me. He's beautifully masculine and handsome in a rugged way that makes my mouth water. With him close to me, I can check him out properly. He's beefy and his faded light blue jeans fall over brown work boots. He's got a black T-shirt on and his big, bubble butt totally fills the jeans. I spring a woody just thinking about how hot that ass would be to fuck.

He says, "You walked by and my friend Alex whistled at you. He thinks you're hot, too."

I nod, saying, "So what do you think?"

"I told him I saw you first."

The DJ mixes a gold '70s tune, "Everybody Dance" by Chic.

I take his hand and lead us to a space in the front of the dance floor. As we dance, my thoughts twist to consider what control I have over my destiny. *Do I avoid future conflicts and risk missing out on experiencing love? Would I trade one memory I've had in return for less pain?* I know I'd do it all again.

As we dance to the next song, Rick Astley singing, "Take Me to Your Heart," some of the lyrics inflame me; *"Are we lovers or only just friends? Come tomorrow will I be lonely again?... "*

"...Cos I think about you when you're far away. And I dream about you, Night and day. Can I make you want me, the way that I want you? "

"...Take me to your heart, Never let me go. If you knew what I'm feeling, You would not say no. "

The words churn more thoughts as I consciously allow the warmth of the lights and watching people dance along with us intoxicate me. Something tells me it will be a long time until I get over Tom, but I'm going to survive this. I have to. Looking at Ed as he soaks me in with anxious eyes, I realize more than ever that life is worth living. I'm far from finished with what I will do.

Maybe one day I'll come to embrace and look forward to the future. Right now, I need to live in and for this moment. And I dance on.

ABOUT
THE AUTHOR

Tom Marino was born in 1967 in Neptune, New Jersey. He's still proud to call Jersey home, and lives there now with his husband Noe and their son, Nicholas. Tom continues a career in retail banking.

This is his first published work.

You can visit his website at **www.tomorrowmaybetoolate.com.**

ABOUT
THE MUSIC

As my colleague Terry Oldes has said, we all have "soundtracks" to our lives, pieces of songs that hit us, reflecting what we're currently feeling or experiencing. Plus, what's a book laced with racy exotic male dancing scenes without that ingredient?

Serving as a tremendous backdrop to my relationship with Tom were the terrific sounds of both romantic and dance tunes that electrified feelings and accentuated my memories of one of the best times in my life. I've captured all the songs quoted in the book here. Huge thanks to these artists and writers:

Terence Trent D'Arby "Sign Your Name"

Taylor Dayne "Prove Your Love"

Donna Summer "Love to Love You Baby"

Eumir Deodato "S.O.S. Fire In the Sky"

Midnight Star "Midas Touch"

Starpoint "He Wants My Body"

Taylor Dayne "Willpower"

Kylie Minogue "I Should Be So Lucky"

Amy Grant "Find a Way"

Carman "Fear Not My Child"

Boy Meets Girl "Waiting For a Star To Fall"

George Michael "Kissing a Fool"

Leo Sayer "When I Need You"

The Boys Club "I Remember Holding You"

The Capitols "Cool Jerk"

Brenda K. Starr "What You See Is What You Get"

Taylor Dayne / Siedah Garrett "Do You Want It Right Now?"

Rick Astley "Together Forever"

Will To Power "Baby, I Love Your Way"

Donna Summer "This Time I Know It's For Real"

Breathe "How Can I Fall?"

Full Force "Love Is For Suckers"

Jellybean *Featuring Elisa Fiorillo* "Who Found Who?"

Taylor Dayne "Don't Rush Me"

The Communards "Never Can Say Goodbye"

Yazz "The Only Way Is Up"

Hall & Oates "Everything Your Heart Desires"

Joyce Sims "Come Into My Life"

Escape Club "Wild Wild West"

Frank Sinatra "Someone to Watch Over Me"

Tavares "Heaven Must Be Missing An Angel"

Tavares "Don't Take Away the Music"

Janet Jackson "Pleasure Principle"

Paul Lekakis "Boom Boom Boom Let's Go Back to My Room"

Robbie Nevil "C'est La Vie"

Dean Martin "Sway"

Phil Phillips & The Twilights "Sea of Love"

Susannah McCorkle "Night and Day"

Fine Young Cannibals "She Drives Me Crazy"

Taylor Dayne "Up All Night"

Bonnie Tyler "Holding Out For A Hero"

Robert John "Sad Eyes"

Tony Terry "She's Fly"

Breakfast Club "Right On Track"

Tony Terry "Lovey Dovey"

Village People "Y.M.C.A."

E.L.O. "I'm Alive"

Olivia Newton John "Make a Move On Me"

Nina Simone "Here Comes the Sun"

The Deele "Two Occasions"

Lime "Your Love"

Carol Jiani "Hit & Run Lover"

Debby Boone "If Ever I See You Again"

Glen Medeiros "Nothing's Gonna Change My Love For You"

Simply Red "If You Don't Know Me By Now"

Dead or Alive "Turn Around and Count 2 Ten"

Gloria Gaynor "I Will Survive"

Erasure "A Little Respect"

Tom Johnston "Where Are You Tonight?"

General Public "Tenderness"

Chic "Everybody Dance"

Rick Astley "Take Me to Your Heart"

EPILOGUE
♥

May 30, 2009

It has been 20 years since I have seen Tom and today my baby son and I stand at his parent's grave site. Both are covered over with clover but I found them easily right beside the tree and not far from the road – just where he said his Dad wanted to be. So you could beep your horn as you passed by. A smile finds its way to my face. The place is always serene – it's a place I've come to for years to think.

As we stand here, I reflect on the fact that this man who I shared 10 months with has consumed exactly one half of my life. In my head I see a movie caption below the scene, *Twenty Years Later*. In silent meditation I remind his parents, who I never met, and myself that my love for him was real. I realize now that I have matured. Wherever you are, I love and cherish the memories. I understand now that I thought I was happy. How I've been fortunate and blessed to learn of and experience new dimensions and degrees of joy. My heart still swells when I look back to our time together. How I have learned to sit up and take notice of today – and to bask in the pleasure of the moment – now knowing how valuable memories can be.

My clever husband Noe once asked me why I chose the title "Tomorrow May Be Too Late" for this story. He was referring to the fact that my life today is much better than any one of my yesterdays, including the chapter of my life with Tom, as described in this book.

I look down at my baby son, recently fed and awake but in a milk-induced trance. He looks just like me. I look over at my beautiful husband, with his warm, brown eyes and thick, dark-brown curly hair. As I do, I'm reminded why I selected the title. I have learned to cherish each moment of joy. It sounds like a simple lesson, but for me it's one that has taken years to learn. I'm hyper and impatient by nature, and the true story that prompted this book is the aftermath: the time it took me to resolve my own confusion over what happened to me. The times captured in this book are embedded in the canvas of my life as an epic learning adventure. Fortunately overshadowed by the subsequent joys and experiences I've encountered, the relationship with Tom still turned out to be well worth the price of admission, and to this day the memories continue to intoxicate me. Rather than frame the story in a "lesson-learned" approach, my intention in writing this was to share a side-by-side action-packed ride into my past, so you can enjoy the journey as I did.

This book is the result of many years of pining away for my first real love, as well as the years that followed that were full of doubt and self-loathing that I assigned to myself. I'm now clear on many things. Firstly, that the experience was wonderful, and in itself something I can truly cherish as a lifetime memory. Second, that the experience was an opportunity to learn and grow individually in ways I never dreamed possible; and finally, and most importantly, that despite my over-analysis and dissection of each aspect of what it was, this time was something meant to happen to me for the duration of time it lasted, and I'm better off for having lived it.

In late 1988, I met a man whose first name was the same as mine: Thomas. When I met this man, I was quite naïve and did some exceptionally foolish things. Reading this book, you may decide that I got what I deserved. I've had to learn to live with the fact that my behavior and some of my actions were unacceptable, and pray for God's forgiveness. I want to believe I'm on a *pay-as-you-go* plan with God — meaning I get punished as I do things wrong — but I don't know if God sees it that way.

When I met Tom, I had a ton of money coming in and another ton in the bank, for I was a resourceful 21-year-old. From a financial and emotional standpoint, I got burned surprisingly badly and went through an interval of being upset with Tom, thinking he had hustled me out of money; and then I blamed myself because I allowed it to happen. As time passed, I got over being pissed off about the money and realized that the relationship had been one of the most defining episodes of my life.

We were only together for ten months, but Tom was to have a lasting and profound effect that will always be with me. Even after analyzing many other relationships before and after Tom, memories of my time with him serve as a comparison to all relationships and lovers, and I look back on those same memories with great pleasure. Not only does this book capture the relationship, it's a time capsule of one of the best periods in my life — banker by day, stripper by night, all while in love with the man of my dreams. Tom wasn't my first love, but he was my first *male* love. He was the first person with whom I experienced love in every sense a person can love another. As I wrote about this incredible experience, I found it difficult to come to the realization that I lived with my first great male love and then let him go. I often wondered if I had reached out enough, or if I could have done more to salvage the relationship.

To some it may seem like a clear case of being taken advantage of, and to them I may appear to be a misguided fool. Still, I hope I'm able to convey the experience so as to show how much of a treasure this relationship was and is to me. It's taken years to ponder this experience, and I've concluded that to some extent, Tom really did love me; however, I've come to the realization that the pain I felt wasn't due to the loss of his love, but rather my own desire to be loved. I'm convinced that love is no accident. It's a combination of many factors — like a specific place, time and that special person to which fate guides us. I've had to realize that my youth and looks weighed heavily on Tom's and other men's attraction to me. Love is much more complex than I once thought. Although I consider love a perfect thing, I don't think any relationship is perfect. Successful relationships don't just happen; they take hard work and mutual respect to make them strong.

I can certainly understand why someone might not adore Tom Marino, circa 1988. I was very immature and still trying to define my persona. I assumed the mixed identity of tough guy and successful professional. I knew I was good-looking, had a great body, and considered myself sexually irresistible to both men and women. It was a gift I never respected.

Based on my own logic and what I heard from friends and associates at the time and after, I learned that Tom Marino was promiscuous, didn't want to grow up, treated people poorly, and lived by his own code of right and wrong. Sometimes I would do things that appeared giving and selfless, but I think there were always selfish reasons for my actions. My wish now is to be perceived as realistic and human. I always hid my emotions well and maintained a certain level of toughness, but I've tried to let my heart shine through. If enough of my heart is shown, I think you might find me decent and just in need of maturity — and perhaps be forgiving, sympathetic or understanding about my character and treatment of friends, lovers and others.

After Tom, when I'd hear love songs or watch romantic movies, via daydream I would insert him in situations or places he probably never aspired to be with me. It took a long time to separate his intense impact on me from reality, and probably cost me the opportunity to improve some post-Tom relationships. It definitely robbed subsequent lovers of being recognized for their individual qualities.

I feel no animosity toward my ex-lovers, especially my former wife Nadine. She takes a lot of heat in this book, but in the end, her decision to leave me was correct. It took time to recognize how many mental obstacles and hang-ups I carried with me from my childhood, and had created in adulthood, that hindered my happiness and growth.

My relationship with Tom was a breakthrough in my personal development, and affected me deeply. After the relationship ended, I kept myself going by telling myself that while being with Tom was one of the happiest times I've ever had, there's life without him. Although there's a part of me that will always love the man I knew, the healing process requires going on with life after a relationship ends. I learned to face today's challenges, to celebrate today's victories, and that I can't give in to sadness. There's an element of being overly preoccupied with something that's over, but the feelings inside me were so strong I felt compelled to immortalize them into something concrete and lasting.

Sleepless nights and an obsession with trying to discover just how deep an impact this ten-month relationship had on me led me to decide to compose this book. Part of me wanted to create something tangible from the experience, to champion it as an example of what real love feels like. Part of me wanted to forget the whole thing ever happened — I imagined writing the story of our relationship would help me get over it, thinking that perhaps as I committed each memory to paper, I would be able to part with it. The chapter of the relationship is the core of memories, but I think the real story may be the tears and years that followed, when I anguished over trying to piece together what happened to me. At the time, I had no idea what life had in store for me. On my journey I've come to experience much deeper and profound loves and relationships, but not one can compare. I believe the stage on which this romance is played, the time in my life, significantly contributed to its intensity. I've learned that love takes on many forms and I cherish the young and inexperienced type of affection we shared. The relationship left me disciplined and enriched. Life has an amazing way of renewal and, through time, change brings new and brighter experiences.

I agonized over this romance for years. I've always been one to live my life with no apologies and no regrets, but the experience with Tom threw me into a tailspin. For years I lived with regret and self-loathing, holding myself responsible for the demise of the relationship. When I started writing this in 1991, two years after we broke up, I was responsible for the construction of my own destruction, allowing my body and soul to fall into disrepair. Originally, my personal agenda was to eliminate my own inner demons. Finally, it struck me that it wasn't just the man I was with that made it so wonderful, but *me*. It was me and the particular time and stage in my life that it was played out on. During the creation of this project, as my self-created demons were chased away, the focus changed to a renewed vision and commitment toward achieving a higher mental balance while gaining a higher respect for my community. I learned to realize it wasn't just Tom who made me proud of my sexuality. It's the spirit of belonging I've always wanted, watching my extended gay family in their fight for equality with me. I found strength to incorporate feelings of loss, regret, and self-pity into inner strength to grow and move forward. I cleaned up my act and began carving out a viable, bright new future. Through time and prayers, I found my own sense of purpose and direction. What started as a form of self-healing and personal recreation has developed into a labor of love in deference to a beautiful yet challenging lifestyle and way of life.

Fast forward to present day. I look at my new surroundings and embrace the changes. I count my blessings and think about those around me today who had a chance to leave but chose to stay. I have learned that one must be willing to explore the possibility of each relationship carefully, but with an open mind. I'm convinced that both people in the relationship have to demonstrate through their actions a willingness to invest in each other. There's risk associated with any endeavor, but I've learned to be mindful of the fact that the quality of life can be significantly less tomorrow. What I've gained over time is an appreciation for every day; and I treasure every moment of happiness, knowing that as bad as things may *seem* today, these could be the *good old days*. When I reflect on my relationship with Tom, I no longer allow the terrible moments to tarnish the whole. I'll never say, *I didn't know how good I had it* again. Rather, I look back, close my eyes and *smile*. That was then, but this is *now* and there is nothing wrong with today. This is the story about a place, a time and a precious person in my life who will be with me always, on my soul like a badge of enlightenment. Life is about discovery and risk-taking, and this book wouldn't be in your hands if I hadn't dared to live it. It's my wish that something beneficial can come from sharing. I'm optimistic that it can empower some to avoid living in regret, to be wiser and more careful than I was, but most of all to value today as I have learned to do. I hope you enjoy reading it as much as I enjoyed living and writing it.

Made in the USA
Charleston, SC
07 December 2010